POWER FOR THE WORLD'S RAILWAYS

GEC TRACTION

and its predecessors – 1823 to the present day

The interior of one of the most famous erecting shops in the world, the English Electric works at Preston, taken at perhaps its peak period for main line diesel and electric traction, the early 1950s.

POWER FOR THE WORLD'S RAILWAYS

GEC TRACTION

and its predecessors – 1823 to the present day

Rodger P Bradley

OPC

Oxford Publishing Co.

Title pages: An important order for English Electric was for the twelve Class EM/2 3,120hp locomotives, for the Eastern Railway of India's Calcutta 3,000V dc electrification. The bodies were constructed at Vulcan Foundry, and power equipment supplied from Preston. Ordered in 1956, this photograph, taken in April 1957, shows No. 4107 starting its long journey.

Above: Queensland Railways 1200 class Co-Co diesel hauling the prestigious "Sunlander" express in the 1950s through lush green forests in Queensland, Australia.

A catalogue record for this book is available from the British Library.

ISBN 0-86093-413-6

Library of congress catalog card number 93-78381

Oxford Publishing Co. is an imprint of
Haynes Publishing
Sparkford, near Yeovil, Somerset, BA22 7JJ

Printed and bound in Great Britain by
Butler & Tanner Ltd, Frome and London
Typeset in Times Roman Medium

Contents

Dick, Kerr & Co. provided the power for the world's first high voltage dc electrification (3,600V), on the Lancashire & Yorkshire Railway's Bury to Holcombe Brook section in 1912.

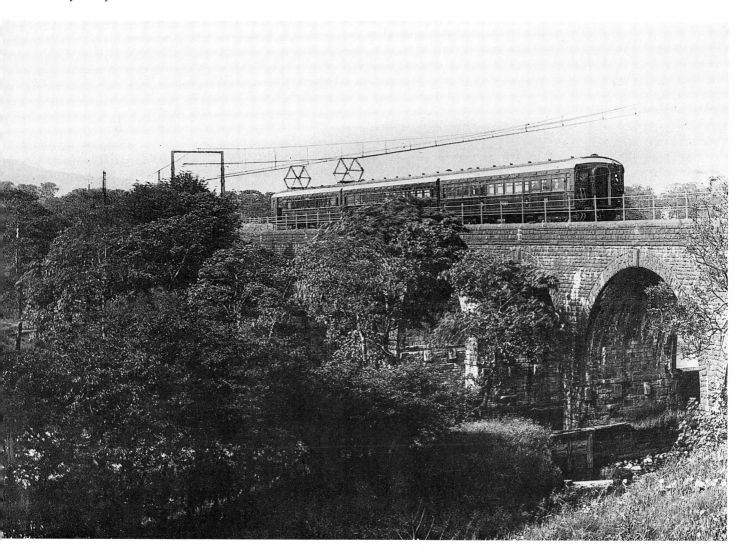

Introduction and Acknowledgements

Where do you begin to review the story of a company that can trace its rail traction activities back to 1823? Well, at least some links can be traced back that far, although as the title implies, this is not a book about steam railways, and neither is it a book specifically about GEC Traction as a company. Rather, it is hoped to reveal something of the diversity of activities, and the development of non-steam traction through the interests of English Electric, Metropolitan-Vickers, and other associated companies, up to the modern day GEC Traction. The companies that formed or were absorbed into GEC Traction read like a who's who of Britain's railway industry involved in diesel and electric traction. Conscious decisions have had to be made to deal in a less detailed way with industrial railways, tramways, and other developments, which would form significant accounts by themselves.

Back in the late 1800s, the upsurge of interest in non-steam railway traction was led by Dick, Kerr & Co. of Preston, Siemens Brothers, and British Westinghouse, in Manchester. If the North East of England was the birthplace of railways, then the North West was the birthplace of diesel and electric traction. In that history, Preston and Manchester have a special place with the former, even as late as 1951, demonstrating that the technology and innovation were still actively applied by English Electric and Metropolitan-Vickers.

The early years were dominated by the activities of Dick, Kerr & Co, English Electric, and British Westinghouse, especially in electric traction. Whilst British Thomson-Houston and Willans & Robinson in Rugby emerged as leading contenders in the diesel traction field. The name 'diesel' we all know is associated with the famous German engineer, and despite the prior claims of Akroyd-Stuart, this generic term has remained.

Over the intervening years, GEC Traction's predecessors have supplied, introduced, or participated in the introduction of diesel and electric traction in many countries. Included in the hundreds of orders and contracts that have been received, have been locomotives, railcars, multiple units, power equipments, transmission components and control systems, from the simplest mechanical devices, up to the most sophisticated and advanced computer technology. Hopefully, the following pages can illustrate something of the diversity of products and activities that have come out of the numerous works, although this study would need to be at least ten times as long to cover *all* the known activities of GEC Traction, and its forerunners.

Before closing these introductory words, I would like to express my particular thanks to Railway Consultant Mike Scott, without whose willing support this project could easily have fallen on stony ground. My thanks too, to a number of railway authorities around the world for their invaluable assistance, in particular, Queensland Railways, National Railways of Zimbabwe, the State Transport Authority of South Australia and South African Railways. I must also mention the assistance provided by Adrian Jarvis of Liverpool Museum for photographs from the Vulcan Collection, the Harris Library in Preston, Bradford Metropolitan Council, the Central Library in Newcastle upon Tyne, the Central Library, Manchester, Staffordshire County Council, Records Office, Warwickshire County Council, Rugby Library, Durham County Library and Mr W. A. Anderson of Kilmarnock District Library. In addition, Mr J. C. Hymas of GEC Transmission & Distribution Projects, Mr G. Briggs of GEC Large Machines, Ray Williamson of Ruston Diesels, and David Gillan of the Railway Industry Association. Lastly, to my wife Pat, who has 'lived with' *GEC Traction* for rather a long time.

NB All photographs are courtesy GEC Alsthom Traction unless stated otherwise.

The reverse of this photograph is dated 1 Oct 1957, and shows one of the first BR Type 1 freight locomotives. Fitted with English Electric 800hp engines, these locomotives are still in service today as Class 20. The order was placed with English Electric, though initially at least they were known as Vulcan Foundry Type 1s, because they were constructed at English Electric's Vulcan Works.

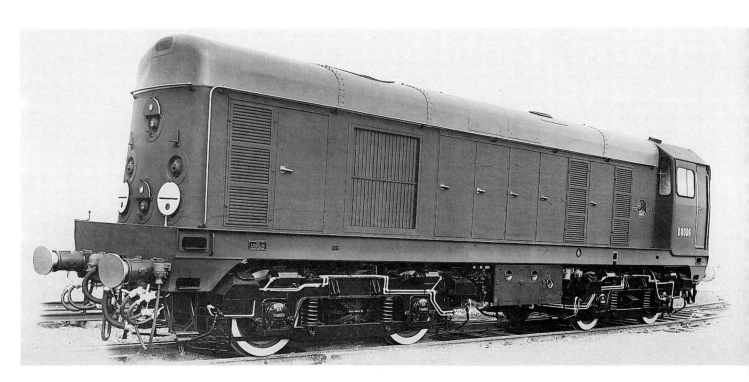

1
The Pioneers

The history of GEC Traction itself dates back to the early 1970s, but the predecessor companies which came together in that grouping can be traced back almost to the introduction of railways themselves. Some of the constituent companies established themselves in the field of steam traction. Today, GEC Traction, as one of the world's leading manufacturers of rail traction equipment is engaging in the same activities as its illustrious predecessors would have done; pushing the frontiers of rail technology forward. Equally today, just as in the last century, there is stiff competition, but the company continues to be successful and prosperous.

Inevitably, steam, and the development of railways are synonymous, and it was fully three quarters of a century before any serious challenge was made to its supremacy. By the time of the Second World War, all over the globe there had been a number of main line and other railway electrification schemes, and important advances in diesel engine design had enabled its use in rail traction service. Admittedly in this latter case, its use was limited in this country, but where indigenous supplies of coal were not so prolific, or where alternative energy sources were not readily available, these new technologies flourished. Electric motors have been put to use, turning the wheels of railway vehicles since before the end of the last century, with this important form of traction having put in its first appearance in the early 1840s.

The simpler technology of steam, which itself had undergone significant change and development by the 1830s and 1840s, was still a more cost effective solution for railway motive power, than the experimental electric traction. By the very early Victorian era, one of the most famous names in the railway manufacturing industry had already established a locomotive building works, at Newcastle-upon-Tyne. The firm of Robert Stephenson & Co., Engine Builders and Millwrights, was born in the North East, but, in partnership with Charles Tayleur of Liverpool, set up the Vulcan Works at Newton-le-Willows in 1830. The creation of this works, which later became Vulcan Foundry, was an important development in the railway industry, and the works continues to this day, designing and building diesel engines for rail traction applications. The middle years of the 19th Century were a period of supremacy for steam, with little competition from the alternative systems – to say the least! – although as early as 1835, a blacksmith in Vermont, USA, was pointing a finger, tentatively, in the direction of the future.

Thomas Davenport, of Rutland, Vermont, has been credited as the first person to use an electric motor to power a 'train'. Although in fact, the first practical application of a motor was for two 50lb motors, designed by Davenport, to drill holes in iron and steel, and for turning hardwood. The idea was patented by Davenport on 25th February 1837. The first experimental locomotive to run on standard gauge track, powered by electricity, was designed by Professor Charles Page, of Washington D.C., and ran on the Baltimore & Ohio Railroad, between Washington and Bladenburg. Three years later, Robert Davidson of Aberdeen, produced a design for an electric locomotive, which ran briefly, on the Edinburgh to Glasgow Railway, and was capable of the staggering velocity of 4 mph, with a trailing load of 5 tons!

Having suggested that the experimental electric traction was no competition at all to steam power, it is interesting to record that this early Scottish electric locomotive met its end at a Perth Engine House, in the Luddite manner! Railway workers may have seen this curious contraption as a threat to their livelihood, and yet, as a form of motive power, it was still 25 times as expensive to operate as steam.

Diesel traction, or perhaps more correctly, the compression ignition system, was not available for another 50 years, until a practical arrangement was devised by Akroyd Stuart between 1886 and 1890. It was, however, through the work of the German engineer Dr Rudolf Diesel, that the engine, and its principle of operation were ultimately successful. In 1893, Diesel produced a technical paper explaining the working and principles of his 'Rational Heat Engine', which was intended to replace both steam engines, and the then more recently developed, internal combustion engines. Although the quest for a practical means of utilising hydrocarbon fuels in this way actually pre-dates the early experiments with electricity, the first real successes came in the 1860s. Rudolf Diesel's work, in practice and on paper, was warmly received by his tutor and his employer, to the extent of the provision of a fully equipped laboratory/research facility at Augsburg. With the support of a number of companies, Diesel successfully persuaded the French to employ his 'rational heat engines', and manufacturing rights had been purchased by a US company before the turn of the century. In Britain, despite the enthusiasm of other countries, the diesel engine, as it became known, was not used in regular rail service until the mid 1920s. The former English Electric Co. were amongst the major manufacturers involved with diesel traction, but here again, not until the 1930s, although other companies, which were later to form part of the GEC Traction organisation, had produced successful internal combustion power equipment for rail and road vehicles before the depression years.

Establishing the Predecessors

Whilst Robert Stephenson & Co. was undoubtedly the first established manufacturer later to secure a place in the history of GEC Traction, a number of other, equally important names arrived in the Victorian era. Stephenson's works was set up in the North East in 1823, whilst his partnership with Charles Tayleur in the Vulcan Foundry began in 1830. Amongst the reasons for the establishment of these works, was the difficulty of transporting locomotives to be used on the western side of the UK, across the Pennines, and often involved lengthy sea journeys. However, neither the Stephenson works in the North East, nor the Vulcan Foundry, was to make an early entry into the field of non-steam traction. The first major step in this direction was taken in 1850, when Siemens Bros UK Ltd, was established in London.

There were three brothers in the Siemens family, all of whom had made significant contributions to engineering development in those early years, and by the late 19th Century, William Siemens had been instrumental in the introduction of electric traction to the British Isles. German influence and technological expertise were much in evidence

A long way from electrification, this view shows a Vulcan Foundry 4-4-0 steam locomotive for India, being loaded at Liverpool. Vulcan Foundry, as part of English Electric and later GEC Traction, built many of the electric locomotives and multiple units for India. (*Ruston Diesels Ltd*)

throughout Europe at this time, and its extension to England was perhaps inevitable. However, it was to be more than 30 years after the arrival of Siemens Bros in this country, that the first major developments in rail traction took place.

Whilst the development of both manufacturing sites and products were sporadic during the middle years of the last century, gradually, towards the turn of the century, the industry became more closely associated with the North West. More specifically, works were established in Manchester, Preston, and Stafford. It is interesting to see, that whilst steam traction had its origins in the North East, in the early 1900s, the genesis of electric traction can be isolated to North West England and Scotland, along with one example in the north of Ireland. In fact, one of the most important names in the history of electric traction; Dick, Kerr & Co., had its origins in a general engineering firm, based in Kilmarnock. Britain though was not a *true* pioneer of non-steam traction, and was heavily influenced by the German and United States railway industry.

In the field of electric traction, an American naval officer, F. J. Sprague, produced an electric motor for traction use in the 1880s, and which was successfully employed on a number of commercial contracts. Sprague's idea and inventive application of the new technologies was, by 1890, absorbed in Edison's General Electric Company, and the influence of American technology was subsequently felt by the UK, through such organisations as the British Thomson-Houston

Co. Home grown technology was arriving too, through the experience and activities of Dick, Kerr & Co., and although the British Westinghouse & Manufacturing Co. was born in Manchester, it too was essentially American in origin. Dick, Kerr & Co. was the most important UK organisation, particularly as far as later developments in the industry were concerned, and the company had been very active in the tramway field, from which the various railway electrification schemes extended their experience and activities.

Internal combustion had not been applied to railway transport with any great success before the turn of the century, and once again, in the main, US, and German technologies held sway. Some British ideas in this context had been produced, even before 1800, but more successful, practical developments did not materialise until the 1860s, as Otto and Langen undertook important experimental work. At about the same time, in the USA, a Bostonian patented the first petrol engine, whilst in Europe, Otto had improved on his earlier work, and patented his 'silent engine' in 1876. In England, efforts were concentrated on stationary and marine engines, with the development of heavier oil engines, and the compression-ignition types made by Akroyd-Stuart. Commercially viable – from the railways' viewpoint – compression-ignition types were more successful following the work undertaken by Dr Rudolf Diesel, again with the support of German industry. Despite this early work, the most significant applications of internal combustion engines in rail traction service were not to materialise until the 1920s. This important period was characterised by an example of European co-operation, at least for one member of the GEC Traction organisation, as the Vulcan Foundry entered into a partnership with A/S Frichs of Aarhus, Denmark, producing diesel powered rail vehicles.

No. 501, the archetypal English Electric diesel shunter, with a 350hp diesel engine and an 0-6-0 wheel arrangement, at work in the Netherlands, many years after the LMS experiments of the 1930s.

Pioneering Establishments

Before the turn of the century, the companies who were later to make GEC Traction a household name, had established their major manufacturing base in North West England and Scotland. Already, Dick, Kerr & Co. had established a sound reputation as general engineers, from their Britannia Engineering Works at Kilmarnock. This company had been advertising their wares as portable railways for mines and plantations, locomotives, and wagons, amongst many other items. In the 1890s, Preston in Lancashire became the focus of attention, as Dick, Kerr set up a works there, for the manufacture of tramcars and associated equipment. Also in Preston, were the works of the Electric Railway, Tramway & Carriage Works Ltd, among others, whilst not too far away, in Trafford Park, Manchester, the British Westinghouse Co. was building up its main plant.

Early Predecessors of GEC Traction

Company	Location	Established
Siemens Bros	Woolwich	1864
Dick, Kerr & Co.	Kilmarnock	1883
British Thomson Houston Co.	Rugby	1896
Dick, Kerr & Co.	Preston	1897
British Westinghouse Co. Ltd	Manchester	1899
Electric Railway, Tramway & Carriage Works	Preston	1898
English Electric Mfg. Co.	Preston	1900
United Electric Car Co.*	Preston	1905
British Electric Traction Co.	Preston	c1900
Siemens Bros Dynamo Works	Stafford	1901
Phoenix Dynamo Manufacturing Co. Ltd	Bradford	1903

* Name was changed from Electric Railway, Tramway & Carriage Works, which was owned by Dick, Kerr & Co.

Siemens Bros, from their London home of Woolwich, or, more precisely, under their new name of Siemens Bros & Co. Ltd, adopted in 1880, were responsible for the electrification of the world's first hydro-electric railway; the Giant's Causeway Tramway. This contract, involving the narrow gauge line near Portrush and Bushmills in Northern Ireland, required Siemens Bros to design and install the electrical equipment. To a degree, it may be said, that this project set a pattern for future developments in guided land transport up to, and beyond the turn of the century. Having said that, Dick, Kerr & Co. had only recently arrived in the transport field, and it was they who were to set the initial pace, concentrating on many schemes for municipal authorities.

In the 1880s Dick, Kerr & Co. specialised in the laying of tramways, adopting the grooved girder tramrail, which subsequently became a universal standard. Dick, Kerr & Co. did however provide steam traction in the earliest days, before constructing the world's first electric conduit line, from Gravesend to Northfleet in Kent. Nearer to home, the company were also responsible for the first section of an endless cable tramway in Edinburgh. In Kilmarnock, Dick, Kerr, or rather the Britannia Engine Works, had been engaged in general engineering activity since 1872, as the business of Messrs Allen Andrews & Co., and as developments in tramways progressed, the works was already occupied in the manufacture of gas engines. In 1883 it became the Britannia Engineering Works, and with its new proprietors, was well placed to take advantage of these emerging markets.

Although the initial application of electricity to rail transport covered municipal tramways, judging by some of the contemporary press reports, there was a curious ambivalence towards the new form of transport. In *The Engineer*, there was the suggestion that the development of this form of electric traction, with the new tramcars plying town and city streets, had been held back by the reluctance of some authorities to allow their streets to be disfigured in this way. Before the turn of the century there was an expansion of the tramway business, enabling Dick, Kerr & Co. to buy the works in Preston, in order to manufacture electric tramway vehicles. During the next few years a number of important contracts were won, in particular, within overseas markets, against stiff foreign competition.

Larger scale contracts, taking Dick, Kerr & Co. into the field of railway rather than tramway electrification schemes, began to appear in the 1890s. In 1890, a contemporary, Siemens Bros & Co. Ltd, provided traction equipment for the

The Indian Subcontinent saw many orders for English Electric and AEI, exemplified in this view of Calcutta, with an EE Co. powered 1,500V dc locomotive leaving the crowded station, with the Howrah Bridge in the background.

first underground electric railway in the world – the City & South London Railway. Three years later, in 1893, the Liverpool Overhead Railway began operations, and soon afterwards, Dick, Kerr & Co. supplied improved power equipment for the rolling stock of the world's first electrified overhead railway.

Perhaps the next important step in the development of electric traction, was the acquisition of land, and the establishment of the Preston Works. Dick, Kerr's in Preston was set up by 1897, although the Kilmarnock based parent then brought into being the Electric Railway & Tramway Carriage Works the following year, 1898, to build tramway rolling stock. There was, perhaps obviously, an overlap in the board of directors of both companies, though it is interesting to note that a famous Lancashire businessman, one Robert S. Boddington was elected to the board of the Preston company. Boddington, a local entrepreneur, had made his name in the brewing industry, a name which is still associated with that trade in the Greater Manchester and South Lancashire areas.

A more pressing reason for the establishment of the new company and its works, recognised the need to provide tramcars and light rail vehicles for the home market, since other-

wise, it was supposed, more municipal authorities would be forced to import these products from abroad. The Dick, Kerr & Co. site, and those of the Electric Railway & Tramway Works occupied an extensive area, along the west side of Strand Road in Preston, close to the docks, and with rail links to both the Lancashire & Yorkshire, and London & North Western Railway systems. There was substantial American influence on the design of the tramway vehicles, the Works Manager at Preston, E. A. Stanley, having already benefited from substantial experience in the USA, at similar works. In addition, a flexible approach by the Preston company was evident, since they offered to fit to their own car bodies, the bogie, or truck designs of such famous American manufacturers as Brill, and Peckham, if these were preferred to Dick, Kerr's own make. The Preston site was able to manufacture around 800 tramway cars each year, with the larger cars and railway vehicles constructed and supplied less frequently. In the late 1890s the works employed between 600 and 800 men, and as the demand for electric traction equipment rose, a second company was formed by directors of Dick, Kerr & Co., and others, for the specific purpose of manufacturing electrical machinery. The name of this company was to remain a household word for many decades, extending across many different branches of the engineering industry, and becoming a major component of GEC Traction. English Electric, or more precisely, the English Electric Manufacturing Co. Ltd, was formed in November

1899, with two of that company's directors also on the board of the Electric Railway & Tramway Manufacturing Co., and Dick, Kerr & Co.

Like the tramway company, English Electric was originally formed as a separate organisation, with the works constructed on the opposite side of Strand Road in Preston, on land later occupied by British Aerospace. English Electric's first foray into rail traction fields lasted just four years, until 1903, when it was amalgamated with Dick, Kerr & Co. It was a successful undertaking from the word go, and electric motors, motor controllers, and other equipment were supplied from Preston to all parts of the world.

During the last years of the 19th Century, the Electric Railway & Tramway Carriage Works Ltd continued its separate existence, but maintained close links with Dick, Kerr. Shortly after the turn of the century, in 1905 the company's name was changed to the United Electric Car Co., and twelve years later, Dick, Kerr acquired overall financial control. From around 1905, the United Electric Car Co. was engaged in negotiations relating to the purchase of the British Electric Car Works in Trafford Park, Manchester, and for the Castle Car Works, at Hadley in Shropshire.

In addition to the electrification and tramway work already mentioned, it is worth recalling that Dick, Kerr were the main contractors in the changeover of the first main line railway in this country, from steam to electric traction. This particular project involved the Lancashire & Yorkshire Railway's line from Liverpool to Southport, with the supply of 600V dc traction equipment, and third rail contact system in 1904. Dick, Kerr's growing dominance in the electric railway and tramway market was emphasised by numerous contracts, including, amongst others, the Portrush & Bushmills Tramway, City & South London Railway orders, and of course the variety of municipal tramways schemes.

It was the prospect of significant growth in the railway electrification business that brought George Westinghouse across the Atlantic, to establish the British Westinghouse Co.'s works in Trafford Park, Manchester. Westinghouse came to this country in 1900, looking for a suitable site for his projected works, though even at this early stage, Dick, Kerr were the UK's main competitor, and with them, Preston came to assume a role of special importance in this developing field. In neighbouring Manchester, in the early 1900s, the competition was coming chiefly from British Westinghouse, and some of the smaller concerns, as was the case with the British Electric Car Co., were not finding survival easy. One of the reasons for this, and for the diversity of manufacture by British Westinghouse, was a marked lack of enthusiasm, and impetus for the progress of railway electrification.

Back in Preston, the British Electric Car Co. were employed on various contracts, including work for the Lancashire & Yorkshire Railway, whilst a very interesting project had been put forward, but not pursued, to combine a diesel/oil engine, with electric traction motors. This proposal was put to the board of the British Electric Car Co. by a certain Mr Dickinson, who envisaged an oil engine coupled to a generator, in a railway locomotive, supplying power to traction motors fixed to the trailing coaches. The idea makes for an interesting comparison with the designs of diesel multiple units produced for British Railways in the 1950s and 1960s, and perhaps even a progenitor, by many decades, of the principles of having many axles in a train with motors, and now being developed for wider use on the latest designs of British Rail's multiple unit rolling stock. Although the board were not disposed to the idea in 1904, its rejection provoked a very indignant response from the said Mr Dickinson, and in retrospect, the company would have been years ahead of any competitors, had the idea been taken up.

George Westinghouse and Trafford Park

An American from Pittsburgh came to England in 1900, looking for a site for his new factory, and was instrumental in establishing one of the cornerstones of the GEC Traction empire. The site chosen, in Trafford Park, Manchester, was literally a greenfield location at that time; parkland, containing the ancestral home of the De Trafford family. George Westinghouse acquired 130 acres of open countryside, and was told that it would take no less than five years to build the factory he required! Since Westinghouse had already accepted orders he needed the British site in production within 18 months, and this was undoubtedly seen by many as a formidable obstacle. Such however was the mettle of the man, that he returned across the Atlantic for the plans of his Pittsburgh factory, and a contractor by the name of James C. Stewart, who promised its completion within 15 months! In fact, the Manchester factory was completed in just twelve months, and included the building – which still exists to this day – that was a replica of the office block back in Pittsburgh.

In 1902 then, the British Westinghouse Co.'s Trafford Park works was in full operation, although the anticipated surge in railway electrification projects did not materialise. The few, isolated, electric traction schemes that did come to fruition, influenced Westinghouse to take a different course, building gas engines and steam turbines instead. But, this was not before a number of important orders had been completed, one of which included ten electric locomotives for the Metropolitan Railway in London, each of which weighed in at 150 tons. Shortly before Westinghouse lost his enthusiasm for the British side of his railway business, the company successfully tendered for work on the Thamshaven to Lokken electrification project in Norway. This scheme was of particular significance, since it was the first example of the use of high voltage, single phase ac electrification, and was carried out simultaneously with the Lancaster to Morecambe & Heysham project in England.

The late 1890s and early 1900s were a period when a number of companies, which subsequently formed part of GEC Traction, were established. The North of England continued to remain the focal point of these developments, with the Phoenix Dynamo Co. setting up works in Bradford in 1900, to manufacture small rotating machines, whilst Siemens Bros & Co. began the production of electrical machinery and switchgear from Stafford. The Siemens Bros works at Woolwich in London, which had been the most profitable sector of the business, producing telegraph equipment, lighting and cables, remained in independent existence until 1956, when it was finally acquired by Associated Electrical Industries (AEI). The General Electric Co. were also extremely active in North Woolwich, at the same time as Siemens Bros, but under the guise of a predecessor, William T. Henley, established in 1837. Like Siemens, Henley's workshops first produced cables and telegraph equipment, and small electro-magnetic machines. Siemens, although prominent in the very early years of electric traction, from the Stafford Works, did not figure quite so prominently over the longer term, unlike Dick, Kerr & Co., Metropolitan Vickers, British Thomson-Houston, or English Electric. A similar situation applied in the case of the General Electric Co., whose pre-eminent position was not established in the UK until the 1960s.

Mention of the British Thomson-Houston Co. refers back to the 1890s, when the company entered into discussions with Siemens Bros, with a view to the merger of their interests, although these were not to have a successful outcome. The British Thomson-Houston Co. itself was originally incorporated as a selling agency of the US parent company,

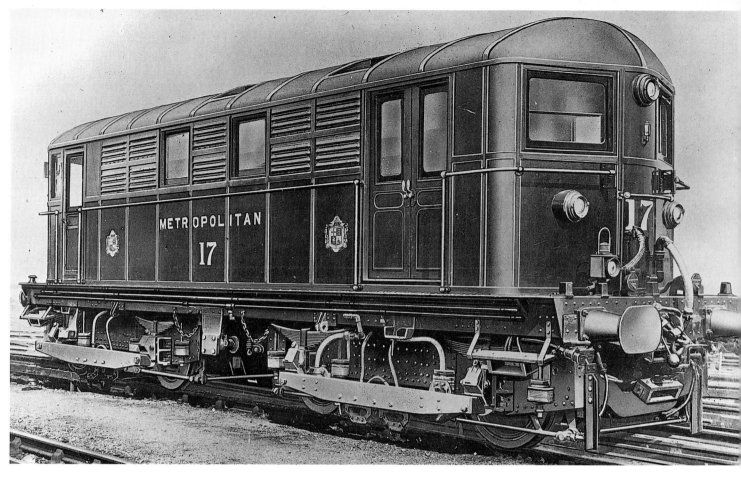

Perhaps amongst the most famous, at least in the UK, of the early electric traction products, were the Bo-Bo locomotives built for the Metropolitan Railway by British Westinghouse, in the American Company's Manchester works.

in 1886. The Thomson Houston Co. of the USA was initially financed by international bankers, but by 1902, the International General Electric Co. had taken over financial control.

In England, BTH was formed in May 1896, as an independent concern, with the exclusive rights to manufacture and sell apparatus under patents purchased from the US parent com-

Another British Westinghouse equipped offering for the Metropolitan Railway was this centre cab Bo-Bo, bearing the railway's attractive insignia, and No. 1 on the bodyside.

pany, in Great Britain and Ireland. BTH built its first works at Rugby, where it concentrated on the manufacture of turbines, heavy plant, switchgear, motors, domestic appliances and lamps. The company acted independently for more than 50 years, but in 1928 became part of the AEI Group of companies, alongside the giant Metropolitan-Vickers organisation. In the early days, BTH was pioneering in other fields, such as the establishment of power companies to distribute electricity supplies around the country. Although the BTH promoted bill in Parliament was unsuccessful in 1899, it did appear to stimulate the promotion of other schemes for electricity supply undertakings, shortly after the turn of the century.

On the transport front, BTH were responsible for the installation of the first electric tramway in the British Isles operated from an overhead trolley wire in Leeds. The line, around 5½ miles in length, was completed in 1891, and taken

over by Leeds Corporation in 1894. Following on from this, and in the first five years of the BTH company's existence, no fewer than 20 tramway installations had BTH equipment, including London, Liverpool, Bristol, Sheffield and Dublin. Some examples, as at Cork, in Ireland, and Chatham in Kent, BTH actually owned the system, whilst early export orders provided tramway installations in Barcelona, Madrid and Ceylon. In 1898, work began on the first railway electrification project, including the provision of electrical equipment for the power station, substations, and electric locomotives. This project, the Central London Railway, opened in 1900, and was referred to as the 'Tuppeny Tube', on account of the standard fare of two pence for any single journey, irrespective of distance. An interesting story connected with this project refers to an incident that took place during test running, when the electric locomotives proved to be too large for the tunnels! During construction, the railway engineers had, it seems, forgotten to take account of the height of the rails! To overcome this difficulty, new springs were fitted to the locomotives, and shallower section rails were laid. However, this was not an adequate solution, since the shallowness of the rails gave rise to problems at the rail joints, where adjoining rail ends dropped badly, severely jolting the locomotive, and resulting in quite serious damage. In addition to the engineering problems faced by BTH, vibration affecting buildings over the tunnel gave rise to legal action from property owners, and with the requirement for improved acceleration of the trains, this led to the development of multiple unit controls. The system first installed on the Central London Railway also incorporated electrically operated contactors, with similar developments of these arrangements provided on equipment installed on the vehicles of many other systems around the world.

The 'Tuppeny Tube' was not, it has to be said, the first underground railway in the world to operate by electric traction, that honour, as mentioned briefly earlier in this chapter, was claimed by the City & South London Railway. This par-

ticular railway began operations in 1890, running from Stockwell in South London, to King William Street, in the heart of the City. The rolling stock was provided with a pair of 50hp motors on each motor car, and collected power from a conductor rail, at 600V dc. Interestingly, the armatures for these first locomotives were wound directly onto the vehicle axles, and no gears, or other means, were employed to drive the wheels. The equipment was actually still in service in 1924, when it was absorbed, and reconstructed within the emerging network of railways that became London's Underground. The next major developments in London involved both Siemens Bros, and Dick, Kerr & Co.

In 1893, powers were obtained for the construction of a railway under the Thames from Waterloo to the City, more specifically, to the Bank. The railway was opened in 1898, and provided a much more direct means of access to the City for those living on the south side of the river, with business there, and which previously involved more convoluted rail journeys. Here, Siemens Bros provided the original equipment for the operation of this 600V dc line, consisting of five four-coach electric trains. At each end of the train, two 60hp dc motors were provided, and once again, just as was used on the City & South London, gearless drive was adopted, with the motor armatures wound directly onto the vehicle axles. Equipment for these two lines was actually manufactured at the Stafford Works of Siemens Bros, Dynamo Works Ltd, which, less than 20 years later was to come under the Dick, Kerr/English Electric roof.

Further north, in Liverpool, the world's first overhead electric railway had been opened for traffic in March 1893, although the electrification contract for this was placed with the Electric Construction Corporation of Wolverhampton. Links with GEC Traction's predecessors can be traced to Brown, Marshall & Co., which subsequently became the Metropolitan Carriage, Wagon & Finance Co., and a partner to Metropolitan-Vickers. The original Liverpool Overhead Railway rolling stock was supplied by Brown, Marshall & Co., with the power equipment from the Electric Construction Corporation. Dick, Kerr became involved with the LOR in 1901, when, in order to meet the growing competition from the electrification of Liverpool's tramways, experiments were undertaken with new equipment to improve acceleration and train speeds on the railway. Following the introduction of electric trams in 1898,

This seven-car District Railway train operated, at 660V dc, an early rapid transit service. All the GEC Traction predecessors were involved in this type of work, at and just before the turn of century, beginning with the City & South London Railway, in 1890.

Dick, Kerr & Co. provided the power and control systems for the unique Liverpool Overhead Railway vehicles. A three-car set is seen here at Gladstone Dock Station in 1930.

(National Railway Museum)

passengers carried in the city by this means rose from 785,064 in that year, to more than 100,000,000 in 1901. Dick, Kerr's of Preston guaranteed to run the overall distance of the LOR, between Seaforth Sands and Dingle, including 16 stops, in just under 21 minutes.

The original rolling stock consisted of 22 two-car units, with a pair of 60hp motors under direct series-parallel control, and drawing power from the conductor rail, energised at 500V dc. With an average distance of only 760 yards between stops, high speeds were not easily achievable, and in many instances, the city's tramways could provide a faster service. The experimental train of 1901 featured four 100hp traction motors, of an entirely new design from Dick, Kerr & Co. The new train consisted of two motor coaches and a trailer car, with the traction motors driving the inner axles of the motor bogies on each of the two power cars. The traction motors themselves were of the totally enclosed design, in a fire and waterproof casing, and with the final drive to the wheels through cast steel spur gears. Some of the 3,945lbs mass of the motor was supported from the bogie frame by coil springs, and with the additional components of the gear drive and housing details, the total weight of the motor and drive reached some 4,387lbs. The original LOR vehicles had the traction motor armatures wound directly onto the axles, whilst the new Dick, Kerr motors had their casings split into an upper and lower half, to facilitate maintenance. Interestingly, the lower half remained in position on the bogie/axle, and the upper half could be lifted off for inspection, which was exactly the reverse of the arrangement commonly employed at that time on tramcar bogies.

Dick, Kerr also provided a new means of train control, with the motors connected in series-parallel, and with the controller in each driving cab linked to both sets of motors in the train, by a bus-line cable. The controllers, bearing the legend 'English Electric Mfg Company Ltd.', were fitted with the recently patented 'magnetic blow-out' coil, to prevent contacts being damaged when making or breaking circuits carrying around 700 amps. The new Dick, Kerr power equipment was a success during the experimental period, permitting significantly improved speeds, and of course, competition with the city's tramways. The following year, 1902, as a direct result of these trials, Dick, Kerr of Preston won a contract to re-equip all of the LOR's existing vehicles. The major changes in the re-equipment programme involved the fitting of two 100hp geared motors to the motor coaches, new type train controllers, circuit breakers, and switches. The Preston company had sub-contracted some of this work to the English Electric Manufacturing Co., also in Strand Road, Preston. The control systems and controllers were known as type Q4 Form D, designed by Sydney H. Short of English Electric, and more familiarly known as the 'Short System'. On the Liverpool Overhead Railway the accelerated services were begun in September 1902.

Liverpool – Southport: A First Main Line Conversion
This route, from Liverpool Exchange station, to Crossens, north of Southport, was the first example in this country of the complete changeover from steam, to electric traction, of a main line railway. The electrification of the line, undertaken with a third rail contact system, and supplied at 600V dc, was the responsibility of Dick, Kerr & Co., with the rolling stock constructed by the Lancashire & Yorkshire Railway themselves, at Horwich and Newton Heath. Originally, the power station at Formby was provided with four 1,500kW generators driven by cross compound steam engines, and a single 4,000kW turbo-alternator. The latter came from Willans & Robinson at Rugby, whose works were subsequently acquired by the English Electric Co. In 1927, the cross compound steam engines at Formby were replaced by Willans-Dick, Kerr turbines, also manufactured at Rugby. Dick, Kerr also provided 600kW rotary convertors for installation in the traction substations, to feed the 600V dc supply to the conductor rails. The power generating equipment supplied by Dick, Kerr

remained in operation for more than 40 years, until its replacement in the 1940s, when increases in traffic demanded modernisation and re-equipment of the line.

For the rolling stock which undertook the first electrified services from March 1904, 38 motor coaches were equipped with four 150hp traction motors, with similar equipment installed in two motorised baggage cars. Each train was made up of two motor coaches, with two trailer vehicles sandwiched between them. The traction motors themselves were self-ventilated machines, and drove the wheels through single reduction spur gears. Power supply pick up was by means of top running contact shoes on each of the motor bogies, whilst the train control systems were quite unique in their day. Each of the two driving positions in the train was fitted with direct, hand-operated controllers, each having two drums, with a solenoid, magnetic blow-out device to protect the contacts. In turn, each drum controlled four motors in a train, linked by means of three power cables. More modern multiple unit type controls were then under development, and the owners of the line, the LYR suggested trials of this type of controller, which had previously been considered for the baggage car, and for which, in 1904, the controller was already built. By 1921, multiple unit controls were in place on new rolling stock supplied by the company, and the reservation which some board members expressed concerning the possible infringement of the Dick, Kerr system, on that offered by Sprague, and Van De Reele, were overcome. One of the original design of controllers was presented by the later owners of the Liverpool to Southport lines, the LMS Railway Co., for preservation in the Science Museum in London.

Still in the North West, electric running began on the Mersey Railway in May 1903, on the former steam railway linking Liverpool with Birkenhead on the Wirral, with Metropolitan-Vickers, as British Westinghouse, responsible for the electrification project. The contract involved the conversion to electric traction, with electric motor coaches picking up a 600V dc supply from a side contact conductor rail. The company provided, in addition to the rolling stock power equipment; conductor rails and feeders, passenger lifts, and equipment for the power station at Hamilton Square, Birkenhead. With around two thirds of the railway's 4¾ mile route in tunnel, ventilation systems were an important part of the scheme, and indeed, the unpleasant atmosphere on the original steam operated line was one reason advanced for electrification. With a service operated by two, three, or five-car formations, in addition to benefits of comfort, speed and cleanliness for the passenger, electrification reduced operating costs and maintenance, from 33.5d (13.95p), to 15.9d (6.6p) per train mile.

Power station equipment supplied by Metropolitan-Vickers (British Westinghouse), provided a total capacity of 7,735kW, with three 1,650hp, vertical, cross compound steam engines driving 1,200kW dc generators. Other hardware installed, included a pair of 200kW sets for lighting, with a switchboard of 19 panels controlling the outgoing power supplies. The original rolling stock equipment comprised 24 motor coaches, each carrying four totally enclosed traction motors of 100hp, with train control using an electro-pneumatic system, and drum type controllers. Additionally, there were 33 trailer cars in the original fleet. When first built, the vehicles did not carry air compressors, only storage reservoirs, which were refilled from 'compressor stations', at intervals along the route. The electro-magnetic control system, unlike more modern arrangements, received its required low voltage supply from 14V batteries carried on the train, rather than auxiliary generators.

First Single Phase AC Electrification

The former Midland Railway's line from Lancaster to Morecambe and Heysham, occupies a unique position in the development of electric traction in this country. In April 1908, operations began on this 9½ mile route, with motor coaches collecting power from an overhead contact wire, supplied at 6.6kV, single phase, 25Hz, ac. Just over 40 years later, the same route was used as a testbed for the now

AC electrification was adopted for the Midland Railway's Lancaster to Morecambe and Heysham line, at 6,600V, in 1908. The 360hp motor coaches were equipped by Siemens Bros, Dynamo Works, and Metropolitan-Vickers.

The world's first ac electrification was carried out in Norway, between Thamshaven and Lokken. Metropolitan-Vickers powered Bo-Bo locomotives began a pioneering tradition of this company, which has been continued to this day.

standard, 25kV ac, 50Hz, single-phase electrification systems of British Railways.

On the original project, British Westinghouse were once again involved, as were the Siemens Bros, Dynamo Works in Stafford. The latter provided the power equipment for two of the three motor coaches, with British Westinghouse (Metropolitan-Vickers) providing the hardware for the third. The power supplies for the line originally came from a power station at Heysham Harbour, from gas engine driven generators supplied by the Manchester company, but was later obtained from Morecambe Corporation at 6.6kV, three phase, 50Hz, and converted to 25Hz, single-phase, at Heysham. The line, normally operated by three motor coaches and four trailers, was entirely a passenger service, and the original vehicles, built at the railway company's Derby Works, were still in service over 40 years later. The power equipment supplied from the Stafford Works of Siemens Bros, consisted of a pair of 180hp, series wound, commutator motors on each motor coach, and controlled by electromagnetic contactors tapping into the low voltage side of the main transformer. The British Westinghouse equipment was slightly different, comprising an electro-pneumatic control system, with an oil immersed auto-transformer. An auxiliary transformer provided the low voltage for the control systems, with the transformers and switchgear carried on the underframe, below the floor of the vehicle.

Essentially the same systems were installed on the first export contract for a single-phase electrification, secured by

the British Westinghouse Co., and opened in the same year as the Lancaster to Morecambe and Heysham line. The particular contract referred to here, was a 17 miles long route in Norway, running from Thamshaven to Lokken, for which British Westinghouse installed the overhead contact system, and provided locomotives, and a single motor car, for use by the railway's directors. The locomotives were a box type design, and weighed 20 tons, with two four-wheeled bogies, and a single roof-mounted pantograph, feeding the auto-transformer by way of a circuit breaker. Electro-pneumatic control was used again, with drum type controllers at each end of the locomotive. The motors too, operated on single phase, and were series wound, rated at 40hp, with the four motors carried on each locomotive, driving the wheels through spur gears. The locomotive bodies were constructed by W. G. Bagnall of Stafford – later to become part of GEC Traction – and the motor coach – also equipped with a pair of 40hp traction motors – came from the United Electric Car Co.'s plant in Preston. In total, three of the 160hp locomotives were supplied from this country, along with the 80hp motor coach, for this metre gauge line, whilst the Skabo Railway Carriage Works in Oslo (then Christiania), provided the remainder of the rolling stock.

Above: The LSWR was busy pushing ahead with its dc third-rail electrification, and for which, Metropolitan-Vickers supplied the power and control systems for these first units, one of which, No. E12, is seen here at Wimbledon in 1915.

Below: English Electric introduced electric traction to many countries. Here, in 1924, an EE Co. equipped motor coach is seen newly built, and destined for the Campos do Jordao Railway, and the Rio de Janeiro branch, in Brazil.

Power for the line came from a hydro-electric power station at Skjenald Fossen, which also supplied electricity to villages in the vicinity of the line, and the mining machinery at Lokken. A substation was erected at Thamshaven to convert the three-phase supply of 15kV, to 6.6kV, 25Hz for the catenary. Two motor generator sets, switchgear, and oil-cooled step down transformers were supplied by British Westinghouse. The catenary was designed by British Westinghouse and consisted of a single copper contact wire, suspended from the steel catenary cable, carried on insulators. The simple construction used 'T' section support arms on woooden poles, with spans varying from 68 feet on curves, to 150 feet on straight sections of track. Whilst this was not the only contract secured by any of GEC Traction's predecessors, Scandinavian orders were few and far between, and in Norway, the AEI Group's only other recorded order for new equipment, was for a batch of four battery electric locomotives in 1948 for Lorentzen and Wettre Ltd. L&W were actually the Scandinavian sales agents for AEI, and it is not known whether these locomotives were ever put into traffic, or how they were used.

Just before the outbreak of the 1914-1918 war British Westinghouse were involved in another major contract, when, in Australia, Victorian Railways embarked on the electrification of Melbourne's suburban lines. This was the first electrification work in Australia, and in 1913, the company received orders for no less than 400 multiple unit type vehicles, with each motor car carrying four 140hp traction motors. This equipment was used on broad gauge lines, although the project's completion was delayed by the hostilities, and not finished until 1919. The substation equipment was also supplied from the UK, and by 1916, totalled more than 20 rotary convertors, to provide the 1,500V dc supply to the conductor rail.

In the 25 years or so that spanned the period from the 1890s to the end of the 1914-1918 war, considerable progress had been made with non-steam railway traction, though rather less with internal combustion than electricity. The same period had seen the arrival of the major constituent organisations of GEC Traction; Siemens Bros, British Thomson-Houston, and Dick, Kerr & Co., although a number of others were yet to emerge. The development of the use of electricity in transport was applied rather more effectively at this time to tramways – the Victorian and Edwardian equivalent of 1980s/90s light rail and rapid transit systems – than the main line railways. Progress with internal combustion was very slow, although narrow gauge locomotives from Dick, Kerr for the war effort, equipped with petrol engines, brought in another company, which later became closely involved with GEC. In Bradford, the Phoenix Dynamo Works, established for the production of smaller classes of electrical machines, provided the generators for the Dick, Kerr locomotives. The generators were coupled to the four-cylinder petrol engines, which in their turn, powered a pair of Dick, Kerr traction motors. After the end of the First World War, Phoenix Dynamo Works became part of the English Electric Group. The arrival of compression ignition engines are discussed in more detail in the following chapter, though for many years in this country, there seemed a great reluctance to accord the design with the name 'diesel', preferring in many cases to refer to oil, or heavy oil engines. However, as diesel engines they became universally known, despite the prior claims of Akroyd-Stuart, and those produced by the various predecessors and associates of GEC Traction were very successful. The 90 petrol-electric engines from the Dick, Kerr stable during the war years were another useful landmark however, proving the practicality of an internal combustion engine allied to an electric transmission system. In retrospect, it seems a pity that Dick, Kerr & Co. did not fully exploit the suggestion which, it will be remembered, had been put to that company's board some ten years earlier.

2
The Arrival of Diesel Traction

The development of internal combustion engines in Britain dates back, perhaps surprisingly, around 200 years, with proposals for engines using volatile fuels first published in 1790. Further British work in the field can be traced to the 1820s, with additional pioneering work undertaken in France, Germany, and the USA. The basic principles of the working of such hydrocarbon fuel engines were laid down in France, in the 1860s, demonstrating applications of the four-stroke cycle. These principles, outlined by the French in 1860 to 1862, were also applied, independently, by the German researchers Otto and Langen in 1866, and resulted in more experimental work. Meanwhile, across the Atlantic, in Boston, Massachusetts, George Brayton patented the first petrol engine in 1872, followed four years later by Otto's four-stroke engine in Germany.

Two-stroke engines were patented in the early 1880s, with development of the oil engine for stationary and marine applications from Priestman appearing in 1888. At about this time too, Dick, Kerr's were establishing a reputation, building gas engines in Kilmarnock, where the Works Manager, H. Sumner, had previously spent a number of years 'with the makers of the Otto Gas Engine'. Gas engines were especially useful for industrial applications, and at about the same time, another important partnership became forged. P. W. Willans joined with Mark Robinson at Thames Ditton, manufacturing small, high speed marine steam engines. Thames Ditton may not have obvious connections with the development of either diesel engines, or rail traction, but established an important

From the locomotive perspective, these petrol engined, narrow gauge examples for the War Department, represented the earliest batch order for non-steam locomotives. Built at Preston by Dick, Kerr & Co. during the First World War, and fitted with 40hp engines, with electrical equipment from the Phoenix Dynamo Co., of Bradford.

cornerstone of English Electric, as the Willans-Robinson partnership moved north to Rugby in the early 1890s. In 1897, the new works were opened at Rugby, constructing 'reciprocating engines', with the site later becoming the Willans Works of English Electric.

However, even more important developments took place in the two years between 1888 and 1890, when Akroyd-Stuart completed his work on the compression ignition engine. The first patents were taken out in 1890, two to three years before Rudolf Diesel, who ultimately, was to give his name to this particular form of internal combustion. In the east of England, Herbert Akroyd-Stuart, established an association with the engineering firm of Richard Hornsby & Sons, and in 1892, the world's first commercially successful oil engine was produced. Only four years later, the world's first oil engine powered locomotive was manufactured by Hornsby-Akroyd; a 9½hp four-wheeled design, for 18in gauge track. The Hornsby-Akroyd association is important in considering the growth of the GEC Traction organisation, particularly in the sphere of diesel powered rail traction. A brief example of the successful development of this association shows Ruston, Burton & Proctor, partnering Richard Hornsby between 1919 and 1940, when Ruston & Hornsby Ltd, were joined by Davey Paxman of Colchester, coming under the umbrella of English Electric Diesels Ltd in 1966, and finally, in 1975, to their last association, as GEC Diesels Ltd. Not only had the diesel engine crossed the Pennines, but it had progressed from the early links with the development of British agriculture, to provide some of the most successful and renowned diesel engines anywhere in the world.

Although the Akroyd-Stuart compression ignition engines spawned one of the world's leading rail traction engine builders, Rudolf Diesel's work was most influential in its

design and commercial development. Diesel himself was a pupil at the Technical High School in Munich in 1878, and learning that the steam engine converted only 6% to 10% of the energy supplied by the fuel, into useful work, channelled his activities into a practical realisation of the principles expounded in the Carnot Cycle. Experimenting in his spare time, and working in Paris and Berlin, it was not until a further 15 years had elapsed before Rudolf Diesel was able to publish his theories. In 1893, his paper, entitled, 'The Theory and Construction of a Rational Heat Engine to Replace Steam Engines and Present Day Internal Combustion Engines' was first published. With support from his teacher and employer, Diesel conducted a series of experiments at Augsburg, between 1894 and 1897, resulting in a successful design of engine, in which the air was compressed to some 35 atmospheres (bar), with fuel injected in the form of a fine spray. Selling the new design of engine proved difficult in Germany, whilst he persuaded the French to adopt it for use in submarines, and again with the support of his sponsors, travelled widely in an attempt to market his ideas.

Across the Atlantic, the United States and Canadian marketing rights were obtained by the Diesel Engine Company of America, which soon resulted in the appearance of a 60hp diesel engine, manufactured in St Louis, Missouri. This two-cylinder design became the world's first commercial engine in regular service. Whilst the diesel engine's early success had attracted worldwide attention, the first units were cumbersome, and not easily suited to traction purposes, with even the existing petrol engines demonstrating greater efficiency. Nevertheless, back in Britain, the British Army took delivery of 80hp locomotives, between 1898 and 1902, fitted with prime movers of the Hornsby-Akroyd design.

Willans & Robinson – Rugby
An important development in the long term history of English Electric, and later, GEC Traction, took place in the same year that Rudolf Diesel achieved success with his compression ignition engine. In 1897, the Victoria Works of Willans & Robinson Ltd, were opened at Rugby, extending the activities of this partnership from stationary steam engines, into the field of diesel engine manufacture. However, it was not until 1906 that the works produced its first unit, a single-crank engine, developing 130bhp. This design was the forerunner of the world famous 'K' series engines which began life in 1934, and the latest developments of this same family could be included in new diesel electric locomotives, which will take Britain's railways into the next century.

Willans & Robinson had previously been located at Thames Ditton as stated, where they specialised in the manufacture of high speed marine steam engines. Interestingly, the company supplied a six-cylinder steam engine in 1895 to Brown Boveri for installation in a curious combination of steam-electric locomotive. It could well be argued that this was the earliest connection Willans & Robinson had with rail traction, a connection very much strengthened by their successors at the Victoria Works in Rugby, the English Electric Co.

The steam-electric locomotive, with a Do-Do (eight axles) wheel arrangement, was constructed for the French railway Chemins de Fer de L'Ouest, by Brown Boveri, and is believed to be the first example of the pairing of a heat engine, with electric transmission, for rail traction. In December 1894, the directors of Willans & Robinson paid their first visit to Rugby, seeking a location for their new works, which were completed just a year later, on this 'greenfield' site.

The Victoria Works was employing just under 1,000 people in 1899, with the buildings illuminated and supplied with electricity from a dynamo powered by a Willans engine. Just as there was no electricity in Rugby at that time, neither was there a telephone service, although telegrams could be sent from the works, by a telegraph operator transmitting in morse code, into the Post Office telegraph system. Willans & Robinson's new works at Rugby attracted the attention of visitors from all over the country, and overseas too! Its advanced design was inspected by a party from the USA in 1900, when members of the American Society of Mechanical Engineers came to visit the works. Two special trains were provided by the LNWR from London Euston for the outing, and equipped with electric light, amongst other contemporary 'modern conveniences'. An ironic comment passed by one of the American visitors to the Rugby works was that, nowhere else was there any works so advanced in the manufacture of steam engines!

Just 18 years later, in 1919, Willans & Robinson were merged with Dick, Kerr & Co., Siemens Bros, Dynamo Works, and the Coventry Ordnance Works, to form the English Electric Co. At that time, the Victoria Works of Willans & Robinson were, like the other three manufacturers, under the control of John Brown & Co. Ltd. John Brown's principal claim to fame was in the application of Bessemer steel production, introduced in the 1860s, in the production of railway rails, and armour plating for the Royal Navy's 'Ironclads'. The later fame of John Brown & Co. in shipbuilding, dates from the purchase in 1899, of a shipbuilding yard on Clydebank, near Glasgow.

It is perhaps something of an irony that one of the world's most famous builders of diesel railway locomotives should have been established through the enterprise of what subsequently became a major shipbuilding concern. John Brown's of Clydebank has long since disappeared, but the English Electric Co. and its works, formed over 70 years ago, continued to live on under the name of GEC Traction Ltd.

Early Developments in Diesel Traction
From the formation of the English Electric Co. in 1919 it might have been supposed that both engines and transmissions could have been built 'in house', but for the home market at least, engines from Beardmore & Co. could be found paired with electrical equipments from Dick, Kerr of Preston. This arrangement was adopted for the prototype diesel multiple unit trains used on the Blackpool to Manchester lines by the LMSR. The Glasgow based engine builders Beardmore & Co. were the principal suppliers of engines for the English Electric Co.'s early export orders, for Spain and Argentina. In addition, GEC, as the General Electric Co., provided electrical equipment for a diesel-electric locomotive design, with Beardmore engines, for India, by the end of the 1920s.

For the later members of the GEC Traction fold, perhaps the most important successes were achieved in the 1920s, as the use of diesel, or oil engines began to take off. At home, interest in this form of traction was slower to materialise than overseas, where, in some countries, coal was not found in such abundant supplies. The British Thomson-Houston Co., with their petrol-electric bus of 1907, had demonstrated an interesting application of new technology in the field of mass transportation, without the use of rails or electrical contact systems. In later years too, the BTH Co., from their base at Rugby, had produced a number of locomotive designs for rail service, with their first essay in diesel locomotive design being an export order – a shunting locomotive for New South Wales, in 1933. Like English Electric, BTH's early rail transport contracts were in the field of electric traction, extending into the design and supply of power equipment for diesel locomotives and railcars.

With English Electric traction motors and Beardmore engines, this was the first diesel train to operate successfully for the LMS Railway, in 1928.

Vulcan Foundry, whose works had been building steam locomotives for around 100 years, first ventured into diesel traction in the early 1920s. In 1926, the company entered into an association with A/S Frichs of Aarhus in Denmark, to build diesel-electric locomotives, based on the Danish company's existing successful designs. Frichs had actually been in the business of diesel engine manufacture since 1910, exploiting the lead achieved by Britain's European neighbours in this area, and their relationship with Vulcan Foundry was only terminated by the hostilities of World War II. Diesel locomotives continued to be manufactured alongside steam at Newton-le-Willows during the inter-war

Overseas railways were really the mainstay for diesel traction equipment, certainly until the 1950s, from EE Co. Metropolitan-Vickers, BTH, and others. In this view, two Tasmanian Railways 660hp Bo-Bo Class XEs, from Metrovick, celebrate the 1951 Festival of Britain in some style.

period, and afterwards, until 1956, when, just a year after Vulcan Foundry's absorption by English Electric, the last steam type was built. Locomotives, both diesel and electric, continued to emerge from the Vulcan Foundry works until 1970, when the manufacture of diesel engines alone became the principal output. Nowadays, from an emphasis on railway locomotives, the Newton-le-Willows output has diversified into almost every sphere where diesel engines can be utilised, whether for generating sets, powering locomotives, or ships.

Some Notable Products

Whilst the Ruston-Akroyd-Stuart pioneer oil engines, and the Dick, Kerr petrol-electric locomotives represent the first stage in the evolution of the diesel railway locomotive, the next significant orders began to arrive in the 1920s. The first order for the home market took to the rails in 1928, on the LMSR's line from Blackpool to Preston, and was followed in the very next year by the first export success. These latter orders involved the design, manufacture and supply of electrical equipment for railcars for Argentina, and a 100hp locomotive for Canada.

Contemporary press reports of the earliest of these multiple unit type trains suggest that it fell neatly between the duties of steam, or oil engine driven railcars, and electric multiple units. It may then be that from the UK manufacturers' point of view, English Electric had provided the first true predecessor of today's multiple unit designs. For the London, Midland & Scottish Railway four vehicles were built for this train, which in the original scheme of things, had been intended for the dc electrification of the same company's Bury to Holcombe Brook lines. The modifications to the two third class motor coaches, and two third class trailer cars were carried out at the Derby Works of the LMSR.

Described as a 500bhp oil-electric train, the engine itself was built by William Beardmore & Co., in Glasgow, with eight cylinders of 8¼in bore and 12in stroke. The engine was similar to that supplied by Beardmore for railcars in service with Canadian National Railways, and was in fact based on engine designs for airship propulsion. It did not, after its service trials, prove particularly successful, and it was generally considered that the engine design was unsuitable for rail traction. The engine and generator set were carried in a section of the leading coach, 22ft long, and partitioned from the luggage compartment, with a driving position at the outer end.

The electrical equipment, generator and control gear, were supplied by English Electric, and were designed and built at the Preston Works. The main generator, with its shunt winding, was of the single bearing type, with an overhung exciter at the outboard end, and developed a maximum output of 340kW at 900 rpm, on a one hour rating. Described as a 'traction type', the shunt windings were energised by the exciter, or battery, according to the engine speed, whilst at speeds of more than 600 rpm, the exciter functioned as an auxiliary generator. This arrangement has, at least in basic principle, survived almost until the present day, with diesel engines coupled to main generators, on a common shaft, with overhung auxiliary machines. Just as they do in many locomotives today, the LMSR's four-car multiple unit train's exciter/auxiliary generator, supplied power for lighting, train control, and brake exhausters.

The two traction motors, rated at 200hp, were arranged to drive the axles of the trailing bogie on the power car, through single reduction spur gearing, with a ratio of 18 to 60. The English Electric works at Preston, it will be recalled, were formerly those of Dick, Kerr & Co., whose experience in the design and manufacture of tramway equipment was of long standing, and the design of the transmission on the LMS train bore some resemblance to that in use in many city streets. In addition, the type of motor used in this early

diesel-electric multiple unit was similar to that adopted for the rolling stock on the Euston to Watford electrified lines. The motorman's position also owed a great deal, in concept and layout, to the familiar arrangements on tramcars, with, in this case, the main switchboard and contactor gear carried in a frame over the main generator. An electro-mechanical control system was used, with a seven-notch controller, having five running notches, and the final two corresponding to two stages of field weakening in the traction motors, which were permanently connected in parallel with the generator, through a remotely controlled circuit breaker.

This development on the LMSR was not the earliest of its kind, since in Europe, the first multiple unit/railcar had been put to work in Sweden in 1913, also with electric transmission. In view of the later enthusiasm with which diesel traction was pursued in the USA, during the 1940s, it is an irony to recall that the Westinghouse Co., undertook to build Beardmore diesel engines under licence in the 1920s. Westinghouse, as is well known, had come across the Atlantic at the turn of the century, to build their factory in Manchester, taking account of the anticipated growth in electric traction. In mainland Europe, diesel traction was finding success easier than in Britain, especially in Denmark, where between 1926 and 1935, no less than 40 locomotives, 45 railcars, and eleven locomotive tractors were built. The Germans, Swiss, and French were equally busy, exploiting the virtues of the new form of motive power. Developing the growth of expertise in GEC Traction's predecessors, the name of A/S Frichs of Aarhus, Denmark and Vulcan Foundry, although linked from 1926, it was not until 1933 that agreement was reached to build Frichs diesel engines at the Newton-le-Willows site.

Perhaps the next major step in this growing expertise was the winning of an order to supply a 100hp Bo-Bo petrol-electric locomotive to Canada. The locomotive, delivered in 1929, was put to work in Montreal, on the Harbour Commission's lines. However, it was petrol engined, and strictly speaking was something of a parallel, rather than a forward looking step. In the same year though, an important success was the completion of the order for power equipment for diesel railcars/multiple unit trains for Argentina. This order was for three sets of electric transmission equipment, installed in eight-coach trains for the Buenos Aires Great Southern Railway, for working suburban services around Buenos Aires. At the same time, the English Electric Co. supplied electric transmission equipment for a 1,700hp locomotive, for use on the main lines of the Buenos Aires Great Southern system.

These orders for the Argentine were amongst the company's earliest export work, though they were not the first such diesel traction contracts placed by Argentina. A variety of manufacturers had, by the late 1920s seen their products at work, and foremost amongst these names were the likes of Sulzer, Beardmore, Armstrong-Whitworth, and of course, Metropolitan-Vickers. The latter became a member of the GEC Traction fold many years later, through GEC's acquisition of the AEI Group of companies. In the 1920s, diesel engine manufacturers figuring prominently in this slowly unfolding market were Beardmore and Sulzer, with English Electric from their Preston and Rugby works, whilst Ruston & Hornsby in Lincoln were still resisting the use of the term 'diesel'.

Petrol Electric Rapid Transit

At the time the Argentine orders were placed, Sir Sam Fay, of Great Central Railway fame, was also on the board of the Buenos Aires Great Southern Railway, and an enthusiastic supporter of non-steam traction. Referring to the use of petrol engines in rail traction service, with the Great Central

Built in 1933, this 1,700hp twin unit for the Buenos Aires Great Southern Railway was fitted with English Electric traction motors, Sulzer 850hp diesel engines, and main generators from Brown Boveri. The mechanical parts came from Armstrong Whitworth. These early diesel locomotives for Argentina were amongst the first orders for main line diesel traction, with Metropolitan-Vickers also supplying electrical equipment for 1,200hp locomotives built in 1930.

Railway in England, Sir Sam Fay had seen some evidence of the suitability of these power equipments, just prior to the 1914-18 war. The Great Central's railcars were manufactured by the forerunner of Metropolitan-Vickers, the British Westinghouse Electric & Manufacturing Co., and according to the makers, were an attempt to overcome some of the drawbacks of steam rail motors in urban and branch line workings. The 90hp design supplied by British Westinghouse to the GCR consisted of a six-cylinder 90hp engine mounted in the coach body, at the leading end, and driving a 60kW dc. generator. The generator was directly coupled to the engine, and supplied power to two, totally enclosed traction motors, from the Westinghouse stable.

The Great Central Railway's petrol-electric car was supplied in 1912, but again, as was the case with early electric traction orders, overseas railways seemed much more enthusiastic about the development of non-steam motive power. The British Westinghouse railcar design had been supplied to Hungary, where 16 such vehicles were in service on the Arad to Caanad Railway, with another 18 running on the Ooster Stoomtram Mattschappij in Holland, and smaller numbers of similar types at work in France, Germany and Sweden. The Westinghouse car built for the Great Central in England was, at the time, the largest such vehicle in operation. The slow take up of interest in the new form of traction in the UK may be emphasised by the fact that, in Hungary, the petrol-electric vehicles had been in service since 1905.

The engine and generator in the car were arranged at one end, with the traction motors on the bogie at the opposite end.

Two driving compartments were provided, separated by two seating compartments, accommodating 46 passengers, with standing room for another 14. The six-cylinder engine, with 140mm by 156mm cylinders, developed its 90hp at 1,150 rpm, and was water cooled, with the radiators mounted on the vehicle's roof. Intriguingly, hand starting was possible, and the engine was fitted with a 'de-compression cam', enabling the engine to be 'turned easily by hand'.

The generator was a shunt-wound machine, with interpoles, the introduction of which in 1905, had contributed not a little to the development of heavy duty motors, at higher voltages than was possible previously. This particular advance was more pronounced in electric traction service, enabling the use of higher line voltages, and increasing the spacing of traction supply substations. The Westinghouse traction motors on the GCR petrol-electric car were of the dc., series-wound variety, whose design had followed a standard pattern adopted for many tramway and rail systems around the world. The two motors were hung from the axles of the bogie, and drove the wheels through simple spur gearing. Power control, or, more specifically, regulating the traction motor voltage was again, an adaptation of existing tramway controllers, governing the excitation of the generator field coils.

In extolling the virtues of the use of these early petrol-electric railcars, the British Westinghouse Co. were emphasising the economic advantages, and technical superiority of the type over their steam powered equivalents. Electric transmission was seen by Westinghouse as the most effective and flexible means of powering rail vehicles of this design, though mechanical transmissions were, and indeed still are, used to equally good effect.

Ruston & Hornsby

The association of this company, formed in September 1918, by the amalgamation of Ruston, Proctor & Co., with Richard Hornsby & Sons, and its relationship with the development of the compression ignition engine, has already been briefly mentioned. Curiously perhaps, little progress was made in the construction of locomotives, or other vehicles equipped with such engines until around the time of the 1914-1918 war. Most of the locomotives built by Ruston & Hornsby, whether petrol or 'oil' engines, were narrow gauge, and normally employed in quarries, mines, and other industrial locations. It has also been suggested that Richard Hornsby & Sons undertook locomotive building in the 1930s especially, as a relief measure to offset the effects of the economic slump of this period. Whilst R&H may well have been reluctant to adopt the term 'diesel', and preferred 'oil', or 'heavy oil' engines, their work did contribute significantly to the long term development of diesel traction, particularly in the industrial field.

The company later took over messrs Davey Paxman & Co. (Colchester) Ltd, who had been successfully building rail traction diesel engines for a number of years, and as discussed in Chapter 4, were responsible for the engine in the pioneer 0-6-0 shunter ordered by the LMSR. Overall however, the diesel traction market came to be dominated by English Electric, who's success was challenged in the 1920s and 1930s by the likes of Beardmore, Vulcan Foundry and Sulzer, from within the UK. Vulcan Foundry were of course assisted in this area by their partnership with A/S Frichs. Many of the orders for this new form of traction came from overseas, and for both English Electric, and Metropolitan-Vickers, these were predominantly colonies in the British Empire.

Europe in general had stolen the march on the UK, for the adoption of diesel power in their domestic systems, and indeed, in the development of this new form of motive power. The first generally acknowledged diesel locomotive, was a 1,000hp direct drive unit, from Sulzer-Diesel-Klose, appearing in 1912. The first true diesel powered railcar was put into service a year later, in Sweden. Perhaps in some ways, it was a good thing that full advantage was not taken of the British lead in design of compression ignition engines, or we would today be referring to them as 'Hornsby-Akroyds'! Sections of the British contemporary technical press described such installations as oil-electric, in preference to diesel-electric for many years, despite even, the early

publication of the 'Diesel Railway Traction' supplement to *Railway Gazette*.

Dick, Kerr & Co., who were the major constituent of English Electric in 1919, had, oddly, rejected a scheme to produce, in combination with others, a diesel-electric locomotive of 800hp in 1904. Works Committee Minute Books for this period reveal that rejection in some interesting references to an unnamed syndicate and 'Mr Dickinson's Locomotive'. The specification put to the Dick, Kerr committee, was for an oil engine coupled to a generator, with traction 'motors on the coaches'. Evidently, the proposal was for a multiple unit formation, but it was recorded that Dick, Kerr did not consider it of great value to services which were frequent, with many stops, but could be useful for a few trains!

At the time, it was pointed out that a similar system was then in use on the North Eastern Railway, running into Filey, and there was nothing new in the arrangement at all. Questions were also raised on the performance figures claimed for the proposed engine, and the company were advised by the Works Committee that 'it would not be advisable to take in the type of work proposed at that time'. Following an apparently acrimonious exchange of correspondence with the said Mr Dickinson, the idea was again considered by the Works Committee, and again rejected. Some members felt that the proposal was simply to experiment on the suitability of diesel-electric power equipment, whilst another considered that direct drive to be a more appropriate form of transmission.

Only a decade later, Dick, Kerr & Co. began their major essay into petrol-electric transmissions, with the narrow gauge locomotives ordered by the War Office for war service. At the time the Dickinson proposal was made, Dick, Kerr were the major, wholly British force in the electric traction market, with stiff competition from the American

Effectively the start of the diesel era at home was the work undertaken by the LMSR, which, in addition to the multiple units, developed the standard British 0-6-0 shunter, and characterised by English Electric-equipped Hawthorn, Leslie No. 3842 of 1935, seen here in LMS colours and numbered 7070.

backed British Westinghouse, and British Thomson-Houston. It may well have been the consideration of consolidation in existing markets, that dissuaded the company from progressing at an earlier stage, with oil engines and electric, or some other form of transmission. Had the proposal been taken up, the UK may have been as much as seven years ahead of its nearest rivals in the diesel traction field.

The period up to around 1920 seemed to be dominated equally as much by changes in company organisation, notably the formation of two of the cornerstones of the GEC Traction empire; Metropolitan-Vickers and English Electric. During this time, George Westinghouse and his British Westinghouse protege disappeared, the latter of course becoming Metropolitan-Vickers – joining Dudley Docker's Metropolitan Carriage & Wagon Finance with Vickers Ltd. By the mid 1920s, Vulcan Foundry had also taken a significant step forward in diesel traction terms, in association with A/S Frichs of Aarhus, Denmark, further establishing the interest of another GEC Traction predecessor in non-steam traction.

A Summary of Developments

Summarising the involvement of the pre-GEC Traction companies in this pioneering era, it may perhaps be fairly stated that diesel engine construction was predominantly the work of no single company. But, its growth, particularly in commercial terms, was distributed between the likes of Davey Paxman & Co., Ruston & Hornsby and Willans & Robinson. English Electric and Metropolitan-Vickers were rather later into this field, along with Vulcan Foundry. Metropolitan-Vickers, in company with British Thomson-

Houston, and the General Electric Co., had been providing electric transmission equipment, to be paired with the diesel engine designs of different suppliers, such as William Beardmore & Co.

All the later components of GEC Traction began the commercial manufacture of diesel engines for railway locomotives soon after the turn of the century. The exception to this rule being, naturally, the Hornsby-Akroyd design of 1896. Metropolitan-Vickers, like Dick, Kerr & Co., had entered the field by way of manufacturing gas engines. The first 20th century diesel engines were built in 1904 at the Rugby Works of Willans & Robinson, acquired by Dick, Kerr in 1916. In Manchester, Metropolitan-Vickers, as British Westinghouse were building gas engines for royalty, with the first order in 1903, for King Edward VII, and delivered to Sandringham Hall in Norfolk. The earliest diesel engines from the Trafford Park works were produced in 1912, still under the British Westinghouse flag, and were a four-stroke design. Diesel engine manufacture was encouraged by the 1914-1918 war, and by the end of the hostilities, British Westinghouse had constructed a number of diesel engines for the Royal Navy's submarines.

Like English Electric, Metropolitan-Vickers entered the 1920s under something of a cloud, with orders in the electrical industry falling off, and a three months long dispute with the engineering unions at Trafford Park. The main compo-

A beautifully clean engine compartment showing the emerging standard 350hp power unit, from English Electric. The 0-6-0 design was so obviously based around a steam engine's mechanical framework at this time.

The important diesel order from the LMS for English Electric, showing four of the 350hp 0-6-0s under construction at the Preston Works. Perhaps even more interesting in this view, and seen under the crane in the top left hand corner, is the experimental *Bluebird* railcar.

nents of GEC Traction, even in the diesel traction field, were very much affected by the ups and downs of the electrical engineering industry, though this was perhaps less true for Ruston & Hornsby, or Vulcan Foundry. The former company, despite their early progress, were not as successful in the railway arena as the others, from their initial developments, whilst Vulcan Foundry's association with A/S Frichs, undoubtedly gave them a significant edge in the traction field. At home, the four main line railways only toyed with the advantages of diesel power during the inter-war period, with the most important progress being made by the London, Midland & Scottish Railway.

During the next two decades, the work of the big two companies, Metropolitan-Vickers and English Electric, with Vulcan Foundry in second place perhaps, were far more successful in overseas markets. This export success, and two more decades of experience, stood the home manufacturers in good stead, when the railways in this country finally came to take the new form of traction seriously. Although at the same time, to demonstrate their wares, the companies concerned would have to take their potential customers to some rather widely scattered locations around the world. Both English Electric, and the AEI group of companies after 1928 (Comprising Metropolitan-Vickers, British Thomson-Houston, and others), suffered a little from this lack of a 'shop window' at home. Up to the end of the 1920s, major orders comprised the following, with various contracts emphasising the wide customer base,

which, as discussed later, was widely extended during the 1930s and 1940s.

Early Diesel Traction Orders

Argentina	Six sets of diesel railcar equipment. English Electric Co.	1927
War Department	90 petrol-electric locomotives. Dick, Kerr & Co.	1914–18
Harbour Commission (Montreal)	One, 100hp Bo-Bo petrol-electric locomotive. English Electric Co.	1929
LMSR	Set of electrical equipment for Preston to Blackpool train. English Electric Co.	1928
Spain	Three sets of electrical equipment for San Sebastian to Pamplona. Metropolitan-Vickers	1928
Argentina	Three sets of electrical equipment for 8-car trains. Metropolitan-Vickers	1929
Venezuela	Three, 200hp diesel-electric coaches. English Electric Co.	1929

3
Progress of Railway Electric Traction

With the outbreak of the First World War, the greatest progress in rail electrification was in what we would today refer to as rapid transit systems – tramways! Dick, Kerr and British Westinghouse were, as has already been discussed, the major British companies in this field, but although some main lines overseas were being electrified, progress was not so rapid at home. In the North West, there was the Liverpool Overhead Railway, the Midland Railway's line from Lancaster to Morecambe and Heysham, and the Lancashire & Yorkshire Railway's Liverpool to Southport lines. In the south of the country, the growing London Underground was already exploiting the advantages of electric traction, with equipment from Siemens Brothers, Dick, Kerr & Co., and another later member of the GEC Traction fold, the British Thomson-Houston Co. Overseas, only the Norwegian, Thamshaven to Lokken line had acquired the benefits of ac electrification, with an overhead contact system.

British Thomson-Houston, who came into the GEC Traction arena as a member of the AEI Group, following the dramatic takeover bid by GEC in November 1967, had been instrumental in the installation of the first overhead wire tramway in 1891. Home orders for tramways and trolleybus systems were substantial during the period under review, from 1900 up to the outbreak of war, whilst after the hostilities many countries around the world embarked on electrification programmes for main lines. A number of these had been in the planning stage before the 1914–18 war, and were concluded during the 1920s. The expertise of British Thomson-Houston, British Westinghouse, and Dick, Kerr &

Almost new, these Liverpool to Southport units for the LYR, were fitted with English Electric traction motors, and camshaft control. The photograph was taken in 1924, although EE Co., and Dick, Kerr had supplied the equipment for trains operating over this route in 1904 and 1921.

Co. was spread around the globe, from Denmark and France, in Europe, through Hungary and Poland to Canada, Argentina, India, and even Japan. It is an interesting thought that, bearing in mind the later enthusiasm for, and progress with electrification in France, a later GEC company was involved in the earliest projects there. Similarly it is believed that in Hungary, the project with which these early GEC companies were involved, was amongst the first to adopt power supplies to the contact systems, using industrial frequency, single phase ac.

A Period of Mergers

Before looking at some of the developments in the decade from 1913 to 1923, there were a number of important changes in the organisation of the industry, that had far reaching effects. Recalling the pre-eminent position of the Preston company, Dick, Kerr & Co., in association with the Phoenix Dynamo Co., and Siemens Brothers (Dynamo) Works Ltd, these were merged by John Brown & Co., to form English Electric Co. Ltd. John Brown & Co. were first established in Sheffield, though later of course, acquiring the famous shipbuilding yards on the River Clyde. In the 1800s, John Brown's were rather more famous for steel products, including rails from the newly developed Bessemer process, than they were for ships or shipbuilding. Following the turn of the century, and various agreements and associations with other manufacturers, John Brown's expanded rapidly during the First World War, acquiring the Carnforth Iron Co., and shortly afterwards, the Cravens Railway Carriage & Wagon Co., taking the group more obviously into the railway world.

In the same year the English Electric was formed, another famous name emerged from the shadows, the Metropolitan-Vickers Electrical Co. This particularly important company resulted from the takeover of the Metropolitan Carriage, Wagon & Finance Co. by Vickers Ltd. Vickers, like a num-

In 1915, the LYR ordered 60 sets of motor coach equipments from Dick, Kerr & Co., just prior to the formation of English Electric. The five-car trains were set to work on the Manchester to Bury section, picking up a 1,200V dc supply from the conductor rail.

ber of other companies at the time, were seeking diversity in their product range, which, like John Brown's, had previously been confined to heavy engineering, shipbuilding and the like. The Metropolitan Carriage Co. had bought out the American British Westinghouse Co., with its works in Trafford Park, Manchester, where the United States parent had apparently abandoned the venture as a result of the lack of enthusiasm for electric railways in the UK. From 1899 to 1926, including the takeover period, the company, as British Westinghouse, and subsequently, as Metropolitan-Vickers Ltd, was not financially successful. Vickers Ltd later sold off their interest in the railway rolling stock business, as part of a financial reconstruction, following the onset of the economic depression in the early 1920s

So then, at the start of the First World War, two of the key pieces in GEC Traction's history had finally emerged, both English Electric in Preston, and Metropolitan-Vickers in Manchester, emphasised the importance of the North West in the development of non-steam rail traction. Further south, albeit only slightly, the Vulcan Foundry had established its famous works at Newton-le-Willows, which assumed very considerable importance during the mid-1920s, as diesel traction continued to grow within the railway industry. The evolving English Electric empire had the advantage of the switchgear factory established by Siemens Bros Ltd in Stafford, in 1901. Again, Siemens Bros, like many others in the UK during the 1914–18 period, had its finances and activities thrown into confusion by the war, and the company's capital was sold to a finance house in 1917. The Stafford base of Siemens Bros (Dynamo) Works Ltd, was sold to English Electric in the year of the latter company's birth, 1919.

Other GEC Traction predecessors were engaged in electri-

fication work too, like the British Thomson-Houston Co., who, it will be remembered, introduced the world's first petrol-electric bus in 1907. BTH were another example of the American influence on the development of electrical technology in this country, and as mentioned earlier, were responsible in 1891, for the first installation in Leeds, of an overhead catenary on a tramway system. One of the first experimental trolleybuses – a natural extension of the tramcar perhaps – was equipped by BTH in 1909. In trolleybus services, Siemens Bros had supplied equipment for its first installations, commercially, in the UK, in 1910, for service in Leeds and Bradford. The BTH works at Rugby, were neighbours of the English Electric works, which in their turn were formally the Victoria Works of Willans & Robinson Ltd, and which had come into the GEC Traction fold through the formation of English Electric in 1919.

Some Important Projects

Having noted the establishment of the cornerstones of GEC Traction, from a number of smaller companies, following the 1914–18 war, two major projects then undertaken, set something of a pattern for future electrification in Britain. Almost at opposite ends of the country, and at almost the same time, providing electric traction on its main lines, was a policy pursued by two far sighted railway companies. In the North East, the North Eastern Railway embarked on a programme to electrify its Newcastle to Shildon line, with an overhead contact system, whilst south of the Thames, the London & South Western Railway equipped its lines with conductor rails. The NER had already seen the use of electric traction on the Tyneside suburban system, but the larger Shildon project was another first for Metropolitan-Vickers. This time, it was the first use of an overhead contact system energised at 1,500V dc, for which Metropolitan-Vickers supplied the power, and Siemens Bros (Dynamo) Works, the contact system, and locomotive equipments.

The Newport to Shildon line of the NER consisted of 19 route miles, over which in 1922, some 50 million tons of coal and ore were transported from the marshalling sidings at Shildon, to the blast furnaces of steelworks in the Middlesbrough area. Metropolitan-Vickers provided the sub-station equipment, whilst Siemens Bros (Dynamo) Works Ltd, in Stafford, provided the electrical equipment for the locomotives, and contact equipment. Two traction substations were employed, one at Aycliffe, and the other at Erimus, and supplied with power from the Cleveland & Durham Electric Power Company. The electrical equipment from Metropolitan-Vickers consisted of transformers, switchgear and rotary convertors – the latter comprising two 800kW units at Aycliffe, and an 800 and a 1,200kW unit at Erimus. The incoming ac supply at 40Hz was thus converted to 1,500V dc, and supplied to the overhead contact wire, which, it had been decided, would be used on this principal, heavy freight route. Current was collected from the overhead by roof-mounted pantographs, and returned via bonded running rails.

Under the guidance of Sir Vincent Raven, the North Eastern Railway was pioneering 1,500V dc electrification with overhead catenary, though the Tyneside Suburban scheme, again with the support of Metropolitan-Vickers, had adopted third rail contact. It is interesting to reflect that, at least a part of the Newport to Shildon line coincided with the route of the former Stockton & Darlington Railway – also famed for its pioneering activity!

Enthusiasm for electric traction was most evident in three areas of the UK, including the North East, London, and the North West. Elsewhere, countries of the British Empire were popularising this form of traction, which was of course particularly suitable where coal was not such an abundant fuel for use in steam locomotives.

The Newport to Shildon line's success here in the UK, provided the NER with the necessary impetus to consider the even grander scheme to electrify some 80 miles of its main line out of York, in the early 1920s. Motive power for the Newport to Shildon line was equipped with power and control equipment from Siemens Bros Ltd, with ten locomotives built from 1914, each having a pair of two-axle bogies, and exerting a maximum tractive effort of 19,600lbs. They were, as previously referred to, not the first electric locomotives for the NER, since British Thomson-Houston had equipped a

pair of 604V dc shunting locomotives back in 1904 for quay side duties in Newcastle's docks. The Siemens equipped locomotives were the first production series of any size, and built in the railway company's own workshops, they had the following main dimensions:

Newport–Shildon Bo-Bo Locomotives

Wheel arrangement	Bo-Bo
Gauge	4ft 8½in
Voltage	1,500V dc
Drive systems	straight, twin gear
Traction motor rating (1 hr)	1,100hp
(cont.)	635hp
Tractive effort (1 hr)	19,600lb
(cont.)	10,400lb
Speed (maximum)	22.8 mph
Length	39ft 4in
Width	8ft 4in
Height (pantograph lowered)	13ft 1$\frac{5}{16}$in
Bogie wheelbase	8ft 9in
Wheel diameter	4ft 0in
Axle load	18tons 12cwt
Weight of electrical eqpt.	24tons 5cwt
Weight of mechanical eqpt.	50tons 3cwt

Of this class of ten locomotives, it was stated that, at the time, five of the new locomotives could do the work of 13 steam types, and infinitely more cheaply. In fact, in a paper read by Sir Vincent Raven to the North East Coast Institution of Engineers and Shipbuilders in 1921, total running costs for the electric locomotives for 1920 came to 1.5d (less than 1p) per mile, whilst the equivalent for steam engines reached some 11.5d (very nearly 5p) per mile. All ten of these electric locomotives survived to British Railways days, and a decade or so later, at least one was still in departmental service, working at Ilford carriage sidings.

The North Eastern Railway was as famous an innovator as the company who supplied the electrical equipment for this locomotive – Metropolitan-Vickers. The locomotive remained a one off, since, sadly, the railway company's far reaching plans never materialised for the electrification of the main line from York to Newcastle.

Only four years after the opening of the Newport to Shildon line, the NER published plans to electrify the York to Newcastle main line. The details of the scheme were worked out with consulting engineers Merz & McLellan, who were later responsible, with Metropolitan-Vickers, for the Natal electrification in South Africa, in 1922. For the NER scheme of 1919 it is interesting to record that dual contact equipment – both conductor rail and catenary – was to be installed, and was to be suitable for high speed running.

The motive power likely to be used on this main line scheme was the subject of some intensive testing on the Newport to Shildon line in 1922. Whilst Metropolitan-Vickers won the order for the power equipment for the passenger locomotives, a proposal was submitted at the same time by the General Electric Co. of the USA, for an articulated 4-6-6-4 locomotive, with a gearless drive. The decision to press ahead with the 4-6-4 arrangement, with M-V equipment was influenced by the satisfactory performance of symmetrical locomotives at high speed, on a number of European railways. It was suggested that one of the reasons for the symmetrical layout being out of favour in the USA, notwithstanding the articulated version, was due to the staggering of rail joints, common on US railroads.

However, despite the late entry from the American General Electric Co., Metropolitan-Vickers were successful, and the locomotive which appeared in 1922, had to meet a number of interesting design specifications from Sir Vincent Raven.

(i)   The adhesive weight was to be at least 17 tons per axle.
(ii) The complete electrical equipment to exert sufficient torque to skid the wheels, without damage to themselves, or any part of the equipment.
(iii) The traction motors were to be able to exert a total, average starting tractive effort of 16,000lbs.
(iv) The complete equipment was to be able to start a trailing load from rest of 450 tons, on a gradient of 1 in 78, and accelerate it to normal running speed.
(v)   The traction motors were to be designed for normal operation at a speed of 90 mph.
(vi) On level track, the locomotives were required to be capable of hauling 14 main line coaches at more than 65 mph.

A series of successful trials were held on the newly electrified Newport to Shildon route, but the planned electrification of the York to Newcastle main line never got off the ground, and the fleet of locomotives was not needed. Only two years later, the far sighted North Eastern Railway was swallowed up in the amalgamated London & North Eastern Railway.

Metropolitan-Vickers equipment provided in the solitary express passenger locomotive, consisted of three pairs of traction motors, each developing some 300hp, and driving the wheels through quill shafts. Two motors were carried above the quill shafts on each driving axle, to which they were connected by spur gears. Force ventilation, and electro-pneumatic control systems were employed, with the motors grouped either all series, or in two, or three parallel groups. Under test, the 4-6-4 locomotive, with its twin, roof-mounted pantographs, was able to sustain a drawbar pull of 6.6 tons up a 1 in 103 gradient, with a trailing load of 460 tons. Over the 18 miles from Newport to Shildon, rising more than 400ft, average drawbar pull under test was 5.5 tons.

Metropolitan Vickers and the LSWR Electrification
At the opposite end of the country, another British railway company was demonstrating its initiative with the then 'new technology'. The scheme was to electrify the London & South Western company's London Suburban lines also involved a degree of co-operation with one of Metropolitan-

Vickers' competitors – Messrs Dick, Kerr & Co., of Preston. The latter were already renowned for their expertise at home and abroad, and pioneering work in the area of electric tramways and railways.

At the time of introduction of electric traction on the LSWR routes, Metropolitan-Vickers was not in existence, because in the autumn of 1915, the Manchester company was still known as British Westinghouse. For the LSWR, Metropolitan-Vickers were responsible for the power equipment on the rolling stock, whilst Dick, Kerr had provided five 5,000kW turbo alternators, and three 400kW turbo generators in the Durnsford Road power station at Wimbledon. The turbo alternators supplied power at 11kV, 25Hz, whilst the generators gave power at 220V dc for the switchboard, auxiliaries, and power station lighting. The 11kV ac was supplied – with a duplicate circuit – to each of nine traction substations at Waterloo, Clapham Junction, Raynes Park, Kingston, Twickenham, Barnes, Isleworth, Sunbury, and Hampton Court Junction. The substations, with their associated transformers and rotary convertors, were then required to convert the incoming three-phase ac supply, at 11kV, into 600V dc feeders into the conductor rails.

The LSWR, and its Chief Electrical Engineer Herbert Jones, had studied in detail the available systems of the day, and came down in favour of using 600V dc, with a conductor rail – running rails were used for the return path. But, it is interesting to note the comment made, that this decision was reached on the basis of the LSWR's intensive suburban traffic, and in contrast to the prevailing tendency to adopt 1,500kV dc as standard. The LSWR scheme though, established a standard pattern followed south of the Thames by other railway companies, despite the relatively brief and minor flirtation of the London, Brighton & South Coast Railway with single-phase ac, and an overhead contact system.

A total of 100 route miles of suburban track were covered in the 1915 LSWR project, with electrification completed in two stages of 50 miles each. The company had put forward three reasons in support of the introduction of electric traction: (i) to recover lost traffic, (ii) to induce new traffics, and, perhaps obviously, (iii) to meet the growing competition from neighbouring railways. With electric traction it was possible to provide a more frequent and rapid service. The competition driving the LSWR down this path came from the LBSCR, Metropolitan District, London's tramways, and a growing network of bus services.

At this point in the development of non-steam traction, the familiar names in the industry were rather more involved in the production of power equipments, than complete vehicles, or integrated projects. This was especially true at home, and in the production of multiple unit type rolling stock, and in the LSWR scheme, the railway company provided the vehicles, and Metropolitan-Vickers (alias British Westinghouse), the electrical equipment. The railway company produced 252 coaches, normally employed on steam hauled services, modified to include the electrical equipment, and formed into three-car sets, or multiples thereof. The three-coach formation included a motor coach at each end, sandwiching a trailer car, with the set powered by four, 275hp traction motors.

Due to the restriction of size placed on the motors by virtue of the 4ft 8½in track gauge, and the use of normal diameter coach wheels and axles, these were the largest dc motors that could be used. A pair of motors were mounted on the bogies under the leading end of each motor coach. Each of these pairs of motors had its own separate control equipment, carried in the cab, immediately above each bogie. Train speed was effected by means of the Metropolitan-Vickers 'All Electric Control' – an electro mechanical system.

Traction Motor Design

It is worth reviewing the progress, and general development of the design of traction motors at this point, as some standard practices had, by the time of the 1914–18 war emerged. There were also a number of differences between the type of motor that had proved suitable for tramways – the construction and operation of which were by this time very numerous, at home and abroad – and those which were more applicable to railway service.

Generally speaking there were two main types of traction motor available; the split frame, and box type. The former had been used for the smaller classes of machines, more especially for tramway installations, with broadly similar designs being adopted on early underground stock, as for the City & South London line. The box type, which, as its name implies, comprised a one-piece casting, and provided a stronger construction, suitable for the rigours of main line railway service. Interestingly, this form of construction was also being adopted for smaller tramway motors around 1915, and although at first, some manufacturing problems were experienced with the larger type traction motors, these were soon overcome, and the design was produced by Metropolitan-Vickers, and contemporary makers in some numbers.

The majority of traction motors were self-ventilated, incorporating a fan, built on to the armature shaft. This was referred to as the 'standard' arrangement at that time, although the motors more recently supplied (c1915) to the North Eastern Railway, incorporated force ventilation. On the LSWR project, Metropolitan-Vickers had provided the self-ventilated variety, with 'commutating poles', later referred to as interpoles. Another 'standard' feature already in use, was the arrangement of suspension from one side of the axle, with the nose of the motor suspended from the bogie frame, with a rubber buffer to reduce shocks, transmitted by the vehicle/track to the traction motor. Production processes too, from all the principal manufacturers, had adopted some advanced techniques, with extensive use of jigs and gauges to reduce maintenance time and costs. In general, designs of traction motor, and manufacturing techniques, had evolved considerably since the early days when the products of BTH, for the City & South London Railway, incorporated rotors wound directly onto the vehicle's axles.

Some Special Projects and Other Suburban Developments

The LSWR electrification was a landmark in the evolution of third rail systems south of the Thames, whilst the London & North Western Railway (LNWR), and subsequently the LMSR's outer suburban lines continued to expand. A couple of interesting projects that began life during this era were the Swansea & Mumbles Railway, and the world's first automatic electric railway, built for the Post Office, beneath the streets of the City of London.

By the time Metropolitan-Vickers became involved in London's expanding outer suburban rail network, more specifically the routes from Euston and Broad Street stations to Watford Junction, electric services had been operating since 1908. In 1923, as the London, Midland & Scottish Railway, the electrified lines in this area covered some 41.5 route miles (94 track miles), and included the former Midland Railway line to Barking, and the London & North Western's route from Willesden Junction to Earls Court. Also included was the Elephant & Castle service to Willesden Junction, by way of Queens Park, operated by the London Electric Railway, whose operations were later extended by way of joint stock workings with the LNWR to Watford Junction. In 1922, the LNWR electrified the route

from Euston and Camden Town to Queens Park, giving a through service from Euston to Watford Junction.

Metropolitan-Vickers again supplied some traction motors for the three-coach trains, and switchgear for the eleven substations on the North Western lines. In the Stonebridge Park power station, power was generated at 11kV ac by turbo-alternator sets, before conversion to 630V dc supply to the conductor rails. The Stonebridge Park station was built to supply the North Western section, whilst the former Midland Railway lines obtained their supplies from the London Electric Supply Co.'s Barking Power Station. In the original installation at Stonebridge Park, Metropolitan-Vickers provided turbines and condensers for the four, 5,000kW turbo-alternators, along with some low voltage switchgear for auxiliary services. In 1927 this was supplemented with a 10,000kW turbo-alternator from Trafford Park, to a new design.

The three-car suburban trains on the Euston to Watford routes of the LMSR consisted of a motor coach, intermediate trailer, and driving trailer. Metropolitan-Vickers supplied 66, 280hp traction motors, four of which were employed on each motor coach. The first 48 motors supplied were provided with one field tapping, whilst it was later decided to adopt a standard pattern of motor, with two field tappings, which was suitable for both the London Suburban and Liverpool to Southport lines. The second of these two field tappings on these later standard motors was used on the stock working the Southport services, where the average traction voltage was lower than in the London area. The three-coach trains in London were operated under the Group Control System, whilst Metropolitan-Vickers also supplied lighting and heating equipments.

Much further west, in South Wales, the Swansea & Mumbles Railway, originally opened for traffic in 1807, was converted to electric traction, with Metropolitan-Vickers supplying all the equipment for the Blackpill Substation. The Swansea & Mumbles Railway was only 5.75 miles in length, and had only adopted steam traction over horse power in 1877. On completion of the electrification, the service was provided by motor coaches, collecting a 650V dc supply from the overhead contact system.

Power was obtained from Swansea Corporation, and supplied at 6.6kV from the St Helens Power Station to the substation at Blackpill. Metropolitan-Vickers equipment in the substation consisted of rotary convertors, transformers and switchgear, and was controlled so that the whole operation was completely automatic. In the event of a fault in the supply line for instance, a second ac incomer was provided, whilst protection against such mechanical faults as overheated bearings in one of the rotary machines, allowed the offending device to be switched out, and a backup machine started automatically. Metropolitan-Vickers referred to this particular project as 'modernising the antique'.

Last but by no means least of these domestic 1920's projects, was the design, construction, and commissioning of the Post Office Tube Railway. This project occupies a special, if not unique position in the annals of railway history, as the first example of wholly automatic operation. In this country it pre-dated such schemes as the Birmingham 'Maglev' by some 60 years. The civil engineering work for the Post Office tube, including the running tunnels and tracks, were laid down before the 1914–18 war, although it was not until 1924 that electrification work was begun, following the acceptance of the English Electric Co.'s proposals. English Electric's contract with the Post Office included the provision of rolling stock, substation equipment, automatic control systems, signalling and cabling.

The route covered in the project was 2.5 miles long, with tracks laid to 2ft 0in gauge, and power supplied at 440V dc,

The world's first fully automatic electric railway, equipped by EE Co. for the Post Office, beneath the streets of London. The first orders were for the complete electrification of the line, at 440V dc, and the provision of 44hp locomotive tractors for the 2ft gauge line.

and fed to the conductor rails from three substations. From Paddington to Liverpool Street the deep level tube was constructed to link the principal GPO sorting offices, with two running tracks in 9ft diameter tunnels. At each station, an island type platform arrangement was adopted.

In each of the three substations, English Electric installed rotary converters to provide the dc traction supply, and auxiliary motor generator sets provided power for battery charging. The batteries themselves fed into the track signal circuits, with the whole line track circuited and sectionalised throughout, to allow minimum headway, with entry and exit from stations controlled automatically. The camshaft control system provided for the trains was claimed to enable one of the small wagons to enter a station at any speed, and be brought to a stand within eight feet of a designated point. Actual vehicle speeds were set at 32 mph in the tunnels, slowing to 8 mph at the station platform roads. The rolling stock order consisted originally of 90 two-axle trucks, though these were replaced a few years later by 50 wagons on 'maximum traction trucks'. These were fitted with a pair of 22hp dc traction motors, reverser, and electrically operated brake gear.

English Electric were justifiably proud of this narrow gauge railway, and in a review of progress published by the company in 1951, considered it to be unique in the whole railway world. The Post Office Tube did have some human intervention, at a distance, as the operation of a switch was

necessary to start a train on its way, and control of the points on the track was exercised remotely, guiding the vehicles on their way. At the time of writing, the Post Office Railway has been in operation for some 60 years, and until recently, retained its unique position as an automatic railway.

The Importance of Overseas Projects

Until the early 1920s, both English Electric and Metropolitan-Vickers were very successful in winning contracts around the world, mostly in the British Colonies. That success continued, and indeed, increased significantly thereafter, even in Europe with these most famous names becoming a major force in the industry. In the Far East, the English Electric Co. had won major orders in Japan as well as New Zealand, whilst Metropolitan-Vickers had been awarded contracts to supply locomotives for the first main line electrification project in South Africa. Orders for electric traction equipment for South African Railways have been an important market for GEC Traction and its predecessors, ever since the first report from consulting engineers Merz & McLellan was completed in 1919.

Furthest away from home, the New Zealand electrification scheme was a 'comprehensive contract', awarded to English Electric for the conversion to electric traction of the line from Arthur's Pass to Otira on the South Island. The contract involved the installation of catenary through what was at the time, the longest railway tunnel in the British Empire. The tunnel, 5.5 miles long, on a ruling gradient of 1 in 33, was hewn out of the solid rock, beneath Arthur's Pass in the Southern Alps. The route itself was very important, linking two of the South Island's provinces, Canterbury and Westland.

Thirty years after they first entered service, in 1922, these 720hp locomotives are seen here, still hard at work, on mixed traffic duties, on New Zealand Railways' Arthur's Pass to Otira line. The route was electrified by English Electric at 1,500V dc, and was one of the first composite contracts, for a 3ft 6in gauge line.

The equipment provided by English Electric consisted of the following:
5 complete, 720hp, 50-ton Bo-Bo electric locomotives.
1 complete, 400hp, Bo-Bo battery locomotive.
1 steam generating station, with two 1,200kW, 1,650V dc turbo-generator sets.

The overhead line equipment was also to be provided by the company, with the conductors energised at 1,500V dc. The success of this first scheme also resulted in the electrification of the seven miles long, suburban section of the same route, between Christchurch and the port of Lyttelton, which again involved a 'comprehensive contract'. The use of 1,500V dc was rapidly becoming standard, as both English Electric and Metropolitan-Vickers had clearly demonstrated at home. However, its use developed far more rapidly and extensively outside that 'home market', as the succession of export orders for these cornerstones of the GEC Traction empire, and the rail traction industry demonstrated.

The fixed structures of the New Zealand project included 'double catenary' in the open, and 'single catenary' through the Otira Tunnel. The conductors were supported in the open on wooden poles, with insulators attached to angle iron brackets, with more complex girder structures in stations and yards.

Locomotives were Bo-Bo double ended types, rated at 720hp for those in use on the main line, and a single 400hp battery locomotive. The latter had 50hp traction motors, driving the wheels through single reduction gearing, using a ratio of 15.83 to 1. The more powerful 720hp types, had four 179hp motors, with force ventilation, and connected permanently in series, as two pairs of motors. The tractive effort produced was 14,200lbs at the one hour rating of the traction motors.

These 'box cab' locomotives, with their twin, roof-mounted pantographs used the Westinghouse air brake, and a rheostatic brake, where the electrical energy of the motors was dissipated as heat through banks of resistances. The reason why regenerative braking systems were not employed – although it was considered – was due to the fact that the power station was there purely to supply power to the railway, there being no other load to share any regenerated energy that might otherwise be fed back into the line.

The success which attended this first project encouraged the extension of electrification of New Zealand's 3ft 6in gauge railways. Here again, English Electric supplied rotary convertors for the substations, but this time the principal source of power was the hydro-electric station at Lake Coleridge. Six 1,200hp Bo-Bo locomotives were supplied, with power equipment similar to that installed on the Arthur's Pass locomotives, with the English Electric Co.'s camshaft control system. The introduction of suburban services over the line from Christchurch to Lyttelton was completed in February 1929.

South Africa

Still in the southern hemisphere, consultants Merz & McLellan had reported on the suitability of two important routes in South Africa, for the use of electric traction. It is something of an irony perhaps, that, electrification was most popular in countries, or areas, where coal as a fuel was in short supply, the Pietermaritzburg to Glencoe route in Natal should have been selected. This line actually passed through some of the most productive coalfields in South Africa! And, interestingly, South Africa became one of the last strongholds of steam traction.

Three UK companies were particularly involved in this project, with British Insulated & Helsby Cables Ltd supplying the complete overhead line and droppers, and Metropolitan-Vickers, just three years after formation, were the main contractors for the 1,200hp locomotives. Intriguingly, the mechanical portions – 35 bodies at least – were subcontracted to Vickers Ltd, with a further 60 coming from the Swiss Locomotive & Car Works. The whole project was expensive – especially by 1920's standards – with overall expenditure coming in at more than £5.5 million.

South African Railways saw English Electric Equipment in use on the early Cape Town suburban system, from 1927. This view shows one of the early 748hp motor coaches, seen here with one pantograph raised, at the maker's works in Preston. EE Co. also supplied the control equipment for the trailer vehicles. The company were however, overall, less successful in winning orders from South Africa than its chief competitor, Metropolitan-Vickers.

The scheme had in fact been under consideration since 1903, covering the Durban to Pietermaritzburg, and Cape Town to Simonstown routes. The electrification of the latter was postponed shortly before contracts were placed, due, amongst other reasons, to the rapid growth in traffic on the Natal Province lines. It was, at the time, the largest single undertaking of its kind in the former British Empire.

Power was supplied to the overhead catenary at 3,000V dc from twelve substations spaced, in the original scheme, at 15 miles apart. These in turn were supplied from an 88kV, 50Hz power transmission system, from the main power station at Colenso on the Tugela River. Amongst the reasons put forward in favour of 3kV dc supplies to the catenary were its suitability for general commercial, as well as railway applications, and the locomotives employed on this 3ft 6in gauge line could be of relatively simple construction. The fixed equipment supporting the simple catenary was similar in design to that adopted for the Melbourne Suburban lines in Australia, with a 0.25sq in copper contact wire. The lattice steel masts were bolted down to concrete foundations, with gantry, or portal structures, used at multiple track locations. One of the earliest problems to arise in the first year of electric operation, was as a result of frequent electrical storms in Natal during summer months. Flashovers caused by lightning discharges in the vicinity of electrical equipment resulted in the need to install some kind of protection to prevent any major damage to insulators, supporting arms, and related hardware. An initial solution to guard against the induction of momentarily high voltages in the contact system was to pro-

vide lightning arrestors at intervals. Subsequently though, a better solution was found, with the installation of high speed, automatic circuit breakers in every substation, sectionalising the catenary, and minimising the damage arising out of such storms, to such delicate components as insulators.

The locomotives constructed by Metropolitan-Vickers at Trafford Park, and delivered to South Africa, were the first of many such orders from that country, and the Manchester Works' association continues to this day, through GEC Traction. The general design was evolved by Metropolitan-Vickers in consultation with the project's engineers, and the Railway Administration, and included the first large scale application of a regenerative braking system. Careful consideration was given to the performance specifications, having regard to the expected considerable growth in traffic over the 171 miles route, with the line's many sharp curves. Bearing in mind the then unsatisfactory performance of side rod driven locomotives, it was decided to adopt a double four-wheeled bogie (Bo-Bo) layout, with axle hung traction motors, and a final drive through reduction gearing. To negotiate the minimum radius curves of 300ft, the maximum permissible wheelbase for each bogie was fixed at 9ft 3in, with an axle loading of 18 tons. Some of the major dimensions and characteristics of these important locomotives are noted in the accompanying table:

Unmistakable in this case, is the large 'Metropolitan-Vickers' builder's plate, on the cab side of these, the first electric locomotives for South Africa. The locomotives were put to work on the Natal electrification and the 1,200hp Bo-Bo units were an outstanding success. For Metro-Vick, the order represented the beginning of a long and equally successful relationship between South African Railways and the Manchester company.

Leading Dimensions – SAR Locomotives

Class	1E
Main contractor	Metropolitan-Vickers
Introduced	1923
Total No. in class	95 (supplemented later by a further 87 units)
Overall length	43ft 8in
Overall width	9ft 2¼in
Overall height	12ft 11½in (pantographs lowered)
Wheel arrangement	Bo-Bo
Bogie wheelbase	9ft 3in
Wheel diameter	4ft 0in
Bogie pivot centres	21ft 8in
Weight in working order	67 tons
Traction motors	Four, Metropolitan-Vickers type 182R; 300hp
Maximum tractive effort	21,200lb
Continuous t.e.	16,400lb
Maximum speed	45 mph
Track gauge	3ft 6in

The locomotive was very much a box shape, with a cab at each end, and connected by a corridor along the right hand side. Leading off this was the high tension (HT) compartment, housing the cam operated switch groups, resistance banks, motor-generator resistances and contactors, and various fuses. Behind the cab bulkheads, and outside the HT compartment, were the motor-generators themselves (one 28kW and one 16kW set was provided on each locomotive), in two machine compartments, along with the traction motor blowers. Roof-mounted equipment included two pantographs, lightning arrestors, electrical chokes, and the pantograph isolating switches.

The fabricated four-wheeled bogies were coupled together at their inner ends, through an articulated joint. South African Railways have used bogie intercoupling for many years since, which offers such benefits as reduction in wheel flange wear through restricted transverse movement. Buffing and drawgear were mounted on the bogie frames, with laminated springs forming the main suspension. The 300hp series wound traction motors were four-pole machines, hung from the axle, with nose suspension, and with connections in either series or parallel modes. Each pair of motors was permanently connected in series across the 3kV dc line, and controlled by Metropolitan-Vickers electro-pneumatic control system, enabling four locomotives to be operated in multiple from a single master controller in one of the driving cabs.

The regenerative braking system was supplemented with conventional air brakes for the locomotive, and vacuum brakes for the train. The system proved eminently suitable for controlling the speed of trains down the long gradients in the Drakensberg Mountains with safety, and at higher line speeds than was possible previously, with steam haulage. Overall, electrification of this route was successful from the word go, with the new motive power giving considerable operating improvements, and significant reductions in journey times. From Glencoe to Pietermaritzburg with steam engines, and 1,000-ton loads, a 16½ hour schedule was needed, but with the new 3kV electric types, 1,500-ton trains were taken over the same route in only 10¼ hours !

Japan

From the other side of the world, Japan had demonstrated a progressive attitude towards railway electrification, and by 1922, for both government and privately owned lines, it had

The largest electric locomotive for Japan at the time of its construction. In 1925, No. 8000 was the first of eight 2-Co-Co-2s, on the Imperial Government Railways' 3ft 6in gauge line from Tokyo to Kobe. The locomotives were rated at 1,836hp, and fitted with English Electric power equipment.

become a national policy. In 1922, English Electric secured its first orders from the Far East, consisting of two complete 1,200hp Bo-Bo locomotives for the Tokyo Suburban lines. The locomotives were dual voltage types, for use on either 600V dc, or 1,200V dc systems. The order was placed by the Imperial Government Railways, as work began on electrification of a stretch of the Tokaido Railway, covering some 590 kilometres, between Tokyo and Kobe.

This first order for English Electric locomotives was referred to as samples, and the two box cab units used for trial running in the Tokyo area. Each locomotive was equipped with four 350hp traction motors, camshaft control, and weighed in at 59 tons. The dual voltage of 600V and 1,200V dc was not the standard adopted for major electrification work; with the main line systems adopting 1,500V dc, as used on many railways around the world. In 1922, the plans for the Tokyo Railway provided for an overhead contact system, energised at 1,500V dc, and included the construction of the Tanna Tunnel, with which some difficulty was experienced. In 1923, progress with the project suffered a temporary setback in the Great Earthquake, which affected the whole area.

This pair of locomotives were a successful experiment, and resulted in an order being placed on English Electric for a further 26, box cab type locomotives. Nine of the units in this order were for local passenger duties, with the remainder for freight work, and the only differences between the two types being the gear ratio of the final drive, and the brake gear. Other than this, they were essentially the same, particularly in external appearance, although on the passenger types, exhausters were provided, since Japanese Railways then still operated vacuum braked passenger trains. Locomotive control equipment again featured English Electric's standard camshaft system, with a pair of 305hp motors permanently connected in series, and series-parallel control of the four motors on each locomotive, with four stages of field weakening. The traction motors themselves were force ventilated, with the ducting supplying the cooling air built into the loco-

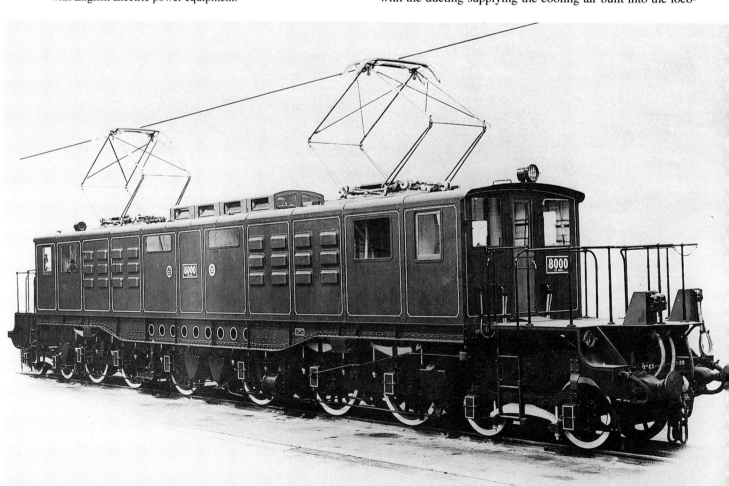

This photograph shows one of the 173 motor coaches, with equipment from English Electric, supplied to various Japanese private railways, between 1923 and 1930. This view shows one of the 360hp twin sets for the Nagoya Railway. Notice, in particular, the tramway type overhead trolley pole collector.

motive underframe. Equipment contained in the body of the locomotive was housed in separate compartments, with interlocks on the high tension compartment. This design strategy was similar to that employed by such as Metropolitan-Vickers in their South African order, and set a pattern for future equipment layouts in locomotives. On English Electric's Japanese locomotives auxiliary power supplies were provided by motor-generator sets, with the voltage output for lighting and control purposes, and fans for ventilating the traction motors, driven directly from the motor-generator sets.

Eight express passenger locomotives were also supplied by English Electric at Preston, of 1,836hp, and weighing 100 tons, sporting a 2-Co-Co-2 wheel arrangement, with leading and trailing bogies. Overall, the design was an extension of the Bo-Bo box cab types, but this time, equipped with six of the 305hp traction motors. English Electric's camshaft control was used, with these pairs of motors permanently coupled in series. Two control groupings were possible, with the first having all motors connected in series, and the second with three series pairs connected in parallel, and with two stages of field weakening available. The main trucks, or bogies, were not true bogies, since they were articulated, and coupled together at their inner ends, through vertical and horizontal joints. The heavy, fabricated sideframes supported the wheels through outside bearing axleboxes, with a for-

ward extension of the locomotive frames projecting over a four-wheeled bogie. Overhung, compensated leaf springs provided the main suspension, with 4ft 7in diameter 'driving wheels', and 3ft 1in diameter carrying wheels in the leading and trailing bogies.

An unusual incident befell these locomotives during their delivery in 1923. At the time of the Great Earthquake, in that year, the ship carrying the locomotives from Preston to Tokyo was in Tokyo Harbour, and unloading was in progress. Unfortunately the bogies (for the Bo-Bo locomotives) and the motors were on the wharf, with the superstructure and control gear on barges, which sank during the earthquake. The bogies and traction motors disappeared beneath the sea too, as the wharf on which they had been deposited also collapsed. Replacement locomotives were built, and subsequently shipped out successfully. Equal success was the lot of these early Japanese projects, and further orders were awarded to English Electric in the 1920s.

The Midi Railway

Much nearer to home, English Electric won important orders from France in 1922, as the Midi Railway adopted 1,500V dc as its standard for electrification work. This railway already had some experience of main line electrification, even before the 1914–18 war, with some tracks operating under a 12,000V ac system. These first English Electric orders, which were for power equipment only, for locomotives and rolling stock on routes at, almost, the opposite ends of the country. In the north, traction motors only were supplied to the 1,500V dc Paris to Orleans and Paris Suburban lines of Chemins de fer L'Etats in 1922, with complete loco-

The earliest locomotive for Japan, from EE Co., were these box-cab, double-bogie types. Weighing in at 59 tons, they were equipped with four 300hp traction motors.

motives, and locomotive and power equipment for motor coaches, for the Tarbes to Pau route of the Midi Railway.

The choice of 1,500V dc was made as a result of the desire for unification of standards, and pressed for by the French government. It was also seen as something of a compromise too, since on railways where third rail contact systems were being retained, engineers were advising that this was the maximum safe voltage that could be used. Another argument in favour of 1,500V dc that may have been considered – it was certainly mentioned in the contemporary railway journals – was the lack of experience in the use of high voltage mercury rectifiers, and the desire to avoid motor-generators and rotary convertors connected in series. In fact, the following decade saw the arrival of the glass bulb type mercury rectifier, which in its turn provided for further advances in the design of traction substations, without the need for rotating machinery to produce the dc traction supplies. The electrification of the Midi Railway provided pioneering examples of the use of the 'mercury vapour' rectifiers in substations – five of which were installed with this 1920's project, and worked successfully. *The Engineer*, in a far sighted editorial comment, suggested that: 'the mercury vapour rectifier, or, some other form of rectifier, will be very widely used on direct current railways'.

English Electric, in association with Les Constructions Electriques de France, provided literally hundreds of power equipments for locomotives and motor coaches, as electrification spread rapidly in the Pyrenees Region of south west and south east France. The first order with which English Electric were, involved in 1922, comprised the electrical equipment for ten 1,400hp Bo-Bo locomotives, weighing in at 67 tons, with the four series wound traction motors capable of operation at the full line voltage of 1,500V dc. English Electric's camshaft control system was used, with, in addition to conventional braking arrangements, a regenerative system, with the 350hp traction motors acting as generators, with field settings controlled by way of an auxiliary motor-generator set. A similar arrangement was adopted for the initial order for 19 motor coach equipments, which also included rheostatic braking and camshaft control, with a pair of 350hp traction motors.

The mixed traffic locomotives were complemented with, initially, four 2,100hp express passenger types, weighing 91 tons, and with a 2-Co-2 wheel arrangement. These latter were a remarkable design, with twin vertical shaft motors driving each locomotive axle, through bevel gears and a quill shaft. The box cab layout incorporated leading and trailing bogies, with a rigid frame in the centre, supporting the driven axles. Main suspension was provided by compensated leaf springs, and outside bearing axleboxes, whilst the current collection gear included three roof-mounted pantographs, each having two collector bows. Later, a second series of largely identical locomotives was built for the Midi

Above: In 1922 the Chemins de Fer du Midi, or Midi Railway, in France, put four 91-ton 2-Co-2 locomotives into service on the Tarbes to Pau section. English Electric, who supplied the power equipment, had also equipped trains operating over this route in 1904 and 1921.

Below: The orders from Chemins de Fer du Midi in 1922 included electrical equipment from English Electric, in addition to the complete locomotives illustrated earlier. In this case, 19 of 45 700hp motor coaches were equipped from the Preston Works, and the remaining 26 by CEF to English Electric designs.

Railway, but with a fourth driven axle, with the rated power output up to 2,800hp.

Rapid advances had been made in the setting up of hydro-electric schemes in the Pyrenees, supplying power to the equally rapidly advancing electrified routes. English Electric designed power equipment was manufactured under licence in France, at the works of Les Constructions Electriques de France, from where hundreds of locomotives began to appear in the mid 1920s. In total, English Electric were involved in the design and manufacture of equipment for the Midi Railway, summarised in the table below:

(a) 90–1,400hp Bo-Bo locomotives
(b) 10–2,100hp 2-Co-2 locomotives
(c) 140–1,600hp Bo-Bo locomotives
(d) 35–700hp motor coach equipments.

The French connection was maintained, as English Electric supplied equipment for one of the French Colonies, by way of Chemins de Fer du Maroc in 1925, with an order for ten 1,300hp, 72 ton Bo-Bo locomotives. Electrification work in Morocco involved the installation of 3,000V dc overhead contact systems on the standard gauge route from Rabat to Kourigha. The power equipment for the locomotives was largely made in France, through an associate company, although the motor-generator sets themselves were supplied direct from Preston.

Also in 1922, EE Co., and the French equivalent, CEF (Les Constructions Electriques de France) supplied these Bo-Bo locomotives for Chemins de Fer du Maroc (CFM).

A Period of Consolidation

For all the companies involved in electric traction, the period up to around 1923 was characterised by consolidation rather than extensive growth, whilst the decade that followed was affected very substantially by the general economic depression. Having said that, the limited growth in diesel traction in the UK was about to be given a significant boost, with the establishment of the Vulcan-Frichs association, and the orders for diesel shunters from the LMSR. For English Electric, consolidation was slow to materialise, and the 1920s saw some financial losses, with the company's widely scattered works and factories existing with outdated machinery, and a poor organisation. British Thomson-Houston and GEC were extensively involved, along with many others, in the manufacture of electric lamps, and to a degree this assisted in maintaining their capability to undertake traction work during this difficult period. Siemens Bros also had an extensive interest in the lamp industry, jointly with English Electric at Preston, whilst Metropolitan-Vickers, the former British Westinghouse, were equally affected by the depression in the electrical industry. An interesting development for Metropolitan-Vickers in the 1920s, soon after its formation, was the establishment of the 'group system' in the organisation. In practice, this set up a separate traction department, with the traction section at Metropolitan-Vickers' Trafford Park Works transferred to Sheffield, and the Attercliffe Common Works. G. H. Nelson, as Works Manager of both Sheffield plants – the River Don Works ceased traction manufacture in the 1920s – was very important to Metropolitan-Vickers, and hailed as the company's saviour during the depression years.

4

Developments in Diesel Traction to 1947

The 20 years between 1927 and 1947 saw very little development in diesel railway traction in the UK, with the exception perhaps of an increasing number of shunting locomotives, and the use of narrow gauge types in mines, and other industrial applications. On the standard gauge, only one main line railway company in Britain was committed to the idea of diesel motive power. For the railway industry, several important developments took place, the first of which was the reinforcing of the partnership between Vulcan Foundry and A/S Frichs of Denmark. A second, and perhaps even more far reaching development, was the merging of Metropolitan-Vickers and the British Thomson-Houston Co., under the Associated Electrical Industries (AEI) flag.

Financial performance of the former British Westinghouse Co., and subsequently Metropolitan-Vickers was not perhaps as good as might have been expected from such a famous, and well respected organisation. In fact, it was not until Metropolitan-Vickers had acquired the British Westinghouse Co. that the first dividends were paid to shareholders, following a lapse of more than 20 years. The company's results in the 1920s were not that much improved, with falling dividends in 1923 and 1927. It was in 1927 too, that Vickers Ltd made the decision to leave the electrical engineering industry, and Metropolitan-Vickers was sold to The International General Electric Co. of the USA.

The British Thomson-Houston Co., it will be remembered, was set up initially, in 1886, as a selling agency, and incorporated as a company ten years later. The original finance for the company came from a group of international bankers, but, in 1902, the International General Electric Co. assumed financial control. The dominating influence of the latter was reinforced in 1928, as the US company established AEI, and consolidated the interests of Metropolitan- Vickers and British Thomson-Houston Co. in particular. The then newly formed Associated Electrical Industries was actually a holding company, with International General Electric holding 28% of the preference stock, and 58% of the ordinary stock.

The formation of AEI had no immediate impact, and years later, references to the development in 1928, at least from the Metropolitan-Vickers side, that independence of management and company identities were to be pursued, although co-operation with other AEI Group companies was actively encouraged, as was the exchange of patent rights and manufacturing information with the US General Electric Co.

Vulcan Foundry of Newton-le-Willows, the second oldest manufacturer of railway locomotives in the world, had, it will be recalled, established an agreement with A/S Frichs of Denmark, to manufacture Frichs' design of diesel engines. The agreement – a collaboration agreement, as it was referred to – enabled Vulcan Foundry to take a leading role in the UK, in the diesel railway traction field. The international co-operation exemplified by this agreement could be seen in Vulcan's competitors too, as in say, the Brush-Sulzer association, although English Electric were developing a highly successful range of 'home grown' diesel engine designs. English Electric were 'assisted' in this work by the LMSR, where a range of diesel shunters, and, much later, a 1,600hp main line type, were put to work. Interestingly, the first of the LMS shunters was powered by a Paxman diesel engine, and Davey Paxman, as Ruston Paxman Diesels came under the GEC umbrella many years later.

Once again, in the period under review, overseas orders were far more numerous, and were represented by countries as far apart as Malaya, Brazil, and Eire. Even the Vulcan-Frichs association might be described as being heavily involved in the export market. During the 1920s and 1930s diesel traction was frequently discussed at conferences, where some emphasis was placed on the suitability of various types of transmission system. As an example, at the World Power Conference in 1933, a paper presented by Mr P. Due-Petersen, outlined current trends in design. The paper, entitled *Diesel Locomotives and Cars*, illustrated in particular the Frichs built locomotives for Denmark and Siam (Thailand). In his paper, the author outlined three main transmission systems, as follows:

(a)   Pneumatic – lacking in success due to its complexity and weight.

(b)   Mechanical transmission – at the time it was suggested that this could be considered for transmission at powers in excess of 150 to 200hp, only in exceptional cases.

(c)   Electrical transmission – employed for higher powers almost exclusively, on coaches and locomotives.

The author of this paper made some interesting observations on the latter, thinking that, but for its high cost, it would be unchallenged in the transmission field, with its all round superiority. Interestingly too, hydraulic transmission which later found favour in West Germany, was discounted on the grounds of low efficiency due to leakages. Overall, the impression gained from this important source in the 1930s was that electric transmissions were by far the most popular, yet its critics considered much energy was wasted in the conversion and reconversion of mechanical effort.

Other developments related at this time, considered the English experience, and exampled contemporary designs of Davey Paxman & Co. Ltd's medium speed, four-stroke, airless injection engines. Beardmore & Co., and Armstrong-Whitworth figured prominently in these discussions, whilst a three-car diesel train was proposed, with 800hp, giving a journey time of $1\frac{1}{2}$ hours on the London to Birmingham run. Vulcan-Sinclair hydraulic couplings, used in many hundreds of shunting locomotives, were pushing back the limitations of hydraulic transmissions, and effectively replacing the conventional clutch. Still however, the UK experience was for low powered locomotives, although Vulcan Foundry, in association with A/S Frichs, were building some quite large main line types at this time. Vulcan's Danish partners took the opportunity of the conference referred to above, to demonstrate, apparently quite impressively, a 1,000hp diesel-electric type. The design on display dated from 1931, weighing around 100 tons, and was equipped with the Frichs type 6285CL diesel engine. This was not the largest type then available from the Vulcan-Frichs stable, since a 1,600hp diesel-electric for Thailand/Siam was also on show. Whilst Sulzer are now recognised as being the first in the field with a true diesel locomotive in 1912, by the 1930s, Vulcan-Frichs were certainly amongst the leaders in this field of new technology. The success of the partnership was only terminated by the hostilities of World War II.

In the 1930s, English Electric were embarking on a period of some success, despite the economic recession, which was effectively sustained for more than 30 years, and with that independence terminated only by the English Electric-AEI partnership. The success story that was English Electric over those 30 years was continued in the English Electric-AEI merger, which immediately preceded the setting up of the GEC Traction organisation in 1972. What marked English Electric's projects as being different, and distinct from their competitors was, in many cases, their building of complete locomotives/rail vehicles. This is not to say that they were alone amongst the later GEC Traction stable in this technique, nor was it their sole method of production. The company did design a new 'oil-electric locomotive' for shunting purposes, and heavy goods haulage, but sub-contracted the construction of the mechanical parts to R. & W. Hawthorn, Leslie of Newcastle. English Electric, in addition to this pioneering design work on the 300hp, 0-6-0 shunter, also manufactured the six-cylinder diesel engine at their Rugby Works, with the generators and traction motors being designed and built at Preston. In contrast, a Bo-Bo diesel-electric for the North Western Railway of India was designed by a team of consulting engineers (Messrs Rendel, Palmer and Tritton), and had the complete electrical equipment manufactured by the General Electric Co., with the engines and mechanical portions of these locomotives coming from William Beardmore & Co. Ltd.

The Home Market

From 1930, perhaps the earliest, and most significant developments came from the English Electric stable. First to appear in this period was the 200hp 'Bluebird' railcar. This prototype unit from English Electric was intended as a test bed for a new design of high speed diesel engine, also

English Electric's *Bluebird* diesel electric coach had little impact at home, when it appeared in 1934, but led the company into an important market, with major export successes for later designs of diesel multiple unit.

designed and produced by English Electric. The 200hp engine carried on *Bluebird* had the unusually high, for the time, piston speed of 2,000ft/min, and cylinders with four valves, and, with other features which later became standard, had a three-point mounting. *Bluebird* was tried out on the LMSR, and could be found on routes such as those from Warwick to Northampton, but although it had operated successfully, the LNSR did not consider such single unit railcars as suitable for its traffic.

Ironically perhaps, at that time, the same railway company was considering a quite far reaching scheme to develop the use of diesel traction for shunting purposes. The railcar idea was not particularly popular in the UK in the 1930s, although other countries had made much more use of it, at an even earlier stage, it was not until British Railways' days that diesel railcars, and multiple units too, gained much ground. Comparing however, the *Bluebird* prototype with examples from competitors during the 1930s, of which Armstrong-Whitworth is perhaps the most notable, showed some interesting innovations in design features. In this country, the development of internal combustion engines was more marked in the road transport sector, and Armstrong Whitworth's 'streamlined' railbus of the 1930s, had adopted a 100hp heavy oil engine, of a similar type to that used in road vehicles. Transfer of road technology to rail was surprisingly common at the time, and whilst the Newcastle company's *Tyneside Venturer* diesel-electric railcar had been in service with the LNER since 1932, English Electric's *Bluebird* had a diesel engine specifically deigned for rail traction.

However, from the English Electric view, the most important developments were just coming along, and were aided and abetted by the LMSR, who's early 'stab' at dieselisation set some standards which were maintained, at home and abroad, for many years. The locomotive – a 300hp 0-6-0 type – which emerged as a result of the railway company's policy, incorporated again, a purpose built six-cylinder engine, produced at the Willans Works of English Electric in Rugby. However, this was not the first of its kind here at home, that particular milestone having been recorded across the Pennines, and in fact, south, to Colchester in Essex. In

Later members of the GEC Traction empire, like Davey Paxman of Colchester were responsible for the introduction of diesel traction in the UK. Here we see No. 1831, the LMS Co.'s first attempt at a diesel shunter, with a Paxman diesel engine, in a locomotive with a layout which had a major influence on later English Electric designs.

(Lens of Sutton)

1931, Davey Paxman & Co., later coming under the GEC Traction umbrella, by way of an association with Ruston & Hornsby, designed and built its six-cylinder 6XVS diesel engine for the LMS 0-6-0 shunter prototype, No. 1831. The railway company constructed the mechanical portion of the locomotive, based around the frames of a steam engine, and other details, whilst the Paxman engine was the first rail traction diesel engine, installed in the first diesel locomotive on the standard gauge, for a major British railway company.

The LMS company placed extensive orders in 1933 for diesel shunting locomotives, following the trials with the Paxman engined conversion/prototype, and a 250hp shunter from Armstrong-Whitworth. The light locomotives ordered by the LMS came from a variety of suppliers, including Hunslet, and Hudswell, Clarke in Leeds, the Drewry Car Co., and even Harland & Wolffe of Belfast. The latter may at

In early BR days this English Electric powered 0-6-0 diesel shunter, set standards that were, and indeed still are, maintained. The jackshaft final drive, seen in this example, was not, however, the most common arrangement and usually one or two traction motors were installed.

the time have been considering the diversification that Vickers Ltd had embarked on some years previously, which resulted in the successful development of Metropolitan-Vickers of course. In addition to the shunter orders, the LMS had placed a contract with Leyland Motors Ltd for three 40-seat railcars, with driving compartments at either end. Six of the eight locomotives on order had direct links with GEC Traction's predecessors, since in their transmission they were fitted with the innovative Vulcan-Sinclair hydraulic coupling. The Vulcan-Sinclair coupling became very popular for numerous low speed/power rail traction applications around the world. During the infancy of diesel traction development, comparisons with steam locomotives were inevitable, and in some cases, the locomotive designs, as outlined above, were at least outwardly similar. The Vulcan-Sinclair coupling took the analogy a stage further, and some sections of the contemporary technical press referred to this form of hydraulic transmission as directly comparable with the regulator of a steam locomotive. Such analogies were obviously less suitable where electric transmission was used, although in this country, the attempt to modify the Whyte Notation for describing a locomotive's wheel arrangements lasted well into the post war era.

Prototype 350hp Shunters
In the UK this was perhaps the most significant development of the early 1930s, and whilst Britain was slow to adopt diesel traction, the English Electric shunter design of 1933 established a layout which is still in use to this day. When completed, in 1934, this prototype locomotive was described as a 'general purpose 300hp oil-electric locomotive'. The reference to oil-electric, when in fact the engine was a compression-ignition type, much more commonly referred to as a diesel, persisted in this country until well into the 1950s.

More typical of the EE Co. standard 0-6-0 shunter, is this former Southern Railway example. The 350hp diesel engine, with six, in-line cylinders, became the most common standard, and the shunting locomotive itself represented the face of diesel traction progress in the UK for many years, until the late 1940s.

Whilst 'oil-engine' may be technically accurate, at least to a degree, the reluctance to use the term 'diesel' was due to a desire not to accord any precedence to the invention of Dr Rudolf Diesel, when Hornsby and Akroyd could point to a prior claim. Hornsby and Akroyd were undoubtedly the first to build a 'diesel engine', though perhaps as a result of the sluggish adoption of the principle by British industry, and lack of adequate marketing, the diesel engine was set to become a household name.

Be that as it may, the diesel-electric shunter designed by English Electric was a very significant advance, but like the Davey Paxman engined predecessor, it was constructed along similar lines to an 0-6-0 steam locomotive. In principle, it was intended for shunting and heavy goods haulage, and for branch line passenger services, with English Electric responsible for the overall design, and R. & W. Hawthorn, Leslie & Co. constructing the mechanical parts.

The locomotive had a single driving cab at one end, with a sheet metal casing, or hood, covering the engine and generator compartment, with a radiator mounted on the front face of the locomotive's nose. Below the footplate, the two 1in thick steel plate frames supported six outside bearing axleboxes, with fluted coupling rods linking the 4ft ½in diameter wheels. The engine and generator compartment was separated from the driving cab by a double partition, one function of which was to effect a means of providing some soundproofing for the crew.

The design of the engine itself differed from the type fitted to the *Bluebird* railcar, in that it was a medium speed design, running at 680 rpm, and designated type 6KT. It was a six-cylinder, in-line arrangement, with 10in by 12in cylinders, and with engine bedplate and crankcase fabricated from steel sections, ensuring minimal weight, and a good degree of stiffness and rigidity. The 6KT engine was also built at Rugby Works, and directly coupled to a 240kW generator, and mounted on an extension of the engine's bedplate. The 200hp power unit was, as in the *Bluebird*, carried on a three-point mounting, which also assisted in avoiding any stress on the crankcase or crankshaft, from movement of the locomotive's underframe. Overhung from the main gen-

Above: A later view, taken in 1951, shows the popularity of the 0-6-0 arrangement, but 12,000 miles from what may be considered its traditional home. This occasion, the shunter is in Australia, at the head of a short train, which includes the first of the main line diesels for Commonwealth Railways.

Below: Just to prove that the LMSR were not the only owners of 350hp 0-6-0 shunters. The Great Western Railway in this case, with its example – identical almost to the LMS version, and with the mechanical parts not from Swindon, but R. & W. Hawthorn, Leslie, on Tyneside.

erator was an 11kW auxiliary generator, which, in addition to its use as an 'exciter' for the main generator's field windings, also provided power for battery charging.

The four-pole traction motors were supplied from the main generator, which had a maximum output of 645 volts, and could be connected in either series, or parallel mode, with a single stage of field weakening. The motors were self-ventilated, and mounted on the two outer axles of the locomotive. A later series of shunters, 40 in all, included only a single traction motor, and a jackshaft drive, with which it was thought that the lower gear ratio would provide higher tractive effort, at low speeds. However, two motors were ultimately preferred for these shunter types, with their greater flexibility, and double reduction spur gearing fitted where intensive slow speed operations were commonplace. Later service experience also brought about the use of force ventilated traction motors on these locomotives.

Control of the locomotive was effected from two separate driving positions, on either side of the cab, with a four- position controller governing the engine speed, with intermediate generator field control positions. The loading of the main generator was controlled by a patented torque regulator, which provided instantaneous regulation of the main generator field through a pulsating electric torque relay, varying the electrical loading to suit track conditions and load of the locomotive. These shunters were fitted with straight and automatic air brakes, and vacuum brakes, to handle any kind of rolling stock, with the air and vacuum reservoirs carried below the locomotive's footplate. The mechanical handbrake acted on cast iron brake blocks, carried in front of the wheels, on fully compensated brake riggings.

Fuel was supplied to the engine by gravity feed, with the main tank mounted above the driving cab. Just in front of the cab louvres were provided in the bodysides, to draw cooling air into the generator compartment, from which it was separated by a partition/bulkhead.

Ruston & Hornsby
Across the Pennines in East Anglia, Ruston & Hornsby produced what may be referred to as their first 'diesel' locomotive in 1931, although in obvious deference to the Hornsby-Akroyd engine, early R&H engines were referred to as 'crude oil' types. Constructed at R&H's Anchor Street Works in Lincoln, the 2ft gauge, 10hp locomotive was obviously for industrial use, and was in fact operated by Manchester Corporation on the Hawsewater Reservoir Scheme. Early R&H industrials were fitted with Lister engines, following a period, as with other builders, of producing petrol engined units. Subsequent developments in the 1930s saw a range of in-house designs, of larger horsepowers, and for track gauges from 1ft 8in to 3ft 6in, but producing in 1935, the first R&H standard gauge industrial diesel locomotive.

R&H were amongst the earliest manufacturers to produce locomotives for use in mines, whilst from 1940, an association was begun with another GEC company, Davey Paxman of Colchester. Rustons were however, very much a star of the industrial world, and it was not until after Nationalisation that important standard gauge diesels were offered for service on British Railways. Another association with a later member of the GEC Traction fold, through AEI, saw British Thomson-Houston providing the electrical equipment for a variety of two and three axle diesel-electric shunters by the late 1940s.

Despite however, the push of the London, Midland & Scottish Railway, and some isolated prototypes ordered by other railway companies in the 1930s, a great deal of success was achieved by GEC, English Electric, Metropolitan-Vickers, and others, in foreign markets.

Export Orders
Between 1930 and 1935, once again English Electric saw the most outstanding success, though Metropolitan-Vickers, GEC, and BTH were involved in a number of export orders. And, of course, Vulcan Foundry's partnership with A/S Frichs of Aarhus in Denmark resulted in important overseas

This fine study of the metre gauge version of English Electric's 0-6-0 shunter, seen at Kuala Lumpur in 1948 was the first of 20 such locomotives.

Not all diesel locomotives used for shunting sported either the 0-6-0 wheel arrangement, or were supplied by EE Co. and in this case, the unmistakable BTH logo on the side of this centre-cab Bo-Bo at work in New Zealand demonstrates the origin of the power equipment.

orders. The lack of progress with diesel traction in the UK during the 1930s, in a period of great economic recession was, it has been suggested, a disadvantage from another point of view. The manufacturers of internal combustion motive power had no 'shop window' in the home market to demonstrate their wares, although in fairness, many colonies in the former British Empire were running examples of these new products.

English Electric during the 1930s supplied diesel locomotives, railcars, and electrical equipment to Brazil, Eire, Ceylon (Sri Lanka), South Africa, and Sudan. The last mentioned country was the first to order complete locomotives from English Electric, which arrived in 1936. The two locomotives ordered, were 350hp 0-6-0 shunters, and in design were very similar to the 350hp prototype for the LMSR in the UK – equipped with two traction motors, driving the coupled wheels through single reduction spur gearing. The most obvious, and main difference from the UK order was the rail gauge, which in the Sudan – and later almost standard throughout Africa – was 3ft 6in. The Sudan locomotives weighed 45 tons in working order, and with a top speed of 40 mph, were also capable of transfer workings, in addition to conventional shunting duties. These first locomotives were a success, although it was not until after the Second World

War that a second order was placed, for five more 0-6-0s, to be built at the company's Preston Works. The engine installed in the 0-6-0s for the 1935 order was what became the standard 6KT, six-cylinder series, which in a modified and upgraded version was the power plant in a second export order to South Africa, in 1936. The 1936 contract was for New Consolidated Goldfields, with the 0-6-0s now in industrial use for shunting duties, and rated at 410hp, with seven cylinders under the hood. The basic layout of this design, with a single driving cab at one end, had a long bonnet, or hood, over the engine compartment, and the six coupled wheels, with outside bearing axleboxes, seemed to be following a more or less standard pattern. The South African dominion provided a valuable market for electric traction orders, but curiously perhaps, GEC companies did not achieve the same success in diesel traction, whether for industrial, or main line use.

In 1938, English Electric established another first, following completion of an order it had received from Ceylon Government Railways. This order, for three articulated diesel trains, was the first all-welded design to be built in Britain. They were wholly constructed at Preston Works, and consisted of a pair of coach bodies, with an articulating bogie at one end, and conventional bogies at the two outer ends. Four such articulated pairs made up each train, with a capacity for 300 passengers, with a maximum speed of 55 mph on Ceylon's 5ft 6in gauge lines.

English Electric had also developed a high speed, 1,500 rpm diesel engine, specifically for diesel-electric railcars and trains. The design, designated type 6H, was a six-cylinder

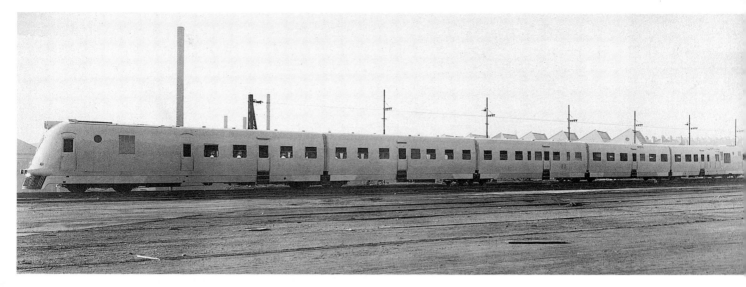

English Electric won important orders for multiple unit rolling stock in the 1940s, including these five-coach articulated sets for Egyptian State Railways. EE Co. were main contractors, with the mechanical parts supplied by Birmingham RC&W Co., at whose works this photograph was taken.

in-line engine, developing 200hp, and directly coupled to a generator at one end. In service, with the Ceylon Government Railways, a 6H engine and generator set was mounted at each end of the train, in a separate compartment, above the vehicle floor, and behind the driving position. The new 1938 articulated trains went into service, principally on the line from Colombo to Gaul, and despite the difficulties of the Second World War, apparently succeeded in amassing no less than 2,000,000 miles in traffic! Such was the success of this experience, the authorities in Ceylon ordered similar equipment from English Electric in 1946, and again powered by the 6H diesel engine, but this time, the railcars were not articulated, and operated either singly, or in pairs. Once again constructed entirely at the Preston Works, they were broadly similar to the previous design in body styling, with the first of the 23 200hp railcars entering service in 1947. Including their 200hp diesel engines, each of the railcars was 64ft long, with sleeping accommodation for 83 passengers and a luggage compartment, tipping the scales at 36 tons.

Under construction at English Electric's Preston Works, seen here, are the articulated motor coaches for the Ceylon Government Railways in 1947.

South America, as has already been mentioned, was a source of some orders for both Metropolitan-Vickers and English Electric, with the majority of the contracts coming from Brazil and Argentina. The former country placed two orders on English Electric in 1936 and 1938, for diesel-electric trains, and locomotives, respectively. In 1936, the São Paulo Railway ordered a pair of 600hp diesel-electric trains, for which English Electric supplied the 200hp traction motors and control equipment. The interesting arrangement of cardan shaft driving a worm gear on the bogie axle was certainly an unusual layout in rail traction. Three years later, English Electric supplied three 450hp mixed traffic locomotives for the Eastern Railways of Brazil. The eight-cylinder engines for these 1-B-B-1 locomotives were constructed at English Electric's Rugby Works, the company having made a policy decision to develop its own range of diesel engines during the 1930s, although of course, the Willans Works had been producing diesel engines in Rugby since 1904. The 1939 locomotives for Brazil bore a number of similarities to the design of steam locomotives, not least amongst which was the use of a rigid frame, forming the 'spine' of the locomotive, with four wheels coupled together. In that respect, these locomotives were similar to the emerging standard 0-6-0 diesel shunter, however, they were also equipped with leading and trailing pony trucks.

Neighbouring Argentina had been developing the use of diesel traction since the late 1920s, which has already been referred to – in particular, the mobile power houses on the Buenos Aires Great Southern system. By 1930, the same railway had obtained a 375hp locomotive from Beardmore's in Glasgow, which was equipped with Metropolitan-Vickers electrical equipment. Further orders were placed for the mobile power house trains in 1930, but this time of 1,700hp, along with a 1,700hp locomotive fitted with English Electric power equipment. Whilst, as in a number of other countries, the Second World War saw a pause in development, following the end of hostilities, plans were put forward to completely dieselise the country's railways. However, the post war plans were slow to materialise for economic reasons, and the orders were not forthcoming as quickly as might have been expected.

Also in South America, Venezuela – not a country renowned for its extensive rail network – placed some work with English Electric during this period. In fact, three 200hp diesel-electric railcars were ordered from the Preston company in 1929, and were similar in design to other 200hp units supplied to the San Sebastian to Pamplona Railway in northern Spain. These diesel railcars followed closely on the heels of motor coaches for the electrified, metre gauge line, from La Guaira to the country's capital, Caracas.

The Second World War
For all the later member companies in the GEC Traction group, the period from 1939 to 1945 involved considerable effort in producing the 'tools' required for the war effort. Vulcan Foundry it will be recalled, were closely associated with A/S Frichs, when the hostilities fairly abruptly ended that association. Vulcan then went on to apply diesel technology, with equal success, to the production of the 'Matilda' tank, of which many hundreds were built at the Newton-le-Willows works. Metropolitan-Vickers in Manchester, and English Electric, were heavily involved with aircraft production. For the Manchester company, jet engine technology, with the able assistance of Sir Frank Whittle was later applied, albeit with less success, in the form of an open cycle gas turbine on rail traction, in the post war era.

During the 1939 to 1945 period, no new orders were placed or completed, with the earliest work afterwards going to the export market. South Australia, Egypt, Ceylon, and Malaya were the earliest operators of diesel locomotives or railcars, whilst nearer to home, the Irish Republic (Eire), and Egypt were a source of major projects. For the home market, the LMSR, and the Southern Railway in particular, an increasing number of diesel shunters appeared, along with the first 'high power' main line diesels. The Great Western Railway, and subsequently British Railways (Western Region), quite typically was developing its own perception of the 'modernised railway', which involved the introduction of gas turbine propulsion.

The major companies of the GEC Traction empire were still heavily involved with the development of electric traction,

These Bo-Bo shunting locomotives were built in Australia for New South Wales Government Railways, but included power equipment from British Thomson-Houston Co. (BTH), in 1954, soon to become AEI, Rugby.

which demonstrated a sustained growth in orders. The impending explosion in the use of diesel power, already witnessed in the USA, and which, in the 1950s here, in the UK, was characterised by a rapid expansion of orders at home especially, from 1950. Company developments in the immediate post war era were aimed at consolidation rather than expansion, although from the mid to late 1950s, more dramatic changes were witnessed. Just before the war, Robert Stephenson & Co. of Newcastle, had joined forces with R. & W. Hawthorn, Leslie in 1937, whilst in 1944, in association with Beyer Peacock, Metropolitan-Vickers had established a separate company, to manufacture locomotives in Stockton.

The Immediate Post War Years
The first orders for diesel power after the war came from countries some 12,000 miles apart – Eire and Australia. The latter came from South Australia in 1945, and was for power equipment only, for two 350hp Bo-Bo shunters. The mechanical portions of the locomotives were constructed in the railway company's own workshops, with both axles on each bogie motored, and English Electric supplying its 'standard' control equipment.

In the same year that these South Australian locomotives were placed in traffic, 1946, Coras Iompair Eireann (CIE), placed an order with Sulzer Bros, as main contractor, for a pair of 915hp locomotives. The bodies of these locomotives, and other mechanical portions, were built at CIE's Inchicore Works, with Metropolitan-Vickers supplying the power and control equipment. For its early diesel units, CIE were adopting a medium speed diesel engine, paired with electric transmission, and avoided the debates which beset neighbouring British Railways some 10 to 15 years later.

In the CIE Bo-Bo locomotives for the 5ft 3in gauge, a six-cylinder, pressure charged, Sulzer designed diesel, running at 730 rpm, was directly coupled to a Metropolitan-Vickers

Closer to home, but still an export order, were these Co-Co diesel-electrics for CIE, and built by Metro-Vick, in Manchester. Full width bodies, and double-ended locomotives retained their popularity in Great Britain and Ireland, although much less so elsewhere in the world.

eight-pole generator. The main generator, and overhung auxiliary generators were self ventilated machines, whilst force ventilation was adopted for the traction motors. Final drive was effected by means of a fairly commonplace arrangement of spur gears, in a ratio of 16 to 65, to the 44in diameter road wheels, giving a maximum speed of 55 mph. Whilst this latter may seem low nowadays, operationally it provided CIE with the opportunity to accelerate schedules on routes where the Sulzer/Metro-Vick diesels were in service. Control systems, with multiple unit facilities was incorporated in the driving position master controller, from a handwheel with ten notches. Power to the traction motors drew a high current at starting, gradually falling away, with the voltage rising, up to a speed of about 25 mph. At this speed, the traction motor field regulator came into operation, progressively weakening the traction motor fields, up to about 45 to 55 mph.

These new locomotives in service with CIE survived for many years with further orders placed with Metropolitan-Vickers, and subsequently AEI Traction. In 1969, the Irish railway authority returned to AEI for replacement power equipment, as the locomotives were then being refurbished.

The Irish order is a convenient break point in the story of the development of diesel traction, since from the start of the next decade, orders for diesel locomotives and railcars came flooding in, to all the major companies. The motive power revolution was perhaps more marked in the field of diesel traction, here at home, than elsewhere in the world, except possibly for the USA. The post war era demonstrated quite clearly, the direction in which the railway companies were planning their future, and the benefits were equally clear to those major cornerstones of the British railway industry.

Above: Again, under the innovative support of the LMSR, the scene is Rugby, but just into British Railways days, in October 1948, as the first British main line diesels are put through their paces. The leading locomotive, No. 10001, had only just been completed, whilst No. 10000 had been outshopped in the previous year, 1947.

Below: The former Southern Railway followed the LMS lead in main line diesel traction, and also selected English Electric to supply power and control equipment for its enormous – at least in weight – 1,750hp locomotives. Mechanical parts for this example, numbered 10202 and sporting the early BR black livery, were constructed at Ashford Works.

5
Developments in Electric Traction to 1945

As outlined in Chapter 3, by the early 1920s the major UK suppliers, English Electric and Metropolitan-Vickers (subsequently for the latter, as part of the AEI Group), were responsible for a number of important electrification projects. This state of affairs continued throughout the 1920s and 1930s, with significant orders for complete projects, and a number of contracts to supply hundreds of sets of power equipment. The larger proportion of these orders were for export, despite the major expansions of the Southern Railway's electrified network, work for London Underground, and a number of lesser schemes. Included amongst these latter is the unique Post Office Tube Railway, a pioneering example of automation, which is now approaching its 60th anniversary.

In 1925, a second series of orders was taken from Australia, as the state of New South Wales embarked on a major suburban electrification project. The Sydney Suburban scheme adopted 1,500V dc supply to the contact system, and

Skirting the coast, and showing some signs of wear, or at least, a lack of cleaning, is this New Zealand Railways 1,240hp locomotive, dating back to 1937. The design sported a 2-Do-1 wheel arrangement, and power equipment from English Electric.

the AEI Group providing the traction substation equipment, which in its turn, consisted of rotary converters and rectifiers. In fact, this was not the first electrification project of this kind, since Metropolitan-Vickers had supplied equipment during the First World War, to the railways of the neighbouring state, Victoria. For the New South Wales project, Metropolitan-Vickers were once again the recipients of the prime contracts for the power equipment. Initially, 150 sets of power equipment were ordered, but followed in 1926, 1927 and 1928 by further orders for 101, 105, and 100 similar sets, respectively. Each of the power cars for New South Wales were fitted with a pair of 350hp motors, and equipped with Metropolitan-Vickers emerging, standard electro-pneumatic control system. Interestingly, just as Metropolitan-Vickers supplied their fourth order for 100 sets of e.m.u. equipment in 1928, arch rivals, English Electric supplied a dozen 375hp dc motors for use on vehicles employed on these same suburban services.

The first New South Wales orders were of a breed that included equipment significantly more powerful than the four-motor cars used on the railways of neighbouring Victoria. There, the power cars were rated at no more than 560hp, continuously. Having said that, another 40 sets to the same design were supplied to Victorian Railways, from Metropolitan-Vickers, in 1925.

A year before, on the other side of the continent, in 1924, the railways of Western Australia saw the introduction of their first electric locomotive, with equipment supplied from Metropolitan-Vickers. A single, 600hp Bo-Bo was built for operation on Western Australia's 3ft 6in gauge lines, working from a 600V dc supply, and weighing in at 44 tons. Like the electric multiple unit vehicles in New South Wales and Victoria, it too was equipped with an electro-pneumatic control system. Unlike the e.m.u. orders, the whole locomotive was the responsibility of the Manchester company.

Australia was one of both Metropolitan-Vickers, and English Electric's success stories for both public rail transport, and industrial railways. From GEC Traction's point of view in later years, the company can point, retrospectively, to the introduction of electric and diesel traction to this continent, as a direct result of the activities of their predecessors. The variety of gauges in Australia was no handicap to the commercial or technical success for both companies, and in 1928, AEI/Metropolitan-Vickers obtained an order from the Broken Hill Pty Co., for two 22-ton, Bo-Bo electric locomotives, running on 3ft 6in gauge, and collecting power from a 600V dc supply, as in the case of the earlier order from Western Australia. Broken Hill itself, at the time the order was placed, was the location of the world's largest silver mine, near the state border between New South Wales and South Australia. Whilst the locomotive order was for the mining company, the town itself was linked by rail with Port Pirie and Adelaide. Further orders from Broken Hill followed in 1929, 1936, and 1941, for another four Bo-Bo electric locomotives.

In New South Wales, more multiple unit equipment orders were placed with AEI in 1938, and after WWII, in 1945. No

One of the earliest four-motor, 880hp multiple units for the Netherlands, with electro-pneumatic control equipment from Metropolitan-Vickers. These first units were supplied between 1925 and 1927.

further orders were won by English Electric until the early 1950s, as part of Victoria's main line electrification project, covering the route from Melbourne to Gippsland. In total, between 1923 and 1945, both the AEI Group and English Electric were responsible for supplying no less than 582 sets of power equipment for multiple units, seven locomotives, and numerous items of traction substation equipment. Of the total, only 2% came from English Electric, with Metropolitan-Vickers securing far and away the lion's share of these first Australian orders.

In the New World too, both Metropolitan-Vickers and English Electric were securing important contracts, with the earliest of these coming from the Montreal Harbour Commissioners in Canada. The Montreal project, which resulted in an order for English Electric, involved the complete electrification of the harbour lines, following an experiment with two electric locomotives rented from Canadian National Railways. At the time, in 1924, CNR had already electrified their Montreal Tunnel Section, at 2,400V dc, with a overhead contact system. This method was, in turn, chosen by the Harbour Commissioners for the new project. As main contractors, English Electric not only provided the nine, 100-

This fine view of one of the nine 1,720hp Bo-Bo locomotives for the Montreal Harbour Commissioners, emphasises the 'box-like' structure of early non-steam motive power. The units were supplied, complete, from EE Co.'s Preston Works, in 1924/25, and collecting power at 2,400V dc, operated under some of the harshest winter weather conditions. The size of the pantograph makes an interesting comparison with modern counterparts.

ton locomotives, but also the motor generator sets installed in the substations providing the traction power supply.

Three 1,000kW motor-generator sets were supplied to the initial installation, with the last two being manufactured at English Electric's Stafford Works. Subsequently, the Harbour Commissioners ordered two more machines from English Electric, each of which consisted of a 2,300kW, 63 cycles, synchronous motor, coupled to a pair of 1,200V dc generators, connected in series.

The Montreal locomotives were a Bo-Bo design of 1,720hp, and were supplied against two orders, and the locomotives were, at the time, considered to be the most powerful units of their type, anywhere in the world. The first four locomotives went into service in February 1925, with the second batch of five in operation from August the following year. The locomotives were built at the Preston Works, and shipped across the Atlantic to Montreal. In design, the units were a simple box cab layout, with a driving cab at each end, although one of these was provided with projecting lookouts so that the driver could have unobstructed vision during some shunting operations. The cab with the projecting lookouts had duplicate controls, a further advantage for shunting service, whilst the cab at the opposite end, with only a single set of controls, and no lookouts, would be used predominantly for long haul operations.

Power equipment layout consisted of four, 430hp force ventilated traction motors, each being axle hung, and driving the wheels through single reduction spur gearing. The locomotives were capable of exerting a tractive effort of

70,000lbs at the wheel treads, and soon after their introduction, one of their number demonstrated these abilities by hauling a train of some 5,240 tons, the heaviest then recorded. Within the body of the locomotive, the remaining equipment was installed in cubicles along either side of a central gangway. This hardware consisted of a motor-generator set, air compressors and banks of resistances, with standard English Electric camshaft control. With the English Electric version of this form of control, the operating current was not switched at the camshaft itself, but on line breakers, connected in series with the camshaft controller. Special provision was made for the high tension equipment, which was housed in a separate compartment, included access through substantial, interlocked, sliding doors, and which could not be opened unless the main switch was closed, isolating the equipment.

In view of the harshness of the Montreal climate in winter, important amongst the numerous design considerations, was the provision of adequate ventilation and heating. Provisions were made to guard against condensation in the traction motor field windings, which could be connected in series to a 220V shore supply, and the driving cabs were double glazed, and heavily insulated against the cold.

Overall, the appearance of these powerful locomotives may be said to have been typically North American, with conspicuously large pantographs–two for each locomotive. They were designed to meet, of course, the details of prevailing standards for Canadian practice.

The Montreal Harbour Commission was not the only Canadian operator to place orders with English Electric in the mid-1920s, with an order coming from Canadian National Railways for power equipment, in the same year, 1924. In this latter case, the order was for equipment only, and consisted of eight, 190hp traction motors, and the camshaft control equipment. The hardware was installed in two 760hp locomotives, which collected power at 600V dc from an overhead trolley wire, in an arrangement very similar to numerous tramway installations. These, even more box like units, with an 0-4-4-0 wheel arrangement, were employed on the Niagara, St Catherines and Toronto section of Canadian National Railways. Montreal Harbour Commissioners went back to English Electric before the decade was out, with an order for a 54-ton, general purpose, petrol-electric locomotive, described in another chapter.

South America

For both English Electric and Metropolitan-Vickers, Brazil was another successful marketplace in the 1920s and 1930s, with contracts for complete electrification projects and power equipments. Between 1923 and 1929 for instance, GEC Traction's predecessors were involved in no less than five schemes in Brazil, Venezuela and Argentina. Perhaps

In 1926 Metropolitan-Vickers supplied five of these 600hp, 46 tons, Bo-Bo locomotives for 1,500V dc metre gauge lines in Brazil. They were a mixed traffic type with electro-pneumatic control and regenerative braking.

the most interesting of these was the Oeste de Minas Railway in Brazil, which was the equivalent of what today would be termed a 'turnkey' project. Metropolitan-Vickers were the main contractors, with responsibility for the complete installation, which included the infrastructure as well as the power equipment and motive power. Source of the power for this scheme was hydro-electricity, and involved the company in ensuring the provision of dams, canals and piping for the three 800kVA generating machines installed in the power house. This latter supplied energy to three traction substations, which in their turn were equipped with eleven 250kW, 750V rotary convertors, to provide the 1,500V dc supply for the overhead contact system. Overall, this was indeed an extremely comprehensive project, with Metropolitan-Vickers providing the substation buildings, transformers, switchgear, and overhead lines. In 1926, the company supplied five 600hp Bo-Bo locomotives for both freight and passenger service, which, like locomotives supplied to South Africa during the same period, incorporated the company's standard electro-pneumatic control system, and regenerative braking.

In 1926, in São Paulo state, Brazil embarked on another 1,500V dc electrification, which this time included seven complete electric multiple units and three motorised freight cars. At the same time, a large 2,340hp 1Co-Co1 locomotive was built for the 3,000V dc system being installed on the Paulista Railway. Unlike the metre gauge schemes referred to above, the Paulista Railway was a 5ft 3in gauge line, and a later connection was made, with the English Electric project, extending the 3,000V dc lines into the region's capital, São Paulo. The Central Railway of Brazil was another 3,000V dc, 5ft 3in gauge line, for which Metropolitan-Vickers were, once again, responsible for the complete project. The Manchester company were contracted to provide the complete overhead equipment, workshops, car shed, and even the building housing the administrative offices, and substations. At the same time as the basic infrastructure for the installation was provided, the power supplies for the two traction substations, including duplicate three-phase transmission lines, and signalling system transmission lines were supplied. In the substations themselves, 2,500kW mercury arc rectifiers converted the incoming ac supply to a 3kV dc output to the catenary. This extensive project was completed in 1935/36, with rolling stock for the initial scheme made up of 60 three-car sets, with one motor coach and two trailer vehicles. Each of the motor coaches was provided with four 175hp traction motors, with electro-pneumatic controls. Two further orders at the end of the Second World War increased the number of multiple units in operation by 50%, with another 30 three-car sets, and 40 more of the 175hp traction motors. The fixed installations too saw a little further development soon afterwards, as extensions were made to the substations, and track sectioning cabins, in 1947.

Staying in South America, but backtracking just a little, to the 1920s, and across to neighbouring Argentina, an important early project covering the suburban lines radiating from Buenos Aires began to see some success. Metropolitan-Vickers were once again the main contractors to this scheme, which ran from Buenos Aires, out through Liners, Monon, Moreno, and the western province of Mendoza. This scheme, the Buenos Aires Western Railway's suburban electrification project, was undertaken on the oldest railway routes in Argentina, and in the 1920s, the Buenos Aires Western Railway's mileage covered a network of just less than 2,000 miles of the 5ft 6in gauge. The railway company actually took the decision to electrify 23 miles of this route before the 1914–18 war, but the scheme lay relatively dormant, and was not completed until 1923. Metropolitan-Vickers provided equipment for the power station, traction substations and

cabling, in addition to the power equipment for the electric multiple unit type rolling stock.

The Buenos Aires Western was electrified using the third rail system, at 800V dc, with 20kV feeders to the four traction substations from a power station at Dock Sud, in Buenos Aires itself. The power station was actually a joint construction with the Buenos Aires Great Southern system. Although for the most part, the Buenos Aires Western lines were equipped with a third rail contact system, some sidings in the port of Buenos Aires had overhead conductors, to which the Buenos Aires Western main lines were linked by a 5km long tunnel. This port section was electrified at the same time as the suburban routes, and two locomotives were used to haul freight traffic through the tunnel, and were capable of collecting current from either the overhead contact wire or conductor rail. More importantly perhaps, Metropolitan-Vickers supplied equipment for all 76 motor coaches, and 97 driving trailers. The motor coaches were provided with a driving compartment at each end, with four 200hp traction motors, picking up power from the conductor rail by means of an underhung (bottom contact) collector shoe. The conductor rails themselves were of channel section, with the collector shoe picking up from the underside of the top flange. The two traction motors on each motor bogie were permanently connected in parallel, with each pair of motors on the motor coaches arranged for series-parallel operation.

The trains' control system was the Metro-Vick electromagnetic design, with all the switchgear housed in dustproof cases below the floor of the vehicles. The makers claimed automatic acceleration of the train through a system of relays, which governed the safe acceleration rate for the unit, and which would not normally be affected by the driver. In service these trains could be arranged in a four-coach formation, comprising two motor coaches and two trailers, with each traction motor drawing an average of 290 amps, at an average acceleration of 1.25 mph/second.

True international co-operation was more obvious in the construction of the freight locomotives, which although powered by Metropolitan-Vickers electrical equipment, were of a Westinghouse/Baldwin design. Each of the two locomotives was fitted with four, 230hp axle-hung traction motors, two roof-mounted pantographs for current collection from the catenary sections, and the same design of bottom contact collector shoe to that used on the multiple units. The traction motors were force ventilated, whilst the standard electro-pneumatic control system was employed. Other equipment provided by Metropolitan-Vickers for these locomotives included reversers, contactors, and banks of resistances mounted on a frame in the driving cab. In general, the equipment supplied for the Buenos Aires Western project was similar to that supplied for the earlier scheme on the Central Argentine Railway.

English Electric's early contribution to electrification in South America involved the suburban, or inter-urban systems, linking La Guaira in Venezuela, with the country's capital city, Caracas, 23 miles away, and 1,000ft above sea level. English Electric designed and constructed the generators, to provide the 1,650V dc supply to the contact system, switchgear, and power equipment and control systems for the motor coaches. The latter were equipped with four 90hp traction motors, with complete motor coaches built for this metre gauge line, at the company's Preston Works, with the units first entering service in 1927.

At the end of the period under review, the English Electric Export & Trading Co. signed a contract for the electrification of the 5ft 3in gauge line from Mooca to Jundiai in Brazil, which included links to the state capital, São Paulo. The railway company's engineers had in fact surveyed the line between 1943 and 1945, in collaboration with engineers and specialists from English Electric.

Overall, both Metropolitan-Vickers and English Electric had been responsible for, or involved with, the following projects in South America, between 1923 and 1945:

(a) Argentina–Buenos Aires Great Western Railway Metropolitan-Vickers
(b) Central Railway of Brazil–Metropolitan-Vickers
(c) São Paulo Railway Company–English Electric
(d) Paulista Railway Company–Metropolitan-Vickers
(e) Oeste de Minas Railway–Metropolitan-Vickers
(f) Bolivia–Peruvian Railway Corp.–English Electric
(g) Venezuela–La Guaira to Caracas Railway–English Electric

The Indian Sub-Continent
The first electrification project in India was the Bombay Harbour branch of the Great Indian Peninsula Railway, begun in 1925. The same company then embarked on what was then referred to as a comprehensive programme of electrification, involving routes from Bombay to Igatpuri and Poona, involving the severe gradient negotiated in climbing the Ghats. Both English Electric and the General Electric Co. were involved in these first projects for Indian Railways. English Electric were contracted to provide equipment for traction substations and motor coaches on the first suburban phase, which, with extensions to the Harbour branch in Bombay, had reached Kalyan by the end of 1928. The line was 5ft 6in gauge, and electrified at 1,500V dc, with 110kV feeders to the substations, converted to dc supplies for the catenary by no less than twelve English Electric 2,500kW rotary convertors. The four-car suburban trains, each equipped with four, 275hp traction motors on the single motor coach, hauled three trailer vehicles, with special provisions being required to protect the undercar equipment during the monsoon season. To allow for running over sections of route that were flooded, originally the traction motors had special air valves fitted, as a means of diverting the floodwater away from the sensitive machinery. The motors were actually the standard self-ventilating type, whilst other items of equipment, including the camshaft control gear were housed in the main body of the car, above the floor. Considering that each four-car train was equipped with a total installed power of 1,100hp, this may have been necessary to some extent, due to the heavy weight of Indian rolling stock during this period. In this case, each of the original four-car sets weighed more than 200 tons when empty.

On the Great Indian Peninsula Railway, English Electric were responsible for the complete project, which, in addition to the provision of the catenary, substations and other items of infrastructure, included one of the largest water generating plants manufactured in the UK. This latter, like similar machinery for the São Paulo Electric Co. in Brazil, was for installation in the Tata Power Co.'s generating station in Bombay. The name of Merz & McLellan, or more precisely at that time, Merz & Partners, appears as consulting engineers to the project, just as they had been in South Africa, and elsewhere in the former British Empire. Whilst English Electric had a major stake in this contract, members of the AEI group of companies–soon to be formed in 1928–such as General Electric and British Thomson-Houston, along with Metropolitan-Vickers, had also secured important orders in this market. The General Electric Co. it will be recalled, was pursuing some other success in India, and by 1930 had provided the power equipment for a 350hp diesel-electric locomotive for the North Western Railway.

On the GIPR, which later became the Central Railway, General Electric provided power and control equipment for a 2,160hp, 108-ton, electric locomotive. This 'high speed' locomotive, delivered in 1928, had the mechanical parts constructed on Tyneside by R. & W. Hawthorn, Leslie & Co., and like the multiple unit vehicles already in service, required some special precautions for the electrical equipment to provide protection during the monsoon season. The locomotive was built to specifications provided by Merz & Partners, and was classed as a 2-A-A-A-2 type, with front and rear bogies having spoked wheels. The driving wheels too were spoked, and some 6ft 2in in diameter, with the final drive through a resilient gearwheel on each axle, mounted on a hollow quill shaft. Three, twin armature motors, each rated

English Electric supplied power equipment for the earliest electrification on the Indian sub-continent, including this motor coach. Interestingly the photograph bears the date, 20-10-24, whilst EE Co. records indicate delivery in 1928, for the Bombay to Kalyan section of the Great Indian Peninsula Railway.

A very colonial picture is presented in this view of Metropolitan-Vickers 2,160hp locomotive No. 4000, for passenger duties on the Great Indian Peninsula Railway's electrification project of 1927.

at more than 700hp, drove the quill shaft through spur gears in a ratio of 4.5 to 1. This flexible drive system, also referred to as the SLM Universal Drive, was developed especially for this work by GEC, in conjunction with Les Ateliers de Construction Oerlikon. In this instance it was constructed by Hawthorn, Leslie & Co., and it was claimed that the flexibility inherent in the design would take account of any possible movement of the quill shaft in relation to the driving axle.

The general appearance of this locomotive undoubtedly gave some weight to the notion that diesel and electric types were simply boxes on wheels. The 'boxy' superstructure was carried on a rigid main frame, with outside bearing axleboxes, and leaf springs to the driving wheels, with a pair of pantographs mounted on the roof. Some aerodynamic styling could be detected at the front of the locomotive, where the driving cabs were formed into a 'vee' shape, to cut down the wind resistance. This first express passenger locomotive for the GIPR electrification was joined by another 21 from 1929, and a single locomotive nine years later, in 1938, just before the outbreak of the Second World War. This locomotive, along with the multiple unit rolling stock for the Bombay suburban lines, was an important step forward in the growth of electric traction on the sub-continent, and represented very

important orders for the AEI Group as a whole. The main dimensions of this pioneering locomotive are given below:

Great Indian Peninsula Railway 2,160hp 2-A-A-A-2 Locomotive

Track gauge	5ft 6in
Introduced	1927
Main contractor	GEC
Mechanical portion	R. & W. Hawthorn, Leslie & Co.
Length over buffers	56ft 2¼ in
Overall width	10ft 0in
Rigid wheelbase	15ft 0in
Bogie wheelbase	7ft 0in
Driving wheel dia.	6ft 2in
Bogie wheel dia.	3ft 0in
Max. horsepower	2,160
	(2,250 at 1hr rating)
Line voltage	1,500V dc
Max. tractive effort	24,000lb at 36 mph

A year later, Metropolitan-Vickers supplied what may be seen as a competing design, but which was designed for freight traffic, with a C-C wheel arrangement, and side rod drive. No less than 41 of these freight types were ordered in 1928, intended for hauling the heaviest goods trains and negotiating the long climbs and descents of the Ghats. In this situation, regenerative braking, just as had been used on the Natal route in South Africa, was once again employed. Whilst GEC/Hawthorn, Leslie supplied the original 2,160hp locomotive, Metropolitan-Vickers, in reference to this early

India's GIPR electrification produced a second order for Metro-Vick, in the shape of 41 of these enormous, 123 ton, 2,600hp C-C locomotives with side rod drive. With electro-pneumatic control, and arriving in 1928, this view shows one of the class under construction at the Trafford Park Works.

period of electrification, noted that sample locomotives were supplied by themselves and their competitors in 1925–26. The 21 additional express passenger locomotives were ordered from Metropolitan-Vickers in 1929, although, the 22nd member of the class did not materialise until 1938.

The Bombay to Poona electrification of the GIPR was, at the time, the most extensive electrification scheme in the former British Empire, and was officially opened in 1929. It represented the activities and work of almost all the later members of GEC Traction, specialising in electric traction, although it was not the only such example of co-operation between the erstwhile competitors in this market. It was not the only example of electrification in India at this time either, since, on the opposite side of the country, English Electric were busily engaged with the electrified Madras suburban lines of the South Indian Railway.

The metre gauge lines of the route from Madras Beach to Tambaram were an entirely new electrification project, and not simply the conversion of an existing steam operated railway to electric traction. A new double track route and stations were provided, electrified at the standard 1,500V dc, and was brought into operation from 1930. The existing steam services in this area were severely congested, and just three months after the opening of the new lines, passenger traffic had trebled, fully justifying the cost of the project. English Electric's contribution to the scheme's success consisted of three-car articulated trains, and a pair of 640hp Bo-Bo locomotives for shunting and yard duties.

The design of the rolling stock for this scheme incorporated some interesting features, at least, in the arrangement of the power equipment. Each of the 17 trains consisted of three coach bodies on articulated bogies, with a driving cab at each end, and the electrical control equipment mounted in a separate compartment at one end of the centre coach. Power was collected from the contact wire by a single pantograph mounted on the roof of the centre car. Access to the camshaft control equipment was straightforward, whilst maintenance and inspection was simplified still further, by having the equipment carried on racks which, in turn, were supported on rollers for easier removal. The traction motors, four in number on each three-car train, and totalling 480hp, were only carried on the two articulating bogies. The motors were of the self-ventilated type, but the cooling air was drawn in at roof level, and taken to the motors by sheet metal ducting, with flexible joints connecting with the motor bogies. Similarly, all air entering the compartment housing the control gear was filtered, and ducted in at roof level.

The pair of 640hp Bo-Bo shunting locomotives were for use at the electrified yards, and each weighed 42 tons. Both locomotives sported a pair of pantographs and four 160hp traction motors, with provisions for operation from on-board batteries, in addition to the normal 1,500V dc from the overhead line. The on-board batteries were actually carried on two 21-ton 440V battery tenders, also supplied by English Electric, which extended the range of the locomotives beyond the shunting yards.

The Madras suburban lines' traffic exceeded all forecasts and expectations for growth, with the passenger traffic requiring additional rolling stock to cater for the surging demand. In 1933, English Electric supplied a further seven, three-car trains.

Electrification began early in many parts of the world, and progressed more rapidly than in the UK. This was translated into numerous orders for the constituents and predecessors of GEC Traction, particularly in the supply of power and control equipment. In addition to the locomotive pictured earlier, the Great Indian Peninsula Railway also ordered motor coaches for the Bombay to Kalyan scheme, with each set fitted with 275hp traction motors, and English Electric camshaft control. The units entered service in 1928.

Like many schemes completed in the 1930s, the impending hostilities of WWII blocked further growth and development for almost a decade, until the later 1940s. Despite this, some very significant projects were established in Europe during the 1930s, notably in Denmark, Poland, and Hungary. Once again, the close co-operation between English Electric, Metropolitan-Vickers and others, was an important feature.

European Orders

Apart from the Danish electrification, there are perhaps two major projects which stand out when looking at the work of former GEC Traction companies in Europe, during the 1930s–Hungary and Poland. There was too, the beginning of an important practical application of technical innovation,

which in its turn, may well have developed even more rapidly had it not been for the gathering clouds of war. The major constituents of the GEC Traction empire had supplied equipment to Denmark, Holland, Italy, and even the USSR during this time.

The first of the two major projects to start up was the Hungarian Railways electrification, where the main line from Budapest to Heggeshalom, a distance of 120 miles, was being equipped with an overhead contact system, supplied at 16,000V ac, single-phase, 50Hz. This was the world's first ac electrification scheme which adopted standard industrial frequency. Metropolitan-Vickers became involved in this scheme from 1931, with orders for the locomotive power equipment. The Hungarian scheme introduced an original and novel method of driving the locomotives, in the 'Kando' system, where a phase converter was used to change the 16kV single phase supply to a 1,000V, polyphase feed, to a single 2,500hp induction motor. This single motor, in turn,

Power equipments for motor coaches were a major source of orders for EE Co., in the 1920s, including the 90hp traction motors on these power cars for the 600/1,200V dc Barcelona suburban system in Spain. The order was placed by the Ferrocarriles de Cataluna. This view taken in 1926.

drove the locomotives' wheels through a series of mechanical rods. The motive power was not the only source of orders for Metropolitan-Vickers on this project, since the company also supplied all the equipment for the four traction substations along the route.

At least one of the reasons supporting the project was, at least indirectly, political, as an international treaty (The Treaty of Trianon) had reduced the physical size of Hungary, and the country lost valuable reserves of natural gas and water, and 60% of its coalfields. The country's remaining coal supplies were insufficient to provide an adequate, efficient source of coal for steam locomotives. The remaining, inferior coal supplies, could be quite effectively burned in power stations, which, in the case of the electrification project, was the station at Banhida. In addition to supplying power for the railway, the Banhida station provided energy for the major part of Budapest, and neighbouring industrial regions. Electricity at 110kV, 50Hz, was distributed over duplicate transmission lines which, in general, followed the route of the railway. The substations which supplied 16kV ac for the catenary, for traction, in addition to being few in number, were simpler in design than traction substations used for dc electrification schemes.

Not surprisingly, economic pressures had some influence over the choice of ac versus dc contact systems, with the lighter weight of the ac infrastructure helping to reduce construction costs. A disadvantage of ac traction systems, and one which helped to reduce its popularity initially, and in general, was the need to immunise the adjacent telephone and telegraph circuits. In Hungary the telephone lines were removed from the traditional position, alongside railway tracks, on wooden poles, and were replaced by underground cables.

The equipment supplied by Metropolitan-Vickers for the substations consisted of a pair of 4,000kVA transformers, oil-immersed circuit breakers, switchgear, track feed equipment, and a number of auxiliary systems. The two 110kV incomers were each taken from one phase, of each of the 110kV transmission lines, through the circuit breakers, to the oil-immersed transformer. The latter, associated switchgear, was located in the outdoor switchyard. In each case, the substations as built, included space for a third transformer. The supply to catenary was fed to a 100mm² hard copper contact wire, suspended from a galvanised steel catenary wire. This simple catenary, supported from masts spaced at 82-yard intervals, and at multi-track locations incorporated a headspan assembly, similar in arrangement to that used on many railway systems today.

Metropolitan-Vickers responsibility on this project included provision of the 2,500hp polyphase traction motors, starters, pole changing switches and auxiliary equipment. The order, placed in 1932, was for partial electrical equipment for 24 1-D-1 passenger locomotives, and two 0-12-0 freight locomotives, in collaboration with Ganz & Co. of Budapest. For the passenger locomotives, Ganz & Co. supplied the phase converters, controllers and instruments, with the mechanical portions built by the Royal Hungarian State Engineering Works, also in Budapest.

Power equipment on the passenger locomotives consisted of the phase converter, a liquid starter, a cam operated, pole changing switch group, the 2,500hp traction motor, and final drive to the wheels through side rods, and the triangular 'Kando' driving frame. In operation, the 16kV ac supply was taken from the two pantographs and passed, by means of a single roof-mounted oil circuit breaker, to the primary windings of the phase converter. From the phase converter, a polyphase supply was taken to a self contained, pole changing switch group. The contacts on the switch group were selected 'manually' from the driver's master controller, and

closed by compressed air. The function of this switch group was to make the necessary tappings on the phase converter, to give various combinations of poles on the machine, which then corresponded with a variety of speed settings, in either direction of travel. The rotor of the huge traction motor was equipped with 16 slip rings, fed from the pole changing switch group, regulating the speed of the motor.

The 'Kando Locomotive' was a complex piece of electrical machinery, and weighed in at some 93 tons, in common with the 0-12-0 version. It was not the fastest of motive power, and in fact, the locomotive's performance specification required it to haul a 590 tons load up a gradient of 1 in 150, in a time of six minutes, to a speed of 51 mph. The freight locomotives were set to achieve a lower speed (9.76 mph), with a trailing load of 1,476 tons, under the same conditions. Evidently, following their tests, and introduction into service, from May 1932, to September the same year, the locomotives proved well suited to their tasks. The Hungarian locomotives were not, as has been mentioned, the only such work for eastern European countries, undertaken by the likes of Metropolitan-Vickers, English Electric, and others, although the 16kV ac 'Kando System' was not repeated.

The main dimensions and particulars of these unusual locomotives were:

Hungarian Locomotives – Leading Dimensions

	Passenger	*Freight*
Wheel arrangement	2-8-2 (1-D-1)	0-12-0
Weight in w.o.	93 tons	93 tons
Overall length	44ft 11in	44ft 1in
Wheelbase	20ft 10½in	25ft 9in
Driving wheel dia.	5ft 5½in	3ft 9¼in
Trailing wheel dia.	3ft 5in	
Cont. rating		
(3rd/4th speeds)	2,200hp	2,200hp
Max. rating		
(3rd/4th speeds)	3,500hp	3,500hp
(based on five minutes rating)		
Max. speed	62.4 mph	32.1 mph

Denmark

Danish State Railways embarked on the first stage of the Copenhagen suburban electrification in the early 1930s, and in July 1932, English Electric received an order for the complete power equipment for 42 motor coaches, and 21 trailer cars. By the end of the period under review, Denmark had ordered 100 sets of power equipment from English Electric, for which all the traction motors were manufactured at the Bradford Works (formerly the Phoenix Dynamo Co.). The rolling stock itself was constructed at the works of Aktieselskabet Frichs, and Vognfabrikken Scandia.

Copenhagen's suburban routes provided a suitable candidate for the benefits of electrification, although Denmark had already seen numerous developments in diesel traction. The initial electrification work took in about 40km of route between Copenhagen and Klampensborg, with a branch to Holte, and equipped with an overhead contact system. This first stage included the circular route from Copenhagen through Vanlose and Nornebro to Hellerup.

The English Electric power equipment–the trains themselves were arranged in three-car sets, with a trailer car sandwiched between two power cars–consisted of control gear housed in equipment cases below the vehicle floor, and of course, the 160hp traction motors. The control system, referred to as 'All Electric Camshaft', was the same as that supplied to Bombay, Madras and Vancouver and, out in the Far East, to Japan. The underframe-mounted equipment cases were provided with dustproof covers, and were inter-

Suburban electrification in Denmark in 1933, brought orders for power and control equipment, for EE Co. Some equipment was manufactured in the UK, whilst others, including traction motors and control equipment were manufactured under licence in Denmark. This view shows one of the then newly built electric trains entering Copenhagen station.

locked with the main power supply isolating switch, and the air supply for raising and lowering the pantograph. The pantographs themselves–two per motor coach –needed to be lowered before the equipment cases could be opened for inspection and/or maintenance work to be undertaken. The auxiliary equipment provided a 65V supply from a motor generator set, for lighting and control circuits. The motor generator sets were also carried below the vehicle floor, within the underframe, and a low tension bus-line ran throughout the train (three-car or six-car sets), with all the motor generator sets connected in parallel.

The English Electric type EE501 traction motors were, like the generators, self-ventilated machines, drawing cooling air through filters in the body of the vehicle, and trunking, similar to that installed on the Madras suburban line trains in India. A pair of axle hung, nose-suspended motors were installed on the motor bogies of each motor coach, driving the axles through single reduction spur gearing.

The first trial runs of these Danish multiple units took place on 29th November 1933, and English Electric continued to supply equipment of this type until long after the end of the Second World War. Whilst the majority of the traction motors were built and supplied from English Electric's Bradford Works, from the earliest orders, some 78 were manufactured in Denmark, under licence, to the same design.

Poland

In the same year that English Electric powered trains began running in Denmark, a major contract, worth £2 million, was signed in London, for the electrification of 250 km of route, on lines radiating from the Polish capital, Warsaw. Both English Electric and Metropolitan-Vickers were joint main

contractors on this valuable project, which involved the installation of the overhead contact system, six substations, locomotives, and multiple unit power equipment.

The initial scheme was officially opened on 15th December 1936, by the Polish Vice Premier. Various British dignitaries were present, and the Boards of Directors of English Electric and Metropolitan-Vickers demonstrated a heavyweight appearance. Both companies were members of the British Contractors Committee for the electrification of the Polish Railways, along with banks and finance houses, whilst British Insulated Cables Ltd carried out the overhead line work, as principal sub-contractor.

The fixed equipment in the substations consisted of steel tank mercury arc rectifiers in two sizes; 2,500kW and 2,000kW. In total, Metropolitan-Vickers supplied four of the former, and English Electric, five, whilst the supply of the four 2,000kW rectifiers were equally divided between these two companies. The associated switchgear was provided by Polish manufacturers, with incomers to the substations taking 35,000V ac, at industrial frequency, and final traction supply to the contact wire at 3,000V dc The catenary was suspended from brackets, in the now conventional manner, although dual contact wires were used for main lines, and a single wire in sidings.

On the motive power and rolling stock front, English Electric supplied the control gear for all the motor coaches and trailers, and 140 of the 320 traction motors, for the multiple units. Metropolitan-Vickers supplied the remaining 200hp motors, two complete 2,200hp Bo-Bo locomotives, and the power equipment for another four. The mechanical parts for the multiple unit rolling stock were constructed in Poland, with each three-car set arranged as one motor car, and two trailer vehicles. Each of the power cars was fitted with four 200hp motors, and the electro-pneumatic control system. In each three-car set, a second driving position was provided, and the rear of the driving and non-driving trailer coaches was carried on a single articulating bogie. Although, as mentioned earlier, the major portion of the power equipment fitted into all the locomotives and rolling stock was

In 1936, along with English Electric, Metropolitan-Vickers received major orders from Poland for electrification work. These 74 ton Bo-Bo, 2,200hp units were supplied from Manchester in 1936.

manufactured here in the UK, some components from the control systems were manufactured in Poland.

Whilst it would be true to say that for English Electric, Metropolitan-Vickers, and other AEI Group companies, overseas orders were most numerous, some developments were also taking place at home. In fairness however, these were not particularly significant, with composite projects from Europe, the Far East, and especially South Africa, taking pride of place in the various companies' order books. In South Africa for instance, the initial scheme for electrifying the line through Natal was very successful, prompting further orders and encouraging other projects. In 1925, the South African Railways began the electrification of the Cape Town suburban system, at 1,500V dc, between Cape Town and Simonstown, a distance of 22½ miles. By 1928, the entire route was electrified, and a service provided by 83 motor coaches, 37 driving trailers and 95 non-driving trailers. Each train originally consisted of two motor coaches and four trailers, for normal operations, which could be increased to three motor coaches and five trailers at peak periods.

Interestingly, English Electric were the main contractors on this first suburban scheme, which was later converted to the SAR standard 3kV dc system. Power for the initial Cape Town suburban lines came from a generating station at Salt River, equipped with three EE Co. 10,000kVA alternators, generating 12,000V, which in turn, was supplied by way of transformers, at 33,000V to the traction substations. English Electric power and control equipment –187hp traction motors (four per power car)–were fitted to the multiple unit sets ordered in 1925, with a second, similar order in 1938, for another 12 sets of power equipment.

Metropolitan-Vickers in Manchester who, it may fairly be argued, were to become the major supplier to South Africa's electrification projects, had also received a number of orders during the period to the end of World War II. However, no multiple unit equipment was supplied at this time, until the Reef Project of the 1950s. Metropolitan-Vickers' work between 1925 and 1944 consisted of another 79 Class 1E (1,200hp) Bo-Bo locomotives for Natal, in four orders, and a new Class 3E (2,700hp) Co-Co design, ordered in 1944. These locomotives were ordered to support the decision by South African Railways to eliminate steam on the Reef section, and to handle a proportion of main line passenger and freight workings. There was a degree of standardisation between these, and the earlier Class 1E locomotives, notably in the design of the wheels and axles, suspensions, use of inter-coupling between the bogies, and the dc control switchgear. Twenty-eight of these Co-Co units were built at Trafford Park, in Manchester, and delivered from 1948.

The Home Market

In Britain, the major electrification works were restricted to the expansion of the Southern Railway's third rail network,

Still in service 30 years after their first introduction in Natal, is this 1,200hp Class 1E Bo-Bo. From the 1920s South African Railways extended the 3kV dc catenary over the 'Reef Area' of the Transvaal, producing further orders for locomotives and rolling stock from Metropolitan-Vickers.

and the underground railways of London. Smaller projects involving English Electric, Metropolitan-Vickers, BTH, and GEC, in either the complete scheme, or the supply of spares and replacement parts, included the LMS' Wirral, and Euston to Watford lines. The unique Post Office Railway in London, and the Glasgow Underground saw important contracts in the 1930s. Notably, no new equipment was supplied, or projects begun using ac traction during this time.

Glasgow Underground, which was opened in 1897 as a cable hauled railway, operates through some of the smallest diameter rail tunnels in the world. The diameter of the running tunnels is a mere 11ft 0in, with a height from rail level to the tunnel roof of just over 9ft 0in, on a track gauge of 4ft 0in. In fact, compared to some recent stock built by GEC Traction for other rapid transit systems, the Glasgow Underground vehicles could be said to resemble a rather large model railway! In 1934, the railway was converted to electric traction, with power supplied to the conductor rails at 600V dc, and 22 sets of power equipment were supplied.

In London, the underground lines experienced significant changes in the period under review, with the formation of London Transport, and the unification of the various lines. Interestingly, the early successes of English Electric, supplying equipment to the old Waterloo & City, and the City &

South London railways, was not repeated. Metropolitan-Vickers, GEC, and initially to a lesser extent, BTH, supplied the greater proportion of these equipments. (From 1938 onwards, BTH got the lion's share of this work.) The contracts were fairly evenly divided between stock for the surface lines, and that for the tubes, which called for different designs of equipment. Both tube and surface lines were energised at 600V dc, and between 1924 and 1948, no less than 1,300 tube stock power cars, including the prototype 1938 stock, were provided with power and control equipment, and around 700 sets were supplied for the surface stock. Included in this latter, was the Metadyne control equipment developed by Metropolitan-Vickers (who held the UK manufacturing rights), in association with its Italian inventor, J. M. Pestrani, in the 1930s. It was first installed on London Underground surface stock in 1936, when 250 sets were ordered, and although the system was initially successful, the equipment was replaced in the 1950s, with BTH camshaft controllers. Similar Metadyne hardware was installed on tube locomotives, whilst a number of sets of control equipment were supplied for use on the battery locomotives of the surface lines.

Metropolitan-Vickers 'Metadyne' Equipment
In its application to the underground network, Metadynes were constructed to convert power at a constant voltage, to provide an output of variable voltage, and giving a much smoother train control system. Rotating machines of the Metadyne type were built by the company for various applications; as motors, generators, and, as a contemporary press report put it; 'as transformers of D.C. power, as applied to train control'.

The Metadyne hardware itself consisted of three separate rotating machines, mounted on a common armature shaft–a shunt wound regulator, the 'Metadyne', and a separately excited generator. The latter provided excitation for the Metadyne's 'variator' winding, whilst the whole assembly was started by the shunt-wound regulator, which kept it running at a constant speed. The Metadyne itself comprised an armature, commutator, and stator, with four brush arms, arranged as pairs of primary, and pairs of secondary brushes. The 'variator' winding provided the means of controlling motor current.

The Metadyne system applied to London Underground stock by Metropolitan-Vickers was designed to 'boost the back e.m.f.' of the traction motors, in order to balance the applied line voltage. In practice it replaced, or was designed to replace, the starting resistances, accelerating relays, switches, and cam groups, which comprised the vehicle's conventional control equipment. This early attempt at improving the smoothness of train control, has some similarities, in principle, with the development, much later, of thyristor, and transistor based electronic control systems. The objective was the same, but there of course, the similarity ended, for the Metadyne equipped stock was not so successful as the more recent developments of 'chopper' and thyristor based control systems. The Metadyne stock was re-equipped in the 1950s, with conventional control equipment from Metropolitan-Vickers, BTH, and GEC.

Outside London, the Manchester, South Junction & Altrincham Railway was electrified in 1931, with an overhead contact system, supplied at 1,500V dc, over the 8½ mile route. The scheme, recommended in the Railway Electrification Committee's Report for 1927, to the Minister of Transport, was the first section of railway to use 1,500V dc with overhead contact and running rail return. Involvement of what later became members of the GEC Traction fold, included the provision by British Thomson-Houston, of the traction substation equipment at Old Trafford and Timperley.

Stretford & District Electricity Board provided duplicate 11kV ac supplies, to both the Old Trafford and Timperley substations, where it was converted to the 1,500V dc required for the contact wire supply. BTH supplied ten 750kW, 1,500V dc rotary converters in 1929, and a single 1,500kW steel tank rectifier in 1930. The Old Trafford substation contained the steel tank rectifier, and four of the 750kW rotary convertors, connected in two pairs, whilst at Timpereley, six more 750kW units (as three pairs), were installed. The substation at Old Trafford was operated manually, whilst that at Timperley was fully automatic, under the direct control of the personnel at Old Trafford. Another 'first' for BTH was the installation at Old Trafford of the 12-anode, steel tank, mercury arc rectifier. This was the first application on a British railway electrification project.

In the 1930s, the Altrincham railway was jointly owned by the LNER and LMS railway companies, and the services worked by steam traction. The fastest journey time over the 8½ mile route was 27 minutes, and 99 trains were worked in a single day. The inauguration of electric traction, from 11th May 1931, included LMS-built five-car multiple unit trains, with control equipment supplied by Metropolitan-Vickers, running between Manchester and Altrincham in less than 24 minutes. In addition to the two new stops en route, and the reduction in journey time, it was possible to increase the number of trains worked daily from 99 to 124!

The 1930s saw further orders from Merseyside too, for the LMSR, who operated third rail dc services on the Wirral and Mersey, and Liverpool to Southport lines. The latter had some stock powered by Metropolitan-Vickers 265hp traction

motors, although the vast majority, including the order for 59 sets of power equipment, placed in 1938, came from English Electric. Across the Mersey, 19 complete motorcoaches were built in 1936-1938, and equipped on this occasion, with BTH 135hp traction motors, and Metropolitan-Vickers control and auxiliary equipment. Essentially, these three-car sets were the same as the Liverpool–Southport units, except for the fact that they collected power at 650V dc, not 630V dc on the neighbouring lines. Both designs were in operation well into British Railway's days, and in the 1970s, soon after the formation of GEC Traction, acquired BR's TOPS classifications 502 (Liverpool–Southport), and 503 (Wirral & Mersey).

In the south of the country, the Southern Railway was pushing ahead with the extension of its dc electrified network. Further orders were placed with Metropolitan-Vickers for equipment for the Euston–Watford stock of the LMSR, which had already resulted in major contracts for the company on these routes, in the previous decade. The Southern Railway's electrified network grew significantly during the 1920s and 1930s, aided and abetted by the English Electric Co. in particular. Initially however, the Southern had to settle the question of supply voltage and contact system, having inherited three different arrangements at the great amalgamation of 1923. The former LSWR had installed, as reviewed earlier, a 660V dc system, with outside conductor rail contact, of 168 track miles, with proposed extensions totalling 252 track miles. The LBSCR also operated electrified routes, but supplied at 6.6kV ac, with an overhead contact system, with proposals to electrify a further 662 track miles. Conductor rails were preferred by the South Eastern & Chatham Railway though, but energised at 3,000V dc, but no hardware was actually installed by the time of the 1923 amalgamations. By October 1925, almost three years after its formation, the Southern Railway decided to adopt as standard, a 660V dc side contact system, similar to that in use on the former LSWR lines, equipped by Metropolitan-Vickers.

Despite the Manchester company's involvement with the later standard system on the Southern, English Electric became the principal supplier of rolling stock traction equipment to that railway. All the later members of the GEC Traction empire had provided some equipment for the Southern Railway, from Metropolitan-Vickers, and English Electric, through BTH, and GEC. The important distinction so far as English Electric was concerned, involved the provision of rolling stock equipment. In 1923, English Electric supplied 492 self-ventilated 280hp traction motors, and another 136 of the 225hp variety, but the company did not receive a further order until 1936. The AEI Group were eminently more successful at this time, and between 1915 and 1933, had supplied no less than 1,006 motorcoach power equipments. At this point, it is worth reviewing the major orders for both AEI (including Metropolitan-Vickers and BTH), and English Electric, in the period 1915–1938, for the Southern Railway:

Rolling Stock Supplied to Southern Railway to 1935

Quantity	Equipment type	Supplier	Date
Western Section			
244	Motorcoach equipments, power and control, including 275hp motors.	AEI	1915–1930
628	Traction motors (280hp + 225hp)	EE Co.	1923
Eastern Section			
290	Motorcoach equipments, power and control, including 275hp motors.	AEI	1925–1933

Quantity	Equipment type	Supplier	Date
Central Section			
320	Motorcoach equipments, power and control, including 275hp motors.	AEI	1928/1929
Brighton Line			
52	Four-motor multiple unit coach equipments, complete with electro-pneumatic control system.	AEI	1930
101	Sets of electro-pneumatic control equipment for driving trailer coaches.	AEI	1930
66	Motorcoach equipments, power and control, with 275hp traction motors.	AEI	1932
Eastbourne Line			
34	Four-motor multiple unit coach equipments, complete with electro-pneumatic control system.	AEI	1933
68	Sets of electro-pneumatic control equipment for driving trailer coaches.	AEI	1933
122	Sets of electro-magnetic control equipments for motor coaches, with two 275hp traction motors, for six-coach and three-coach semi-fast services.	AEI	1934–1935

Rolling Stock Equipment Supplied to the Southern Railway 1936–1950

(All English Electric)

Quantity	Equipment type	Date supplied
165	Two-motor motorcoach equipments for express services (225hp traction motors).	1936–1950
189	Trailer coach equipments for express services.	
630	Two-motor motorcoach equipments, (275hp traction motors), for suburban services.	1936-1950
519	Trailer coach equipments for suburban services.	1936-1950
254	Driving trailer coach equipments for suburban services.	1936-1950
3	1,200hp electric locomotive power equipments.	1950

Equipment Supplied to the Waterloo & City Railway

(All English Electric)

Quantity	Equipment type	Date supplied
12	Two-motor motorcoaches, with 190hp traction motors.	1938
6	Trailer coaches	1938

NB The Waterloo & City Railway stock was supplied as replacements for rolling stock supplied in 1899.

In 1936, the Southern Railway placed a 10-year contract on English Electric, subsequently extended to 20 years, to supply all of that railway's needs for rolling stock traction equipment. The traction motors supplied under the terms of this contract were of two types, and interchangeable with the railway's existing designs. The 'suburban' type, rated at 275hp, with two motors hung from each of two axles on the motorcoach's motor bogie, and driving the wheels through spur gears. The standard English Electric electro-pneumatic

control–a unit switch–was housed in sheet steel pannier cases carried below the floor of the vehicle, with the low voltage (65V) for the control circuits, supplied through a potentiometer. Two collector shoes were fitted to each power bogie, one on either side, as standard, and a power cable, or bus-line running the length of each eight-coach train. This was required to bridge the frequent, and extensive gaps in the third rail, present on the network at that time. The 'express' type equipment was very similar to the 'suburban', except that the non-ventilated traction motors were rated at 225hp only, and the low voltage supply for control systems was provided by a motor-generator set.

The Southern Railway orders were undoubtedly a major success here at home for English Electric, and of course, for other suppliers. However, in general, on the electric traction front, the UK market was not the cornerstone of the rail traction industry. Electric traction equipment suppliers both benefited and suffered from the effects of the economic depression, but unlike some specialist railway manufacturers, they had the advantage of a larger, electrical engineering background, and broader commercial base.

Up to the end of World War II, all the big names in electric traction continued steady, and relatively successful progress, with English Electric's main works at Preston supported by the works at Bradford and Stafford. After the end of the war, extensive re-equipment of the Preston Works took place, with the East Works concentrating on locomotive, rolling stock, and diesel engine manufacture. The West Works concentrated on electrical equipment, traction motors, control systems, and the like. Interestingly, in 1947, the Preston Works included a Traction Motor Testbed, a tradition continued there to this day, with GEC Traction's Combined Test Facility–although the present installation is a very much more sophisticated arrangement.

In addition to the ex-Siemens Bros switchgear works at Stafford, English Electric later developed extensive Research and Development Laboratories there, serving the whole English Electric Group. Just after the war, in 1946, the Marconi Wireless Telegraph Co. was purchased, along with its subsidiaries in the fields instrumentation and communications, with works at St Albans and Chelmsford.

English Electric were fast emerging as the foremost company in the field, which at times, it seems, was hard to pin down to one area or another. The same could be said of the AEI Group, which included the British Thomson-Houston Co., with its heavy electrical engineering works at Rugby. The BTH factory was on the opposite side of the LMS main line to the south, at Rugby. Metropolitan-Vickers, the other major member of the AEI combine, had, of course, its headquarters at the massive Trafford Park works in Manchester, which, at their peak, employed more than 20,000 people. By the 1930s and 1940s, some traction activities had transferred to the Attercliffe Common Works in Sheffield–this had been Metropolitan-Vickers' second major site for some years. The formation of AEI effectively gave that group a competitive trading position, which it had been seeking to achieve in the British electrical industry, under the ultimate control of the General Electric Co. of the USA. Metropolitan-Vickers was very much the major partner in this group, and was forced to diversify to some extent, by the economic climate, and not least, by the Second World War. Amongst the diversified activities that were to have some impact in the railway industry, was the production of gas turbines for power generation, and transportation. The successful development into rail traction produced an order from the Great Western Railway for a prototype gas turbine powered locomotive. It was hailed as a jet propelled rail vehicle for the future, which belied something of the research that had gone into its final production,

through Metropolitan-Vickers other wide ranging activities in power and transport engineering. However, that success in the railway field was not to be, as railway gas turbines were consigned to the 'failed experiment' category. Like English Electric though, Metropolitan-Vickers, and AEI continued its successful progress, with reorganisations and re-equipment in the post-war era, but with even more far reaching changes still to come in the next decade.

It may seem strange that the coal industry should adopt electric traction for some mines, but these two 50-ton locomotives were the second such order for English Electric. Industrial and mining locomotives were a significant business area for all the major traction companies. EE Co., had supplied a range of trolley pole locomotives for the NCB's Harton Colliery between 1909 and 1911, rated at from 100 to 280hp. The two locomotives seen here were 400hp, and weighed in at 50 tons, with mechanical parts from E. E. Baguley Ltd, of Stafford.

Summary of Electric Traction Orders 1923 to 1945
English Electric

Railway Company	Year	Order
Southern Railway	1923	Traction motors, control equipment
Southern Railway	1936/50	
LMSR (Wirral)	1938	
Southern Railway	1938	Replacement eqpt for: Waterloo & City
LMSR (L&YR)	1939	Liverpool–Southport
Australia (NSWGR)	1928	Traction motors
Bolivia	1930	Traction motors, control equipment
Brazil	1926	Complete electrification project
Canada	1924	Locomotives & traction eqpt. (CNR)
Canada	1926	Traction motors (British Columbia)

Railway Company	Year	Order
Denmark	1933/50	Electrification project
India	1926/30	Various electrification projects, and traction equipment
Japan	to 1930	Electrification project, and general traction equipment
New Zealand	1929/45	Complete electrification project, and traction equipment
Poland	1936	Complete electrification project, in joint venture with Metropolitan-Vickers
South Africa	1938	Cape Town suburban electrification
Spain	1924	Barcelona suburban electrification
Venezuela	1927	Motor coaches, switchgear, etc.

In 1937 New Zealand Railways placed in service the first of ten 1,240hp 1-Do-2 locomotives for the Wellington to Paekakariki electrification. The locomotive seen here is the only complete unit built in the UK by English Electric, with nine sets of mechanical parts shipped out to New Zealand for completion in the railway workshops there.

Metropolitan-Vickers (AEI)

Railway Company	Year	Order
Argentina	1923/29	Buenos Aires Western, complete electrification
Australia (NSWGR)	1925/45	Motorcoach power and control equipment. Substation equipment and switchgear
Australia (Victoria)	1925	Multiple unit vehicles
Australia (WAGR)	1924	Locomotive
Brazil	1935/36	Complete electrification project (Central Railway of Brazil)
Brazil	1926	Complete electrification project (Oeste de Minas Railway)
Brazil	1926	Locomotive (Paulista Railway)
Cuba	1926	Substation equipment
Eire	1931	Electrical equipment for battery operated railcars
Eire	1937	Electrical equipment for battery operated railcars
LNER	1932/37	Substation equipment for Manchester, Sheffield, Wath project
LMSR	1926/37	Traction equipment (Euston–Watford)
LMSR	1926	Power equipment for Liverpool–Southport
LMSR	1929/30	Substation and other power equipment for London area, and Manchester–Altrincham
Southern Railway	1930+	Various power and control equipment
London Underground	1930	Bakerloo Line power equipments
London Underground	1930	Northern Line power equipments
Hungary	1932	Complete electrification project
India	1927/38	Electrification projects, and rolling stock equipment
Italy	1926	Traction control equipments
Japan	1925	1,220hp electric locomotive
Netherlands	1925/34	Electrification projects, and rolling stock traction equipment
New Zealand	1939	Traction substation equipment
Poland	1936	Complete electrification project, conjunction with English Electric, and 'British Contractors Committee'
South Africa	1925/44	Various locomotive and rolling stock orders
Spain	1925/36	Multiple unit power equipments, for various lines, and 4,400hp locomotive
USSR	1926	Multiple unit rolling stock power equipment

6
Diesel Traction Progress to 1970

Progress with diesel traction had been very limited up to the end of the Second World War, although the railway industry had already built up significant experience, on numerous export orders. Away from shunting and suburban traffic, the development of a successful range of diesel locomotives for main line haulage in the USA was demonstrating the way forward. A new word was being added to the railway dictionary in the 1940s too, 'dieselisation'. This word describing a process which, in many instances, involved the complete elimination of steam traction from some US railroads, and was developing rapidly at this time. It has to be said that this was not the earliest instances of such changes, but it was certainly the most extensive.

In Europe, there were many other priorities to be counted in the post-war era, and dieselisation on a wide scale was fairly low down on that list. AEI Group companies, BTH, and Metropolitan-Vickers in particular, along with the English Electric Group, and, to a lesser extent, GEC, were involved with the completion of numerous orders from around the world, and a couple of important developments on British Railways. Major organisational changes involving the nationalisation of the four main line railway companies also, perhaps indirectly contributed to the slower start in the UK. GEC Traction's predecessors, who were busily engaged on fulfilling, in the main, orders from the British colonies, were spearheaded by English Electric, who had secured the lion's share of this work.

English Electric had also been working closely with the Vulcan Foundry, during the recently ended hostilities, a relationship which developed after the war, as Vulcan Foundry continued to build the mechanical parts of English Electric

The official view of English Electric's 1,600hp locomotive for Egyptian State Railways in 'photographic grey'. The bodyside stripes, seen on this 1949 production from Preston are vaguely reminiscent of the style adopted on the Deltic prototype a few years later.

(*National Galleries & Museums on Merseyside*)

designs. During the war too, the Vulcan-Frichs agreement was terminated, and a new agreement signed with the Drewry Car Co. for the manufacture of diesel-mechanical locomotives. This partnership proved very successful, and an effective competitor to another, later GEC company, Ruston & Hornsby, who had been building small diesel locomotives for many years. R&H it will be recalled were in at the birth of diesel traction, but had disputed, if indirectly in some areas, the claims of Dr Rudolf Diesel as the 'inventor' of this form of power, preferring to use the complex 'heavy oil' description. The Vulcan-Drewry association resulted in the appearance of the earliest low powered (less than 300hp) diesel shunters at work, on the LNER initially, and later for British Railways. John Fowler of Leeds had supplied some very small locomotives for the railway companies some years before, but the Vulcan-Drewry variety achieved far more success in practice, and in the commercial sense.

Mention of Ruston & Hornsby during the war years leads to connections with Davey Paxman of Colchester, whom R&H took over in 1940. Davey Paxman, or Paxmans, became an important part of the GEC stable, later designing and building the engines for British Rail's High Speed Trains. English Electric themselves acquired, in 1942, the developer of the famous 'Napier Deltic' engines, D. Napier & Sons Ltd, who had specialist interests in automobile and aeronautical engineering. The company provided English Electric with additional works at Acton in London and at Liverpool. The later 22 locomotives from the English Electric stable that each carried a pair of 1,650hp 'Napier Deltic' engines were, at the time, the world's most powerful single unit diesel locomotives.

Just before the Second World war ended, another important company development took place, when, in 1944, the Vulcan Foundry acquired the world famous name of Robert Stephenson & Hawthorns Ltd, and their works at Newcastle-upon-Tyne. This was a move not without some irony, since a century earlier, in 1832, Robert Stephenson had travelled

across the Pennines to join Charles Tayleur in partnership, forming the Vulcan Foundry, at Newton-le-Willows. The Vulcan Foundry then, together with its newly acquired works in Newcastle, developed an important relationship with English Electric of Preston, from 1946, although it was not for a further nine years, until 1955, that they became a full member of the English Electric Group. The first work on an English Electric main line diesel type was for an export order in 1949, when the Newton-le-Willows plant provided the mechanical parts for the first main line diesel-electric type to be put to work in Egypt.

Completing a circle, Robert Stephenson & Hawthorns, like Vulcan Foundry, had established a working arrangement with the Drewry Car Co., constructing industrial diesel locomotives for many applications, and in the late 1940s, in any gauge from 3ft 6in, to 5ft 6in. The Drewry designs from both RS&H, and Vulcan Foundry were fitted with mechanical transmissions by and large, incorporating 'Vulcan-Sinclair' hydraulic couplings, or the 'SSS Powerflow' gearbox, and Crossley or Gardner built diesel engines. In 1948, RS&H participated in the agreement between Vulcan Foundry and English Electric, for the construction of diesel-electric locomotives. On the industrial diesels front their main competitors were Ruston & Hornsby, already mentioned, who had been building mine, narrow gauge, and diesel-mechanical locomotives for very many years. Ruston were also involved with the production of industrial type diesels, with a member of the AEI Group, British Thomson-Houston, with the latter supplying R&H with power equipments in the late 1940s.

Whilst it is true to say that English Electric were the principal suppliers of diesel and major electric traction equipment in the post-war years into the 1950s, changes were evolving in the AEI Group too. Towards the periphery of this circle of suppliers in diesel and electric rail traction, the original General Electric Co. had teamed up with the likes of North British Locomotive Co. of Glasgow, and were suppliers of power equipment for home and overseas orders. The AEI Group, formed in 1928 included the giant Metropolitan-

In 1956, Malayan Railways ordered the first of 20 1,500hp diesel electric locomotives from English Electric, with the mechanical parts built at Vulcan Foundry.

Vickers plant in Trafford Park, Manchester, and British Thomson-Houston Co.'s works at Rugby. The inclusion of both these major companies in the AEI Group in the 1920s had no major impact on either or both until the 1950s, with each of the member companies retaining their independence, both externally, and to an almost equal extent, with their internal organisation, and company structure.

Metropolitan-Vickers and another famous name in Manchester, Beyer Peacock, combined to form Metropolitan Vickers-Beyer Peacock Ltd, with works at Stockton-on-Tees, to build the mechanical parts of diesel-electric and other non-steam designs. Overall, at this time, some of the world famous names in the steam traction industry were associated with the electrical engineering companies, building the new forms of traction alongside the old. Robert Stephenson and Beyer Peacock were fairly new to the field, whilst Vulcan Foundry had already developed considerable experience. Others, such as the North British Locomotive Co., and Birmingham Railway Carriage & Wagon Co., were not so successful in turning their expertise to the new forms of traction. The former company were successful however, in the 1950s, in providing the mechanical parts for locomotives, with GEC supplying the electrical power and control systems. At home too, the great steam locomotive builders began to involve themselves in the new era of rail traction, with diesel and electric equipments, and even, on an experimental basis, gas turbine powered locomotives.

The giant Metropolitan-Vickers company, had extended its network of offices and plant all around the world, including affiliated companies, agents and correspondents. In Europe, Metropolitan-Vickers was present in France, Germany, Poland, Russia and Spain, to name but a few. In Africa, the Commonwealth (later Republic) of South Africa, Egypt, and Rhodesia saw a presence. Further east, Australia,

Undoubtedly a photograph of contrast and curiosity, showing No. 20101, one of the English Electric 1,500hp Co-Cos for Malaya leaving Kuala Lumpur with a passenger train. All of GEC Traction's predecessors had supplied equipment for service in some exotic locations, but this particular photograph demonstrates that idea particularly effectively.

New Zealand, India, and even China and Japan had some company representation, whilst there were also offices in North and South America. The main works were of course still in Trafford Park, Manchester, whilst as a matter of interest, the company's London office was at the home of the BBC's World Service, in Bush House – an appropriate location perhaps.

British Thomson-Houston, the second placed member of the AEI Group of companies involved in rail traction, had an equally widespread base of operations around the world. However, BTH were rather more involved in the provision of discreet components such as traction motors and control gear, than the complete package. Having said that, in 1948, BTH were supplying ten, 1,000hp locomotives for the New South Wales Government Railways in Australia, and had built its first complete diesel locomotive in 1928, soon after AEI was formed. In order to meet the challenges of the motive power revolution, of which diesel traction was an integral part, AEI decided in 1957 to restructure the organisation on a divisional basis. In 1958, this resulted in the combination of the Metropolitan-Vickers and BTH activities in the railway world, into a single AEI Traction Division. In the UK this resulted from the emergence from the mid-1950s of

two major names in the diesel traction field, English Electric and AEI. From that time, the two companies outstripped all rivals at home, and were powerful forces of competition for export orders around the world, and not just in the former British colonial areas.

Export Orders in the Post War Era
Amongst the first post war orders to be placed with UK companies, was one that went to English Electric originating from Egyptian State Railways in 1947, and included 15 350hp shunters and twelve 1,600hp main line diesels. The shunters were of what had become English Electric's standard type, and built at the company's Preston Works. The engine installed in the Egyptian shunters was the six-cylinder 6KT type, with 10in by 12in cylinders, and directly coupled to a dc generator at the cab end. This arrangement had also been specified and used on similar locomotives built for Malaya. The standard layout adopted by English Electric had a three-point resilient mounting to help minimise any effects of distortion of the locomotive main frame being transmitted to the diesel engine's crankshaft. The generator supplied the two axle hung, nose suspended traction motors, which, in turn, drove the wheels through double reduction spur gearing. The basic layout of the locomotive followed similar lines to that provided in the shunting types built for the LMSR at home, and used a main frame based construction, rather like a steam locomotive, with six, 4ft diameter, spoked, coupled wheels. The driving cab was positioned at one end of the locomotive, with two driving positions, one on either side of the footplate. The power unit itself was

enclosed by a sheet steel nose, or hood, and divided into three compartments, with bulkheads separating the radiator from the engine, and the engine from the generator compartments. Filters were incorporated in the bulkheads to prevent any ingress of dirt, or oily vapours, and in the access doors to the generator compartment, to take in clean, filtered air from the outside world.

The 15 locomotives supplied to Egypt were almost identical with six ordered by the GWR at home, and later delivered to British Railways (Western Region), in 1948. The Egyptian order was shipped early in 1948, and was followed later that same year, by the first of the 1,600hp diesel-electric main line locomotives. These express passenger designs were intended for operation between Port Said and Cairo, Cairo and Alexandria, and Cairo to Assuan. They were provided with an unusual wheel arrangement, having two four-wheeled bogies, each at the outer ends of the locomotive, and separated by a rigid frame with eight larger, driving wheels in between.

The basic layout of these double ended units, six of which were constructed at the Preston Works, provided for a driving cab at each end, with the 16-cylinder SVT design diesel engine, generator, and all auxiliaries carried within the full width body, in various compartments. The Egyptian order provided an important example of the emerging relationship between English Electric and the Vulcan Foundry, as the mechanical portions of the second group of six locomotives were built at the latter's Newton-le-Willows Works. The 16-cylinder 'vee' form engine is of special interest, since it was also installed in the first main line diesel type to run on a railway in the UK, described in some detail later. The power unit once again incorporated EE Co.'s three-point resilient mounting, but with auxiliary springs under the main generator to support the additional weight. In total, six, four-pole, force-ventilated traction motors were fitted, four on the axles housed in the rigid frame section, and one on each of the inner axles of the two bogie units. With operation in Egypt particular attention was paid to climatic conditions, and special arrangements were made on these locomotives to filter all air intakes, before ducting the supply to the components.

1,760hp Co-Co for Malayan Railways.

In the same year, 20 of the 350hp 0-6-0 shunters were ordered from English Electric by Malayan Railways, but adapted for use on metre gauge lines. The first two locomotives to this order were delivered in mid-1948, and once again included the popular 6KT engine, although on this occasion, the traction motors drove the wheels through single reduction gearing. Apart from the obvious external differences such as the rail gauge, the Malayan locomotives carried only 100 gallons of fuel in a tank behind the driving cab. A redesigned nose showed what might almost be considered a minimal attempt at streamlining, compared with the Egyptian and British examples, although again, special conditions were attached to the filtering of the intake of clean, fresh air. The 20 locomotives on the Malayan order weighed in at 44 tons each – 3 tons lighter than their Egyptian counterparts – but with a similar, 33,000lb, tractive effort. In service, they were to be found shunting in the yards at Kuala Lumpur, Singapore, and Prai.

In 1949, English Electric received yet another major order from Egypt, this time for no less than 19, five-car diesel trains, for suburban and express passenger duties. Ten of these articulated sets were for express passenger services, with the remaining nine on suburban operations. A total installed power of 800hp was provided, from the 400hp, 750 rpm diesel engines, one at each end of the train. The four-cylinder engines were supercharged, and each supplied a pair of traction motors installed on the articulated bogie, connecting the power car with the first trailer car, and of course, the final drive was through single reduction spur gearing. The all up weight of these five-car trains was $149\frac{1}{2}$ tons, with a maximum speed of 75 mph, and seating for 244 passengers. By 1950, all of these standard gauge trains were in service, and were followed the very next year by an order for eleven three-coach trains, again articulated, but powered by a single 400hp diesel engine. Both the three-car and five-car versions were provided with driving cabs in the motor cars at each end of the train, with power equipment remotely controlled. The 1951 order for three-car trains provided seating accommodation for 176 passengers, and each train weighing $90\frac{1}{2}$ tons, but with a slightly lower maximum speed of 65 mph.

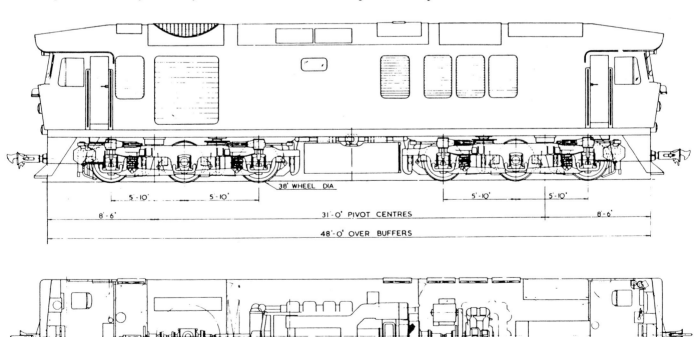

38' WHEEL DIA

5'-10'   5'-10'   5'-10'   5'-10'

8'-6'   31'-0' PIVOT CENTRES   8'-6'

48'-0' OVER BUFFERS

Out in Australia both Metropolitan-Vickers, and BTH, as AEI Group companies, were rapidly extending their experience in the diesel traction field. In New South Wales, British Thomson-Houston provided traction motors, generators and control equipment for ten, 1,000hp locomotives, as main contractor. The engines for these locomotives were supplied by Davey Paxman of Colchester, who had by then, been acquired by Ruston & Hornsby. Each locomotive was equipped with a pair of 500hp diesels, one on either side of the central driving cab, and they were intended for switching (shunting) duties. Although the order was placed in 1950, the locomotives did not enter service until 1952, with the mechanical portions being constructed by Metropolitan-Cammell of Saltley, Birmingham. Paxman engines were installed in 18 similar Bo-Bo switching locomotives ordered in the same year (1950), for Western Australian Government Railways, although these were of only 400hp, and weighed in at a mere 40 tons.

At this time, the only effective competition from the UK for Australian orders came from English Electric, although here again, the Birmingham RC&W Co., and North British

Locomotive Co. supplied small orders in 1954 and 1953, respectively. English Electric's share totalled three major orders during the 1950s. In 1950, 1953, and 1956, 52 locomotives in all were supplied to Tasmania, Queensland, and South Australia. In addition, the company had, in 1949, delivered power and transmission equipment for six three-car diesel trains, built in the workshops of Western Australia Government Railways. The English Electric diesel engines were six-cylinder type 6H, and developed 200hp at a speed of 1,500 rpm. This normally aspirated engine was offered by English Electric, with traction generator, for various railcar and multiple unit applications. The self-ventilated traction motors were axle hung, nose suspended, driving the wheels through the, by then standard, arrangement of single reduction spur gears. The new three-car trains operated on the 3ft 6in gauge, with a weight in working order of 103 tons, a maximum axle load of $19\frac{1}{2}$ tons, and a designed maximum speed of 45 mph.

Tasmanian Government Railways had decided to embark on a major dieselisation programme in the late 1940s, and in 1948, ordered 32 complete locomotives from English Electric. These locomotives were built for Tasmania's 3ft 6in gauge lines, and weighed in at 56 tons in working order, with a maximum axle load of $13\frac{1}{2}$ tons. In fact three separate orders were placed on English Electric for these locomotives, which were constructed at the Preston Works, with the first unit entering service in 1950, as the new Class X/XA. Power

Also running in pairs, but on the other side of the world, in Tasmania, are these 600hp mixed traffic diesel electric locomotives hauling a passenger train on the Coastal Line. A semi-hood type, the first orders were placed with English Electric in 1949.

was provided by an English Electric six-cylinder, in-line, supercharged diesel engine, a medium speed design, running at 750 rpm, to produce a 660hp rating. Each of the axles of the two four-wheeled bogies on which the locomotive was carried, was fitted with a single, 165hp, self-ventilated dc traction motor, driving the wheels through single reduction gears. Maximum tractive effort from these locomotives was 33,000lb. The general arrangement of the superstructure was what could be called a 'semi-hood' type, with a single driving cab at one end of the locomotive. The cab itself occupied the full width of the footplate, with windows on either side giving good visibility along the locomotive's nose or hood, and three large windows across the 'back' of the cab. These it could be said formed the normal 'front' view of the locomotive, since they were normally seen with this end of the cab leading. Numerous hinged doors in the hood gave access to the engine, generator and radiator compartments. These locomotives served Tasmania's railway system well, and by 1962, the fleet of 32 had amassed almost 17 million miles in traffic.

Other important orders for English Electric during this period began with power equipments for the Australian Iron & Steel Co. Ltd, of New South Wales, in 1949, and power and transmission equipment for South Australia. Victorian Railways ordered 13 of the almost standard 350hp 0-6-0 shunter in 1950, with a second order in 1951, raising the total on order to 16. These shunters were all built at the Preston Works, with two traction motors driving through double

Overseas, this Australian Iron & Steel Co. 800hp Bo-Bo diesel electric locomotive, represented a shunting/transfer type, with power equipment ordered from EE Co. in 1949. In the UK market, this power rating was adopted by BR for main line mixed traffic, and freight locomotives.

reduction gearing, a maximum tractive effort of 33,000 lb was achievable, and a top speed of 20 mph.

The equipment supplied to the Australian Iron & Steel Co. for their 800hp shunters, comprised an eight-cylinder, supercharged diesel engine, a directly coupled main generator, and auxiliary equipments. The four traction motors supplied drove the wheels on the two bogies through double reduction gears, with a maximum tractive effort of 33,000 lb exerted, and a top speed of 21 mph. Their duties were arduous, and in very demanding conditions, they were required to haul 250-ton capacity crucible trucks around the steelworks, and 70-ton capacity coal wagons. South Australia too, was busy constructing locomotives equipped with English Electric power equipment, in its own workshops, in 1949. Two diesel-electric locomotives were built initially, of 350hp, and intended for mixed traffic duties, with a similar layout to the Tasmanian locomotives – two four-wheeled bogies, with a single full width driving cab at one end. Further sets of power equipment were ordered from English Electric in 1950, for ten, 1,760hp locomotives, built in the South Australian Railways workshops at Islington. In this case, the locomotives were carried on two, three-axle bogies, with only the outer axles motored, and introduced to freight haulage between Adelaide and Tailem Bend, and passenger duties between Adelaide and Serviceton. Further orders for English Electric arrived in 1955, with more engines, generators, traction motors, and auxiliaries, for ten 750 hp diesel electric types.

English Electric had, by 1951, supplied locomotives and power equipment for service on three of Australia's 'standard gauges'; 3ft 6in, 5ft 6in, and 4ft 8½in. The latter gauge, used predominantly in New South Wales saw the introduction in Australia, of the type 16V, 1,600hp diesel engine, identical to that supplied by EE Co. to Egyptian State

Staying in Australasia, these EE Co. 1,760hp locomotives for South Australian Railways (Nos 901 and 900) bore an uncanny resemblance to an Alco design for the New York, New Haven & Hartford Railroad, amongst others, in the USA. In this case, only ten were ordered in 1950, for main line service.

Railways. The NSW locomotives were a curious, articulated design, carried on three bogies, and built in the railway company's own workshops. The centre bogie was a three-axle layout, and a four-wheeled bogie was provided at either end. The EE Co.'s traction motors were mounted on the underframe of the locomotive, with a cardan shaft drive to the wheels. There had already been an accumulation of experience in NSW, of cardan shaft drives for diesel traction, and the layout on these locomotives provided a lower axle loading than would have been possible with a pair of three-axle bogies. The supply of power equipments against orders from various railway operators had, by this time, adopted a fairly standard format – main and auxiliary generators, a control cubicle and equipment, radiator fan motor, compressor motor, and other auxiliary machinery. In addition, larger orders for power equipments would include the diesel engine itself, and traction motors, where electric transmission was employed. English Electric, in common with their main competitiors, Metropolitan-Vickers, had established offices and works in Australasia, with the principal locations at Brisbane in Queensland, and Sydney, New South Wales.

Still in the Australasian Region, New Zealand provided yet another example of the striking successes of English Electric, and between 1950 and 1962, EE Co. alone supplied all New Zealand's diesel traction needs over 500hp. The earliest orders came in 1950 and 1951, when the Preston Works constructed 15 mixed traffic locomotives, of 660hp, for the 3ft 6in gauge lines. These DE class diesel-electrics first entered service in 1952, and ten years later, between them had covered some 4½ million miles. This first order was followed in 1953 by an order for ten class DF 2-Co-Co-2 locomotives, of 1,500hp, and weighing in at some 105 tons, but with a maximum axle load which, at 11.7 tons, was actually less than that of the smaller DE class. Whilst the DE locomotives were intended for mixed traffic work, including some heavy shunting duties, the larger DF types were purely for main line services. A further series of mixed traffic locomotives were placed in service from 1955 onwards, as classes DG and DH, with 750hp diesel engines, and an A1A-A1A wheel arrangement. These 42 locomotives were supplied by English Electric in two orders, and housed the same engine as the first order for Class DE locomotives of 1950/51. The engine was designated type 6SRKT, and in the first application they were not turbocharged, although for the Classes DG and DH, it had been uprated from 660 to 750hp, with the application of charge air cooling increasing the power output still further, to over 1,000hp in the 6CSRKT version.

British Thomson-Houston also supplied more than 70 shunting locomotives to New Zealand, in several orders, the

Running under the catenary of an electrified line in New Zealand, this 1,500hp diesel electric was ordered from English Electric in 1953, and was the first of the ten in this class.

first of which were supplied from the UK, with the Clayton Equipment Co. building the mechanical portions. Subsequent orders were built in the railway workshops of New Zealand Railway, under licence.

Africa too provided a number of orders for both English Electric and the AEI Group, excluding Egypt, these were received from East African Railways, Ghana, Nyasaland (later Malawi), Mozambique, Nigeria, Rhodesia (later Zimbabwe), South Africa, Sudan and Zambia. East Africa, Rhodesia, Nigeria, and Ghana provided the source for most contracts for the companies in the 1950s, and into the 1960s, and perhaps not surprisingly, in view of the numerous electric traction orders, South Africa placed only a handful of contracts at this time. The late 1950s were the years when most of the orders were received, since the diesel 'revolution' was slower in taking off in many former British colonies, where, for sound economic reasons, the changeover was less justified.

In the period under review, the West African countries were amongst the earliest to order diesel power, by which time, the AEI Traction Division had been formed. This move, brought about in 1959, joined the traction divisions of the two major partners in the AEI Group, British Thomson-Houston and Metropolitan-Vickers, and is reviewed in detail later. By the end of the decade, there were then only English Electric and AEI, as the major UK companies involved in diesel and electric traction work at home and abroad, although of course,

on a smaller scale, a number of other companies continued to supply products, for main line and industrial use.

The African states in the 1950s provided nine orders for locomotives and power equipment, in the higher power ranges, above 500hp. Ghana Railways and Ports Administration ordered a total of 37,750hp mixed traffic locomotives, in three separate orders between 1953 and 1963. The Bo-Bo locomotives for Ghana were built at English Electric's Vulcan Foundry plant, with Preston Works supplying some equipment, shipping the whole out from Liverpool to Ghana. The six-cylinder diesel engine was the same as that used on the New Zealand Railways orders in progress at this time, the type 6SRKT, with the first order for 14 locomotives entering service in 1954. With a total weight of 53 tons, and a maximum axle load of 13 tons, the locomotives were used on both freight and passenger duties, and could work in multiple, if required, on Ghana's 3ft 6in gauge lines. The second order for twelve locomotives arrived in 1958, with a final order for eleven placed in 1963. English Electric's final order from Ghana arrived in 1968, and was for ten locomotives, of 2,025hp, for freight work, and incorporating the type 12CSVT engine. These Co-Co types, which tipped the scales at 84 tons, were significantly different from the earlier design, with two full width cabs at either end, and the engine and generator compartments covered by a narrower hood, or bonnet section, in between. The maximum axle load of 14 tons with these locomotives was only slightly greater than the earlier designs, with construction undertaken at English Electric's Vulcan Works. A repeat order for six more 2,025hp Co-Cos was placed with the company, bringing the total in service to 16.

Between 1964 and 1970, Western Australia placed four orders with English Electric, for 21 of the 1,950hp main line hood type units. Here, four locomotives, working in multiple haul an 8,000 ton iron ore over the 3ft 6in gauge, 307 mile route from the coast to Koolyanobbing.

2,025hp diesel for Ghana Railways.

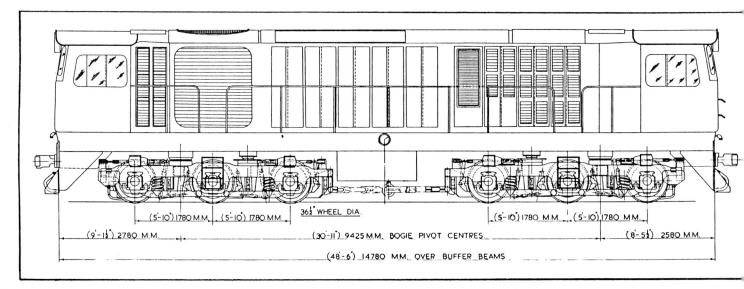

36½" WHEEL DIA.

(5'-10") 1780 M.M.   (5'-10") 1780 M.M.   (5'-10") 1780 M.M.   (5'-10") 1780 M.M.

(9'-1½") 2780 M.M.   (30'-11") 9425 M.M. BOGIE PIVOT CENTRES   (8'-5½") 2580 M.M.

(48'-6") 14780 MM. OVER BUFFER BEAMS

West Africa was not such a frequent source of orders for AEI or EE Co., as the east coast. However, Nigeria had ordered ten 740hp locomotives in 1954, followed some ten years later by these 1,400hp Co-Co locomotives, with a second order in 1966 bringing the total to 29. This is No. 1401 *Lagos*.

Neighbouring West African state, Nigeria, ordered ten of the 750hp Bo-Bos from English Electric in 1954, also for operation on the 3ft 6in gauge, although the locomotive's total weight had crept up to 54 tons. The Nigerian order was broadly similar to the motive power supplied to Ghana Railways, with a single cab, and six-cylinder 6SRKT diesel engine. Just ten years later, in 1964, the Nigerian Railways Corporation came back to the UK with an order worth more than £2 million, for 29, 1,400hp locomotives, but supplied this time by AEI, with Sulzer diesel engines. The mechanical portions of these locomotives were built by Metropolitan-Cammell of Birmingham, with electrical equipment from the Metropolitan-Vickers works in Manchester and Sheffield. The first of these locomotives was completed in March 1965, in just eight months following the award of the contract. Construction of the locomotive in such a short timescale was assisted by the design's similarity to eight locomotives of the 'Zambesi' class for Nyasaland (Malawi) Railways, and the Trans-Zambesia Railway in 1963. In fact, a further order for two more of the 'Zambesi' class locomotives was placed with AEI (Manchester) in 1967. The prime mover installed in the Nigeria and Nyasaland locomotives was the Sulzer 6LDA28 design, which were also fitted in British Railways locomotives at that time, and constructed at the Barrow-in-Furness works of Vickers Ltd. The latter were at the time, curiously perhaps for a major shipbuilding industry, the largest manufacturer of rail traction diesel engines in the UK. Although, it has to be said, not all of these power units were installed in the locomotive designs of GEC Traction, or its predecessors.

Between the Nigerian and Nyasaland orders, there was a difference in power output, which in the Nyasaland 'Zambesi' class, reached 1,200hp with the 6LDA28B engine, whilst in the Nigerian version, 1,400hp was reached with the 6LDA28C variant. Both designs of locomotive were carried on a pair of three-axle bogies, and were of the semi-hood type, with a single, full width cab at one end, with a protruding nose section. The six AEI type 253AZ traction motors were supplied by a 12-pole generator on the Nyasaland locomotive, and a 10-pole machine for Nigeria. In both cases, the generators were bolted directly to the diesel engine crankshaft, with auxiliary generators for supplying power for battery charging, control systems, lighting, and other equipment. The traction motors themselves were four-pole, series wound, hung from the axle, and by then a very well established tradition, driving the wheels through single reduction spur gears.

Irrespective of manufacturer, by the 1960s, traction motor design was essentially standard, with dc machines, force-ventilated, usually four-pole, series wound, and with one or more stages of field weakening, to improve the speed characteristics at the higher end. The design of bogie and running gear on both of these African orders were described as, 'Alsthom Type', and were of fabricated construction, with the roller bearing axleboxes attached to radius rods/arms, fixed to the bogie frame. Two rubber cone pivots, of a type designed by Alsthom, were carried on rubber pads, surmounting fixed bolsters, which allowed shear movement, and, in order to negotiate tight curves, the inner pivot assembly was able to slide on manganese steel pads.

Whilst AEI, as main contractor to both the Nyasaland and Nigerian Railways, were responsible for supplying the completed locomotives, substantially similar power equipment was provided at the time for Commonwealth Railways of Australia. For these latter, built by Tulloch Ltd, of New

South Wales, the Sulzer 6LDA28 engine was paired with the same 10-pole generator as that fitted in the Nigerian locomotives. In the design of the generator, AEI had incorporated their patented form of commutator construction, the 'Pollock' arrangement.

The Tulloch-Sulzer, AEI powered class 'NT' diesels were required to operate in some of the harshest climatic conditions, running on the 3ft 6in gauge line from Marree to Alice Springs. Amongst the hazards faced were temperatures in excess of 100°F, for more than eight days, continuously, and severe sand and dust storms. In order to combat this, and prevent the ingress of the fine, powdery dust to the electrical and other machinery, the locomotive's full width body was pressurised, with air for this equipment drawn in through the roof, to a pressurised, filtered compartment. The 'NT' class diesels began appearing in traffic from May 1965, and amongst other duties, were employed on that famous Australian institution, 'The Ghan'.

In other African states, both English Electric and AEI provided equipment for East African Railways & Harbours, and Rhodesian Railways. For the former, AEI had equipped the prototype 'Explorer', 1,100hp diesel-electric in 1959, which was intended for both branch, and main line duties. The 'Explorer' was the earliest from this company to feature the Alsthom bogie, with its twin rubber cone pivots, but operated on the metre gauge, compared with the 3ft 6in gauge lines of other, later designs. The 'Explorer' prototype also featured a Lister-Blackstone engine, with the mechanical parts completed by the Clayton Equipment Co. The following year, 1960, saw the arrival of the first of English Electric's 2,025hp 1Co-

English Electric seemed most successful in Africa when supplying diesel locomotives compared with Metro-Vick's success with electric traction in South Africa. Here, No. 9003, one of the 44 2,025hp Co-Co locomotives ordered from the company between 1959 and 1967, hauls a freight for East African Railways against a backdrop of savannah.

Co1 designs, which by 1967 had reached a total of 44 locomotives, in four orders. The Class 90 (later reclassified Class 87) locomotives were built at English Electric's Vulcan Foundry plant, and incorporated the highly successful 12 CSVT engine, and were intended to replace steam haulage on the Kenya to Uganda section. These diesel locomotives were amongst the most successful in service in Africa, with orders for similar designs from the Sudan and Rhodesia Railways, all equipped with the 12 CSVT engine. The semi-hood design, with a single full-width cab at one end was popular here, whilst East African Railways ordered a smaller variant of the Class 90 design in 1966, with the eight-cylinder engine, and designated, not surprisingly perhaps, Class 91. With a 1Bo-Bo1 wheel arrangement, the smaller locomotives incorporated a number of components which were common with their larger brethren, and the railways benefited from this standardisation. Here too, the then 1,350hp Class 91 locomotives were built at Newton-le-Willows, and were followed in 1970, by a further order for 10 locomotives in this power range.

Across the Atlantic, in South America during the 1950s, English Electric secured the lion's share of orders, as Argentina rapidly pursued its dieselisation policy. Some equipment had already been supplied for railcars, in the 1920s, but in 1955, the first of two orders were placed for 1000hp A1A-A1A type locomotives, to operate on the metre gauge lines of the F.C. General Belgrano. The first order was for five locomotives, and the second order, placed in 1958, was for 21 locomotives. These orders followed on from an earlier contract, awarded to the company in 1949, for six 880hp mixed traffic types, supplied to the Buenos Aires Provincial Railway, and which entered service in 1952. In neighbouring Brazil, EECo. provided 13 1,000hp locomotives, and a double ended A1A-A1A type, which were put to work on the metre gauge lines of Rede Ferroviaria do Nordeste. The same power equipment included in the designs for this Brazilian contract, was included in another

Above: Emphasising the export success of the diesel business for EE. Co., and the AEI Group too, is this 2,000hp locomotive for Rhodesian Railways. Twenty-three were ordered from English Electric, and built at its then recently absorbed Vulcan Works. Both main constituents of GEC Traction were extremely successful in winning orders from overseas railway companies for diesel locomotives.

Below: Classed nowadays as type DE3 by the National Railways of Zimbabwe, 16 of the class were ordered in 1962/63, and carry the 12-cylinder vee form CSVT engine on a 1Co-Co1 wheel arrangement. This is No. 1310 in Rhodesia Railways livery, although the photograph has been 'doctored'.

(National Railways of Zimbabwe)

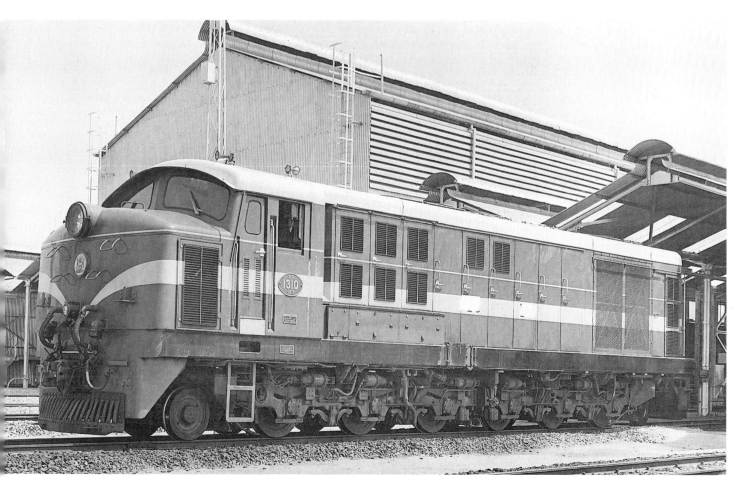

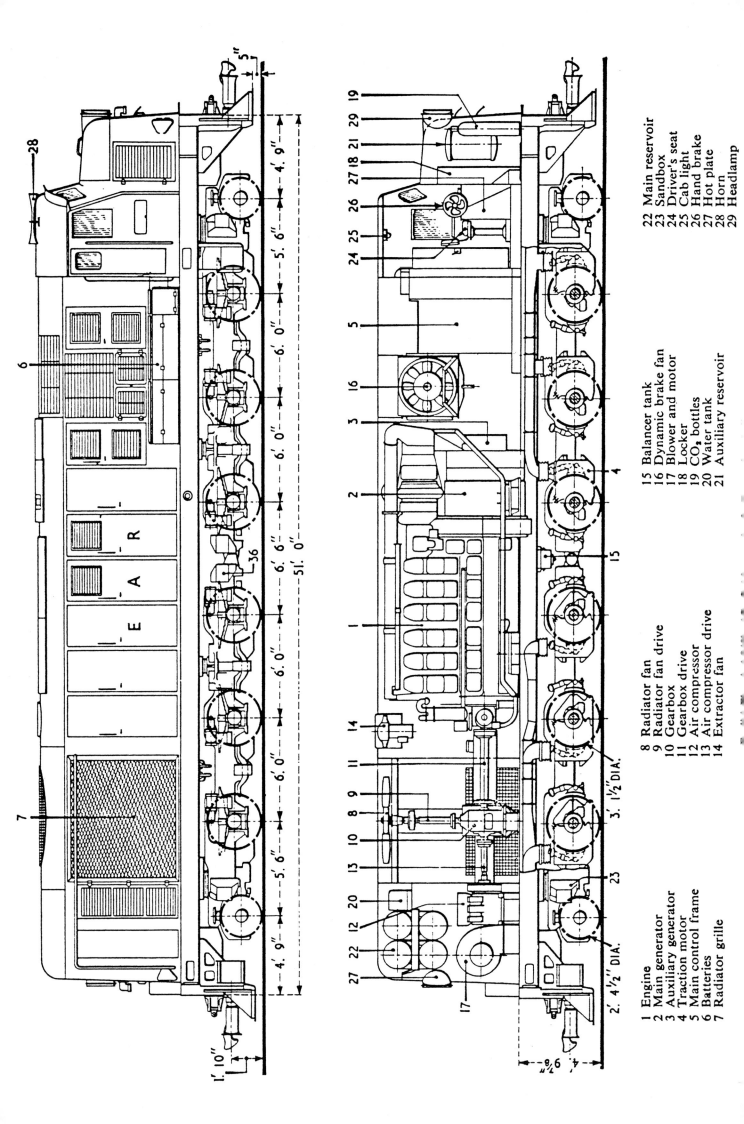

1 Engine
2 Main generator
3 Auxiliary generator
4 Traction motor
5 Main control frame
6 Batteries
7 Radiator grille

8 Radiator fan
9 Radiator fan drive
10 Gearbox
11 Gearbox drive
12 Air compressor
13 Air compressor drive
14 Extractor fan

15 Balancer tank
16 Dynamic brake fan
17 Blower and motor
18 Locker
19 CO$_2$ bottles
20 Water tank
21 Auxiliary reservoir

22 Main reservoir
23 Sandbox
24 Driver's seat
25 Cab light
26 Hand brake
27 Hot plate
28 Horn
29 Headlamp

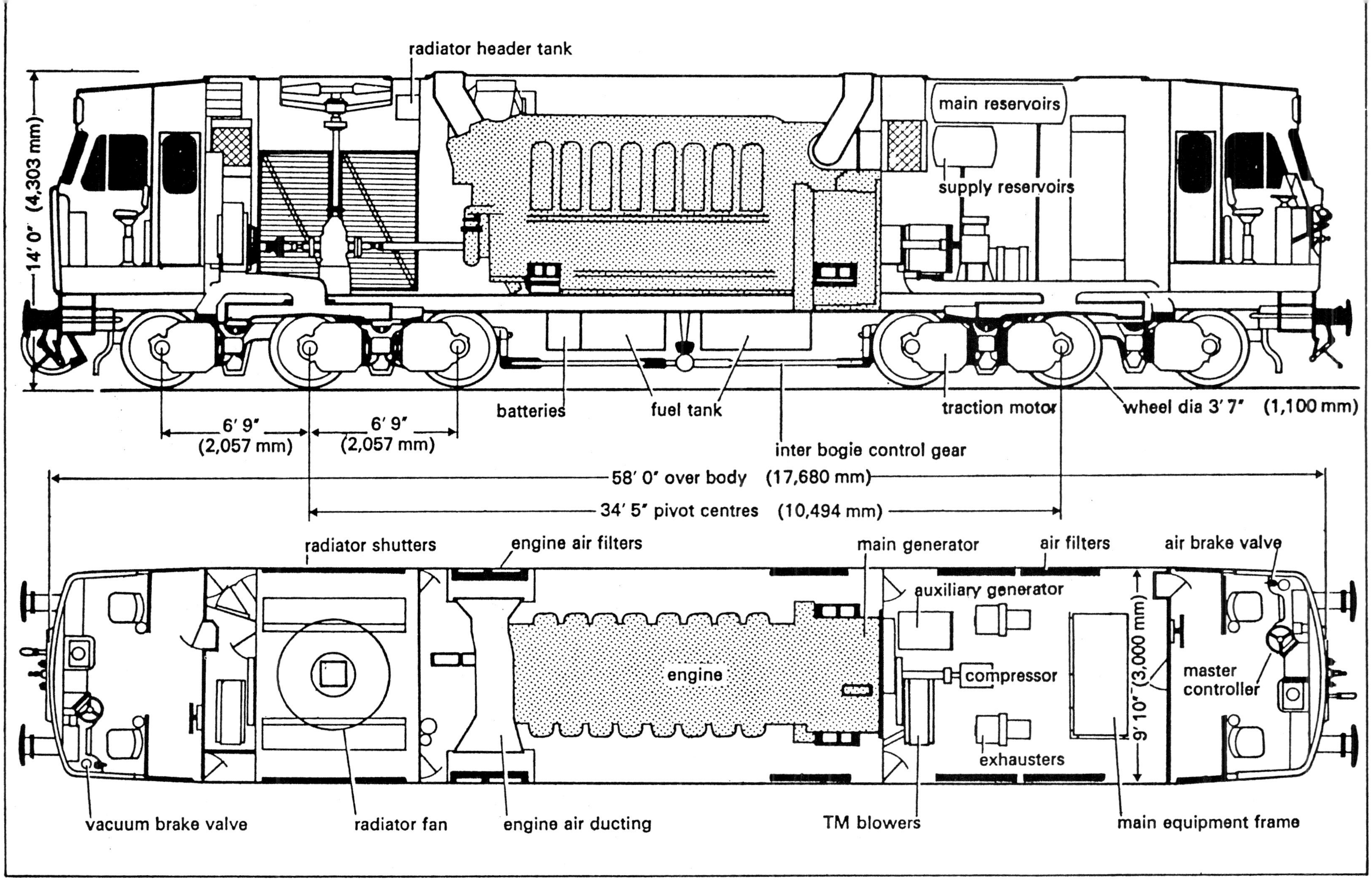

radiator header tank

main reservoirs

supply reservoirs

wheel dia 3' 7" (1,100 mm)

traction motor

inter bogie control gear

fuel tank

batteries

58' 0" over body (17,680 mm)

34' 5" pivot centres (10,494 mm)

6' 9" (2,057 mm)

6' 9" (2,057 mm)

6' 9" (2,057 mm)

14' 0" (4,303 mm)

air brake valve

master controller

9' 10" (3,000 mm)

main equipment frame

air filters

auxiliary generator

compressor

exhausters

main generator

TM blowers

engine

engine air filters

engine air ducting

radiator shutters

radiator fan

vacuum brake valve

English Electric 2,700hp Co-Co for Portugal.

Another view of the Class DE3, but this time, No. 1301 as new, in Rhodesian Railways colours. This excellent photograph clearly shows many external details of these fine locomotives, including the attractive Rhodesian Railways crest on the cab front.
(National Galleries & Museums on Merseyside)

design, which tipped the scales at 72 tons, compared with the all up weight of 73 tons for the locomotives for Argentina. In both cases, English Electric supplied engine and transmission, and constructed the mechanical portions. From entering service in 1956, the motive power for the Argentine had accumulated some 4,700,000 miles by the end of 1962.

British Thomson-Houston Co., as a member of the AEI Group, was busily supplying electrical equipment for industrial locomotives during the 1950s, in both South America and the Caribbean. The latter included a 400hp locomotive from the Yorkshire Engine Co., for Alumina, Jamaica, in 1958. Similar equipment was supplied to the African Manganese Co. Ltd, in British Guiana (later Guyana), in 1957, although these latter were of the Bo-Bo wheel arrangement, rather than rigid frame. The Jamaican Government Railways had ordered 750hp Bo-Bo diesel electrics from EE Co. in 1955, as the first of a group of three orders, with the final contract placed in 1967. Power for these locomotives came from the 6 SRKT engine, but were rated at 750hp, and whose ancestry can be traced back to the early diesel shunters produced in the UK, in the early 1920s and 1930s. Whilst many of the orders from South and Central America in the 1950s and 1960s were for quite small locomotives – with some exceptions – Peru provided orders for no less than 14 1,200hp diesel-electrics, and five 2,000hp units in 1963.

Nearer to home, in 1968, English Electric signed a £2.7 million contract for the construction and supply of 2,700hp locomotives for Portugal, the first of which was delivered in December that same year. The Co-Co locomotives for the 5ft 6in gauge, were based around the same power unit installed in English Electric's DP2 prototype, and British Rail's own Class 50 locomotives. This was the first order for the company from Portugal, since 1,360hp units were already under construction, and were being supplied against three orders for a total of 67 locomotives, between 1965 and 1968. Like the majority of English Electric's motive power orders, the actual construction was shared between the Preston and Newton-le-Willows works.

The Home Market

The period between 1948 and 1970, besides witnessing major changes in the company structures, at both English Electric Group, and AEI Group companies, saw the most important developments on British Railways. The home railways were very much lagging behind in the development of diesel traction, until 1955, when BR embarked on the commendable 'Modernisation and Re-equipment Programme'. Sadly, the changeover advocated in this plan was not adhered to, and a headlong, and barely regulated rush into diesel power took place, which naturally saw a number of 'bad choices', and 'poor designs' take to the rails. For the big names, English Electric, Metropolitan-Vickers, British Thomson-Houston, and GEC, there came the first real opportunity to put some larger designs in service, in the UK's 'shop window'.

In 1948, the four main line railways had been nationalised, although not before the LMSR had ordered, and placed in service, the first main line diesel-electric to run in this country. This was followed quickly by a similar unit for the Southern Railway, and both were powered by English Electric built diesel engines. The old Great Western Railway, obsessed as much by its own individuality, as by a desire to modernise its image, approached the problem from an entirely different route. In fact, the GWR was modernising its motive power by turning to gas turbines, and in this context, contracted with Metropolitan-Vickers to build the second of its two gas turbine powered locomotives.

The period of most interest here at home, effectively began with the appearance of the LMSR's 1,600hp Co-Co locomotive in late 1947. Once again, a curious reticence was displayed by the railways in this country to adopt non-steam traction, despite the numerous and proven export successes of the UK companies, and in particular, the rapid dieselisation of the USA. George Nelson, Chairman of English Electric was keen, in the late 1940s, to stimulate the diesel traction business in Great Britain, and designed and built the 1,600hp diesel locomotive in six months, in 1946. It was not an LMS venture, and in fact, as number 10000, was given free of charge to the railway company, and was joined two years later by a second, identical unit, No. 10001, at the start of the British Railways' era.

Nelson, perhaps like George Westinghouse many years earlier, was not impressed with the way the railways, and indeed

Typically, British Railways entered the new diesel era in a relatively cautious way. At the time this photograph was taken however, the standard British diesel locomotive was still the 0-6-0 shunter, here being No. D3613, with the Modernisation Plan's ambitious ideas still to be seen in operation. Though here too, even in main line traction at home, EE Co., continued to outsell its rivals, with whom, within two decades, it was about to join forces.

the company were treating non-steam traction, and No. 10000 in particular. Apparently, after seeing the locomotive at Stafford, in a less than clean condition, suggested they (the LMSR) did not want it, because they had not even bothered to keep it clean. However, he did believe there was some prospect for diesel traction, although it was slow to materialise, and Nelson had to wait until the mid to late 1950s before that prospect began to dawn into reality. Meanwhile, English Electric continued to sell its designs and products successfully, abroad.

English Electric's last, but in this case, least successful experiment, GT3, a gas turbine locomotive built on the main frames of a 4-6-0 steam locomotive. Designed by EE Co., GT3 was built at Vulcan Foundry, but saw very little active service following its arrival on BR in 1961.

In 1948 therefore, the newly formed British Railways possessed two 1,600hp main line diesel locomotives, and 84 shunting types. By 1951, only four more main line types were in service, and two gas turbine powered designs, along with a significant number of the small diesel shunters. In 1950, the world renowned, North British Locomotive Co., of Glasgow, had teamed up with BTH, and Davey Paxman & Co. to supply an 827hp Bo-Bo type to BR, which, although initially intended for branch line service, actually set a kind of standard for freight types in the home market. It was, in appearance, very reminiscent of the hood types built for many countries, with a casing covering the engine and power equipment only. The single driving cab was the full width of the footplate, and in style, similar to that found on freight units in the USA. North British were responsible for the detailed design and construction, whilst BTH provided the main generator, traction motors, and control equipment. Davey Paxman of course, supplied the diesel engine; a 16-cylinder RPHXL/III, developing 827hp at 1,250 rpm. Interestingly, one contemporary technical journal referred to the design of the traction motors as being 'special', although they were in fact an accepted standard, axle hung, nose suspended design, driving the wheels through spur gears, and

force-ventilated. The details of the motor suspension arrangements could vary significantly between countries and railway systems, but the principles were essentially the same, with four-pole, frequently, series wound dc machines. The locomotive design, overall, bore some comparison to another Bo-Bo type built by North British the following year, for Ceylon (Sri Lanka), and powered by a Paxman diesel engine, but with electrical and control equipment from GEC.

Backtracking a little to 1946/47, EE Co. were obviously closely associated with the 'LMS main line diesel project', and a similar scheme being pursued by the Southern Railway. It is worth mentioning, if only to emphasise the extreme slowness with which diesel traction progress was taking place here at home, that the Southern's project was actually initiated *before* that of the LMSR. The LMS locomotive, No. 10000, turned out into traffic in 1947, was intended for working the heaviest Anglo-Scottish expresses. English Electric supplied the same diesel engine and electrical power equipment to the Southern project, although there were some minor differences in control systems, and the final drive gear ratios. The Southern's first diesel did not appear until 1951! An obvious difference between the two designs was the bogie and running gear, which, on Southern metals, saw the birth of the heavyweight 1Co-Co1 bogie, and which later found fame/notoriety on another famous English Electric powered design for BR.

The Deltic Prototype
Perhaps the most exciting development in the early 1950s, from BR's viewpoint, was the construction and testing of the 3,300hp 'Deltic' prototype, with its unique, triangular engine formation. Once again, English Electric were pioneering, with a private venture, built and equipped at the Preston Works, which took to the rails in 1955, the very same year that the 'Modernisation Plan' was announced. The prototype was intended for main line passenger and express freight duties, developing its 3,300hp on a six-axle layout, with all axles motored, from the twin 1,650hp 'Deltic' power units. The double ended layout – with a driving cab at each end of the locomotive – was still a typically British characteristic, but with a maximum axle load of only 18 tons, and a power-to-weight ratio of 6lb/hp. The basic dimensions of the prototype are given below:

The prototype 'Deltic', initially code named 'Enterprise' – until Hudswell, Clarke used the name on their own new design. After successful trial running on BR for 450,000 miles it was retired to its present home in the Science Museum South Kensington, London, and is seen here en route to there on 24th April 1963.

Deltic Prototype – Leading Dimensions
Length over headstocks	66ft 0ins
Overall width	8ft 9½ins
Overall height from rail	12ft 10½ins
Bogie pivot centres	44ft 0ins
Bogie wheelbase	14ft 4ins
Max. tractive effort	60,000 lbs
Cont. tractive effort	33,000lbs at 33 mph
Fuel capacity	800 gallons
Water capacity	300 gallons
(For train heating boiler)	
Braking system	air for loco., vac for train

The prototype began life in Preston under the code name 'Enterprise' in September 1951, but although it was planned to be carried 'on the locomotive, this name was later abandoned when Hudswell, Clarke of Leeds introduced a new range of locomotives bearing that name. The heart of the locomotive was the 18-cylinder 'Deltic' engine, so called due to its similarity to the Greek letter delta, when inverted. A pair of these, derated for rail traction use, were fitted to the locomotive, each driving a generator through a complex series of 'phasing gears', connecting the output from the three crankshafts, to the input shaft of the generator. The two generators in turn, were connected in series, and six traction motors, in three parallel pairs, connected across the two outer feeders.

English Electric had ordered three such engines from D. Napier & Sons, but the company declined the original order, preferring to supply free of charge, two engines, as a private venture. The engine was originally designed by Napier for naval use, in fast patrol boats, and mine-sweepers, with a layout of three cylinder blocks bolted together to form an inverted equilateral triangle, with the crankshafts and crankcases located at each of the three angles.

The mechanical parts of this locomotive were constructed at Preston during 1954, although the later production version bodies were built at the Vulcan Foundry. The 'Deltic' prototype was turned out in a light blue livery, with yellow 'whiskers' on the noses, and raised aluminium logo and striping on the bodysides, and carried front headlights which gave it more than a passing resemblance to some North American designs. In service from 1955, the prototype's running gave no major cause for concern, although some minor modifications were carried out to improve performance and ride quality, following exhaustive static and road trials. The locomotive, despite not being a British Railways locomotive, was actually the subject of a British Transport Commission Test Bulletin, and which concluded with the comment that the locomotive was capable of hauling 500 tons unaided over the formidable climb to Shap Summit, at 41 mph.

Although spending most of its working life between 1955 and 1959 on the London, Midland Region, it has been said that its full potential was never fully realised in traffic. This idea seems to have transferred into the negotiations with BR over the production series too, since some thinking considered the possibility of the 'need' to run these powerful machines in multiple. In 1960, *Deltic* was at work on the Eastern Region main lines, where it was to end its operating days, and following an engine failure in March 1961, it was taken out of service. Subsequently *Deltic* was removed to the Science Museum in London for preservation – but not before consideration had been given to modifying the locomotive for trials in Canada, where such power might be exploited to the full.

English Electric had hoped to sell the prototype to BR, but

with the extensive modifications required by them, this option never materialised. EE Co. believed, in the early stages of negotiations with BR, that the production versions would simply be copies of the prototype, to fit the 'L2' loading gauge with only minor modifications. However, major alterations in the production version were made, and the later class of 'Deltics' were made to pass the 'L1' loading gauge. It is a tribute to the designers of the 'Deltic' that the 22 production versions, which eventually took to the rails of the Eastern Region's main line, were an outstanding success from their introduction in 1961.

The period between 1948 and 1953 was notable for a lack of development, although that was about to change in a remarkable way. Things were on the move across the Irish Sea too, as Metropolitan-Vickers supplied generators and traction motors to Coras Iompair Eireann (CIE), Irish State Railways, for a pair of 900hp Bo-Bo locomotives. These were introduced in 1950, after completion at Inchicore Works, with a Sulzer engine, coupled to Metrovick main and auxiliary generators. Having said that, the order was actually placed in 1946, taking some four years to complete the locomotives, and place them in service.

The Modernisation and Re-Equipment Programme
In 1955, British Railways embarked on the extensive programme to introduce diesel and electric traction, as a replacement for steam, and more generally, to modernise its infrastructure, ranging from the trackbed to refurbishing stations. The companies that had, during the 1920s and 1930s been in the forefront of diesel traction, such as Armstrong Whitworth of Newcastle, to name one leading light, were no longer around in the 1950s. However, Metropolitan-Vickers, BTH, and English Electric, in particular demonstrated their considerable experience in practical form, for main line diesel traction on British Railways.

Metropolitan-Vickers were amongst the first to supply diesel locomotives to the 5ft 3in gauge Irish Railways (CIE). Here however, in 1954, the company supplied power and control equipment for a 550hp Bo-Bo design intended for branch line and country work.

Some examples were constructed in the railway workshops themselves, at Derby, Crewe and elsewhere, with BTH, and English Electric, Metro-Vick, and GEC supplying the power equipment. At this time, other electrical companies were getting involved in rail traction, including Brush Electrical Machines, and to a lesser extent, Crompton Parkinson. Brush's Traction Division, and English Electric vied with one another to be first on the rails with a new generation of diesel locomotives here at home, throughout this first modernisation period. Unfortunately for English Electric at least, the Brush locomotive, in the Type 2 category, arrived first, though English Electric scored the 'first' in the Type 1 category, with their 800hp Bo-Bo offering, built at Vulcan Foundry.

British Railways sensibly embarked on the programme with a Pilot Scheme for 174 locomotives, in a variety of power ranges, from various builders in the late 1950s. It was however, not carried through, since BR was building up sig-

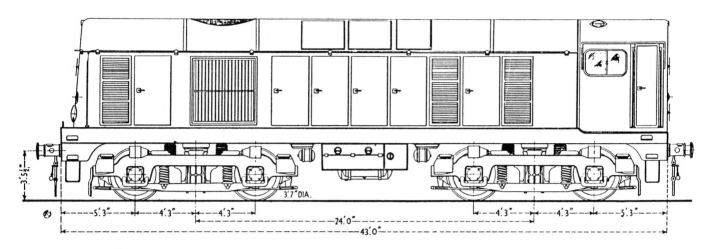

Above: English Electric/Vulcan Foundry 800hp Bo-Bo locomotive for British Railways (Class 20).

Below: Traditionally a major event in the construction of a steam locomotive, was the 'wheeling'. This tradition was maintained during the diesel era too, as this view of the interior of the former Vulcan Foundry shows.

nificant operating losses during the late 1950s to 1960s, and hundreds of diesel locomotives were purchased to replace steam in a very short space of time. Amongst these, the most successful came from the English Electric stable, many of which are still in service in the later 1980s. In fairness however, from this period, or at least in the early 1960s, Brush Traction could actually be said to have produced the definitive British diesel locomotive with electric transmission, and with engines rated at between 2,000hp and 3,000hp. Of all the British Railways diesels for main line service, built between 1957 and 1967, the table below lists those that were constructed by, or fitted with, English Electric, Metropolitan-Vickers, British Thomson-Houston, and GEC traction equipment.

Whilst some later members of GEC Traction fold, namely Ruston & Hornsby, and the Yorkshire Engine Co., were more readily associated with diesel shunting and industrial locomotives, it is curious that there was little involvement with multiple units. Here too, EE Co., Metro-Vick, and others had secured numerous orders for multiple units around the world, but on British Railways these were not to be.

Main Line Diesel Locomotives For British Railways 1957–1967

Date In Service	Type	BR TOPS Class	Rating	Manu-facturer	Power Eqpt.	Total
1957	1, Bo-Bo	20	1,000hp	EE Co.	EE Co.	228
1957	1, Bo-Bo	15	800hp	BTH Co.	BTH Co.	44
1958 (3)	4,1Co-Co1	40	2,000hp	EE Co.	EE Co.	200
1958	1, Bo-Bo	16	800hp	NB Loco Co.	GEC	10
1958/60 (1)	2, Bo-Bo	27	1,250hp	BRC&W Co.	GEC	69
1958	2, Co-Bo	28	1,200hp	Metro-Vick	Metro-Vick	20
1959	2, Bo-Bo	23	1,100hp	EE Co.	EE Co.	10
1959	2, Bo-Bo	21	1,100hp	NB Loco Co.	GEC	58
1961	3, Co-Co	37	1,750hp	EE Co.	EE Co.	308
1961(2)	5, Co-Co	55	3,300hp	EE Co.	EE Co.	22
1967(4)	4, Co-Co	50	2,700hp	EE Co.	EE Co.	50

(1) Only those equipped with GEC motors are shown, the remainder were fitted with motors from Crompton Parkinson.

(2) A 23rd body was constructed, to include the prototype 2,700hp English Electric 16-cylinder engine, and numbered DP2.

(3) The majority of the mechanical parts were constructed at the Vulcan Foundry, with some from Robert Stephenson & Hawthorns.

(4) These locomotives were originally leased to BR from English Electric, but were later purchased outright.

The most successful, overall, of the English Electric designs for BR, were these Co-Co 1,750hp locomotives. At home on both passenger and freight duties, introduced as Type 3 in the BR scheme, most of these are still in service today as Class 37, with many undergoing life extension upgrades. No. D6745 is seen here in BR green on a rake of BR Mk1 coaches in maroon livery.

For many years following the implementation of the BR Modernisation Plan, these English Electric 2,000hp Type 4 (Class 40) locomotives were the backbone of main line passenger traffics. Here, one of the class, bearing BR number D237, is seen at York in March 1967. The family likeness to the first LMSR Co-Co units of 1947/48 is very strong, though these BR units had a 1Co-Co1 wheel arrangement, and sported a massive, fabricated underframe/backbone.

Above: Much of what needs to be said about this 3,300hp Co-Co locomotive has been said, some of it many times over. It was English Electric's most outstanding success, translated as the production 'Deltic' (Class 55) into BR's InterCity service flagship of the Eastern Region fleet, until the arrival of the High Speed Trains in the mid 1970s. For a design which dated from the early 1950s, and which lasted until the modern era on BR, that was a major achievement. This is No. D9001, when new, later named *St Paddy* and re-numbered 55001.

Below: A mistake perhaps, but offered by EE Co. to BR as a possible candidate for a Type 2 locomotive, this design, sported a single 'Deltic' engine. Hence, the obvious nickname for the ten members of this class, "Baby Deltics" represented here by No. D5902. Once again the English Electric family tree is most obvious in the layout of the front end appearance of this design.

No, not another 'Deltic', but the DP2 prototype, which housed the new English Electric 2,700hp 16CSVT diesel engine. This prototype made use of a 'spare' Deltic body in existence at the Vulcan Works, and formed the basis for the later BR Type 4, or Class 50, fleet. Seen at Perth Station on 1st September 1966 . *(Peter Nicholson)*

In addition to those listed, the then GEC company supplied traction motors to Birmingham Railway Carriage & Wagon Co., and the North British Locomotive Co. – 137 in all – for three different Type 2 designs. Only the English Electric design of 1967 was not catered for in the Modernisation Programme, it having evolved from the DP2 prototype, which ran extensive trials in the early 1960s, in the 'spare' 'Deltic' body. Once again, the superiority of English Electric products over its main competitors was marked, no less than 75% of the main line motive power listed, was entirely constructed by that company. In turn, 50% of these were outstandingly successful designs, and are either still in regular service, or were so, until quite recently. Between them Metropolitan-Vickers, and BTH, as the AEI Group, mustered only 64 locomotives! One of these designs was an undoubted failure, whilst the other, from BTH, had a chequered career. English Electric produced the outstanding 'Deltic' Type 5s, a 1,750hp Type 3, which still forms a major element in BR's traction plans, and the 1,000hp Type 1, which has now been in traffic for more than 30 years. The latter, the first main line freight diesel from the Modernisation Plan, in service with BR from 1957, with English Electric power equipment, was built at the Vulcan Foundry works. The early 2,000hp type, with its massively built underframe and running gear was also a first – the first of the Type 4 locomotives for BR's Pilot Scheme, with electric transmission. From EE Co.'s viewpoint, there were some similarities with the recently completed Rhodesian Railways order, and the Southern Region's 1Co-Co1 prototypes.

Of the 174 locomotives, in their various classes, forming the Pilot Scheme order, some were built in BR workshops, but from the private sector, English Electrics were the most successful supplier. There were however, some disadvantages with EE Co.'s products, but affected by 'external' requirements, such as the need to be in keeping with BR's existing operation/maintenance arrangements. It has to be said that these arrangements had more to do with steam traction, and less with the modern motive power then taking to the rails.

Diesel shunters appeared to present less problems in the 1950s, and into the 1960s, and according to one report, very little trouble had been encountered with these types. English Electric had, again, been very successful in this quarter, and although there was some competition from Hunslet Engine Co., Hudswell, Clarke, and Ruston & Hornsby, these latter were essentially suppliers of the smallest designs – less than 250hp. British Railways had, in the 1950s, standardised on a 350hp 0-6-0 design, based on the LMSR locomotives, and those built for overseas customers. These locomotives, of which more than 1,000 were built for home use, were the mainstay of BR's shunting operations up and down the country, and indeed, many still provide shunting and train marshalling functions. However, several minor modifications or versions exist, including some fitted with GEC, and some with BTH traction motors, and surprisingly, even a Crossley powered imitation, with Crompton Parkinson motors. Some of the older LMSR orders, and still then in service with BR, were equipped with one traction motor only, compared with the more usual two-motor arrangement.

English Electric, through Vulcan Foundry were also building a number of the smaller types, notably for the Drewry Car Co., the mechanical portions for which were built at Newton-le-Willows, and fitted with 204hp power units from Gardner Engines of Manchester. British Railways were also constructing numbers of these small, 204hp 0-6-0s at Swindon. Ruston & Hornsby who were later absorbed into the GEC fold, built very few diesels for BR service, but were active in the home industrial scene. R&H supplied a number of 0-6-0 and 0-4-0 designs for internal, BR departmental use, rated at up to 165hp, with, in the main, mechanical transmissions, although the 1953 order for 0-6-0s used BTH traction motors. In 1956, R&H built another 165hp shunter, but this time, with an 0-4-0 wheel arrangement, and incorporating a relatively uncommon form of transmission, essentially mechanical, and using Ruston's constant mesh type gearbox. Six years later, in 1962, BR placed another order on R&H, for ten 0-6-0 shunters, initially to be used in Southampton Docks, although some saw service in later years, as departmental locomotives. The 1962 shunters incorporated a 275hp Paxman engine and AEI traction motors. The list below details the major types and orders involving GEC's predecessors, between 1952 and 1962:

Diesel Shunting Locomotives for British Railways Supplied by GEC Traction Companies

Date	Builder	Type			Total
1952	Drewry/Vulcan	204hp	0-6-0	}	141
1955	Drewry/Vulcan	204hp	0-6-0		
1953/55	English Electric	350hp	0-6-0 (1)		1236
1956	Ruston & Hornsby	165hp	0-4-0		2
1953	Ruston & Hornsby	165hp	0-6-0 (dept. use)		5
1957	Ruston & Hornsby	88hp	0-4-0 (dept. use)		1
1958	Ruston & Hornsby	20hp	0-4-0 (dept. use)		1
1958	Ruston & Hornsby	20hp	0-4-0 (dept. use)		1
1955	Ruston & Hornsby	88hp	0-4-0 (dept. use)		1
1959	Ruston & Hornsby	88hp	0-4-0 (dept. use)		1
1962	Ruston & Hornsby	275hp	0-6-0		10

In addition to EE Co., the following companies supplied traction motors, power and control equipment:

> British Thomson-Houston
> GEC
> Crossley
> Blackstone
> Crompton Parkinson

NB Generally speaking, of the small 204hp 0-4-0 and 0-6-0 shunters, built by, and for BR during this period, the majority were fitted with the Vulcan-Sinclair-Wilson mechanical transmission. The early development and manufacture of this device had involved Vulcan Foundry, prior to the Second World War.

In the midst of the Modernisation & Re-equipment of British Railways, there arrived a certain Dr Beeching, and a major rationalisation of BR, which had serious implications for the railway industry. The streamlining of operations had benefits too, whilst the reduction in the number of goods/marshalling yards for freight spelled the end of the road for the numerous small shunting locomotives. Some of the more obscure main line type diesel-electric locomotives, and certainly all of the diesels with hydraulic transmission were dispatched to the breaker's yard following publication of the National Traction Plan in 1967. Standardising on main line types in higher power ranges was the trend, and a number of the smaller freight diesels produced by AEI/ BTH, and GEC/NBL in particular, were eliminated from future plans. English Electric types survived this purge fairly well, although the centre cab Clayton/GEC Type 1, introduced in 1962, at the same time almost as the 'Beeching Plan' was published, did not survive. In fact, the Type 1 that was 'standardised' for BR freight service, was the 1957 built English Electric/Vulcan Foundry 1,000hp Bo-Bo. Other EE types that figured in this 'standard plan' were the 1,750hp Type 3 Co-Co, whilst the heavyweight 1Co-Co1 Type 4 survived perhaps longer than it ought, and a special place was reserved for the outstandingly successful 'Deltics' on the Eastern Region.

Placed in service in 1967, initially these 2,700hp Co-Co locomotives were actually leased to BR by English Electric Leasings Ltd. The Class 50s were the last of the Modernisation Plan designs, using another innovative English Electric design of diesel engine, first tested in the DP2 prototype. This is No. 404, later No. 50004 *St Vincent*.

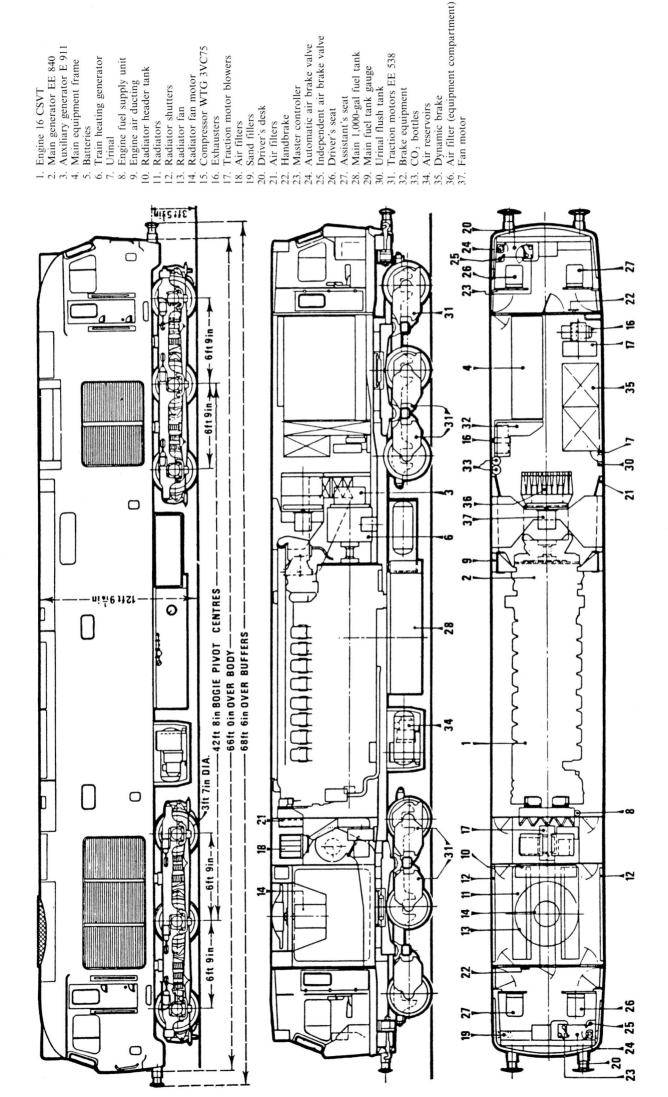

1. Engine 16 CSVT
2. Main generator EE 840
3. Auxiliary generator E 911
4. Main equipment frame
5. Batteries
6. Train heating generator
7. Urinal
8. Engine fuel supply unit
9. Engine air ducting
10. Radiator header tank
11. Radiators
12. Radiator shutters
13. Radiator fan
14. Radiator fan motor
15. Compressor WTG 3VC75
16. Exhausters
17. Traction motor blowers
18. Air filters
19. Sand fillers
20. Driver's desk
21. Air filters
22. Handbrake
23. Master controller
24. Automatic air brake valve
25. Independent air brake valve
26. Driver's seat
27. Assistant's seat
28. Main 1,000-gal fuel tank
29. Main fuel tank gauge
30. Urinal flush tank
31. Traction motors EE 538
32. Brake equipment
33. CO₂ bottles
34. Air reservoirs
35. Dynamic brake
36. Air filter (equipment compartment)
37. Fan motor

The last true English Electric Main Line Diesel for British Rail, the 2,700hp Co-Co the D400 Series/Class 50.

One new type was introduced in the later 1960s, based on the DP2 prototype. This was the Co-Co Type 4, later British Rail Class 50 which arrived in 1968. This series of 50 locomotives was initially leased from English Electric, though later purchased outright. In addition to the 16-cylinder 16CSVT diesel engine, the locomotives incorporated an important development in control systems, based on the use of electronic time delay units. This gave more precise control over field weakening of the traction motors, which extended the performance range of diesel engines. The closed loop control circuits installed in the type were based on systems developed by EE Co., and used on two 25kV ac electric multiple units. These multiple units and locomotives saw the early use of thyristors in traction control circuits on British Rail, although their developments in multiple units, using 'solid state' control with thyristors and transistors was much more rapid than on diesel or electric locomotives. The Class 50, 2,700hp Co-Cos were set to work initially on the London, Midland's West Coast route to Scotland, and in the early 1970s, just prior to the extension of 25kV ac catenary to Glasgow, they were hauling the 'Royal Scot' and other principal Anglo-Scottish expresses.

Whilst a major re-organisation of the AEI Grouping had taken place in the period under review, the 1960s were

Running in pairs, the last English Electric Type 4s for BR, formed the mainstay of the London Midland Region's West Coast Main Line InterCity services during the 1970s, until electrification through to Glasgow was completed. They were subsequently transferred to the Western Region with all being withdrawn from main line service by 1992. This view shows Nos 426 and 443, later 50026 *Indomitable* and 50043 *Eagle* respectively.

brought to a close with further company changes. These, included the takeover of English Electric by GEC in 1969 and the formation of the joint English Electric-AEI Traction Group in the same year. The latter move brought together the two main competitors in the rail traction industry, creating a monopoly situation, which attracted much attention, and the interest of the Industrial Reorganisation Commission. The large company this created, with its vast experience in overseas markets in particular, positioned the one time competitors in Preston and Manchester in the leading group of international companies pursuing railway traction activities around the world. The EE-AEI Traction regrouping was not the end of this brief period of dramatic change, since, three years later, in 1972, the company known as GEC Traction was formed. However, the final developments in that area are discussed in the closing chapter.

7

Electric Traction Developments 1943–1970

Just as had taken place in many other industries, the constituent companies of GEC Traction had all been involved with work for the 'war effort', until the late 1940s. The reconstruction of war-ravaged Europe was a major preoccupation too, although in addition to major electrification projects in Poland, and here in the UK, South America provided at least one major export contract. Unlike diesel traction, there was no 'revolution' in the use of electric motive power at this time; in fact, that revolution had begun more than 50 years earlier.

All over the world, railways had pursued electrification projects for many years, with numerous follow up and repeat orders for power and control equipment forming the bulk of these supplies. Complete electrification projects were few in number in the post war era, coming only from Poland and Brazil, and in 1966, from Pakistan. Here at home, a similar picture had developed, until the massive investment in the nationalised British Railways was begun in 1955. The Southern Railway, and subsequently, British Railways (Southern Region), provide English Electric, Metropolitan-Vickers, and other constituents with major equipment orders, including the world's first electro-diesel locomotives.

The electrification of the LNER's Manchester to Sheffield and Wath lines through the Pennines was completed in the early British Railways' years, at the then main line standard of 1,500V dc, with an overhead contact system. This standard had been proposed and adopted in Britain during the 1920s, following on from various Government committee and technical recommendations. Use of this supply voltage was common to other countries, and involved Metropolitan-Vickers, English Electric, BTH, and GEC as suppliers to New Zealand, Portugal, India, the Netherlands and Denmark. Australia had adopted a 1,500V dc, system too, whilst earlier projects where these companies were involved, provided significant experience, in particular, in Japan, France, here at home, and in the Soviet Union.

Expansion of suburban routes here at home resulted in further equipment orders, as evidenced by the Euston to Watford lines, Wirral and Merseyside, and Manchester to Glossop routes. The large network of London's underground, surface, and tube lines, continued to provide a nucleus of traction equipment orders, with early applications of new and developing technology. Much further north, on the former Midland Railway line from Lancaster to Morecambe and Heysham, the first installation of an overhead contact system energised at the industrial frequency of 50Hz, followed the route's conversion from a 25Hz, to a 6.6kV ac supply. This line was converted yet again in the 1950s, to provide a 'testbed' for the 25kV ac systems adopted as standard for all British Railways' electrification work.

UK Orders and Electrification Projects 1943 – 1955
Looking at the orders placed with later GEC companies during this period, most covered the provision of power equipment for multiple unit rolling stock. Exceptions to this rule could be found in the locomotives from English Electric built for the Southern Railway in 1943, and the LNER's Bo-Bo locomotive of 1941, from Metropolitan-Vickers. The latter was part of a larger electrification project planned by the

LNER some years before the outbreak of war, and the locomotive remained a solitary example until 1954. The Southern Railway's locomotives were built at that company's Ashford Works, with the power and control equipment from English Electric. The first order was placed by the Southern in 1939, and whilst the first two locomotives appeared four years later, the final member of the class, with some detail differences in design, was not delivered until 1948. At the time there were only seven electric locomotives in service, although a number of smaller units had been put to work on industrial sites. The Southern's English Electric powered locomotives were a Co-Co wheel arrangement, collecting supplies at 660V dc, from that railways' extensive network of third rail, with a single pantograph in a well on the roof of the unit, for use in certain yards and sidings. The first two of this Class CC weighed in at 101 tons, whilst the third was 105 tons, although the equipment layout was essentially the same. A number of design innovations appeared with these locomotives, which it was planned, would operate the railway's freight services. Because of the difficulty of maintaining contact with the side conductor rail, in which gaps were necessary at certain places, high speed motor-generator sets were installed, each of which were fitted with heavy flywheels. At gaps in the conductor rail the energy stored in the flywheel maintained the generator's supply to the six traction motors. Each motor-generator set was permanently coupled in series with three traction motors, whose design incorporated the first example of forced ventilation on the Southern Railway. Prior to the appearance of the new locomotives, all traction motors on that system were of the self-ventilated type.

The new locomotives were equipped with eight collector shoes, and operations controlled by a master controller in the driving cab, having 26 notches. This horizontal drum controller was provided with a reversing handle, and a controlling key switch. Each of the cams carried on the master controller operated a contact switch, with the last three notches providing field weakening, through two progressive stages of traction motor field diversion. The motors of the motor-generator sets were connected across the line, and by regulating the generator field excitation, the set could be arranged to oppose ('buck'), or boost the line voltage. In turn, the voltage across each group of three traction motors, could vary from zero to double the line voltage. One of the benefits attributed to the use of the M-G set, with its integral flywheel, was the smooth transition when notching up, reducing any tendency to snatch the train. The closely graded notching reduced the need for a large number of contactors and resistances.

Control systems on existing multiple unit dc rolling stock had used electro-magnetic contactors, carried in the driving cab, to cut out or in, various banks of resistors. The Southern's main line rolling stock had seen, more recently, the introduction of low voltage electro-pneumatic control gear, carried below the vehicle's floor. This equipment layout was subsequently adopted on further orders for multiple unit stock, whilst with minor alterations, it was practical to operate vehicles with both types of control gear in multiple.

English Electric continued to supply power and control gear under a 20-year contract, awarded to the company in the 1930s. Design of the four-pole series wound traction motors

Above: Another Ashford built main line locomotive for the former Southern Railway, with English Electric power equipment, but this time for electric traction. The locomotive, numbered 20003 in BR colours is seen here waiting at Waterloo, and very clearly shows the side, top contact collector shoes, and pick up equipment on each bogie.

(British Rail, Southern)

Below: Definitely not a common sight in Britain, these double-deck multiple units for the Southern Railway were equipped with English Electric traction motors and control systems. Oliver Bulleid, who was the railway company's CME at this time, was renowned for his pursuit of new and innovative ideas. In EE Co. he had enlisted a like-minded ally, the first being introduced in 1949, just after Nationalisation.

for the Southern Railway's rolling stock remained largely unchanged, at least, until 1948. Two designs were being supplied, with the 275hp suburban service motors weighing in at 3.6 tons, whilst for main line or express service, a 225hp motor was used.

In 1948, some 391 suburban, and 85 express types had been supplied, and were to be superseded by a single design for both types of duty, weighing just over half that of the older, suburban design. The new traction motors, of which over 500 had been supplied by 1950, were self-ventilated, with an air duct supplied from a settling chamber in the coach roof. This new design was adopted as standard, with a 180hp, one hour rating, and 140hp, continuously.

Metropolitan-Vickers also had a new locomotive in operation, appearing in 1941, for the LNER's planned electrification of the trans-Pennine, Manchester to Sheffield route. However, full electrification of this route was not completed until 1954, and officially opened between Manchester (London Road) and Sheffield Victoria, on 14th September that year. Under the supervision of the LNER, the installation of catenary supports and other items of infrastructure were progressed until the outbreak of war in 1939, when the work was shelved. The first of the new electric locomotives, for mixed traffic workings, ran trials in 1941, on the Manchester South Junction and Altrincham lines, and in 1946, was loaned to Netherlands Railways in order to gain operating experience, and with an acute shortage of motive power in Holland following the end of the war, served a useful second purpose.

Meanwhile, changes were made to the original scheme for electrification of the Sheffield route, which included construction of the new Woodhead Tunnel, and the provision of a new Co-Co type locomotive, in addition to the Bo-Bo design already planned. Electrification costs for the project had risen to £12¼ million by 1950, and the number of new locomotives to be ordered from Metropolitan-Vickers was reduced from 27 to 7, whilst 58 of the Bo-Bo mixed traffic types were to be completed. Metropolitan-Vickers was not the only company involved in this scheme, as British Thomson-Houston Co. provided the switchgear, and other equipment, for the line's five traction substations. GEC, in company with Metropolitan-Cammell, and the Birmingham Railway Carriage & Wagon Co. provided eight three-car multiple unit trains for the Manchester to Glossop and Hadfield service in 1954. Based at Reddish depot, these sets were similar to those supplied for the recently inaugurated Liverpool St. to Shenfield service, with sliding doors, a single pantograph mounted on the roof of the motor brake vehicle, and powered by four GEC built 185hp traction motors.

The locomotives, both four axle and six axle types, were provided with control and power equipment from Metropolitan-Vickers, with the mechanical portions con-

The former LNER were the leading British railway company following the one-time standard 1,500V dc overhead electrification. Here, the second, and more powerful EM2 class Co-Co units, represented by No. 27004 *Juno*, with Metropolitan-Vickers power equipment sets off, with a very light train over the Manchester to Sheffield, or Woodhead, route. The project to electrify this main line was not completed until BR days, but had ben planned since the 1930s.

structed in British Railways' own workshops. Classed as EM1 and EM2 by BR, the general layout of the locomotives was very similar; double-ended, box-like structures, with two pantographs collecting from the overhead contact wires. The two driving cabs were slightly smaller in profile than the main body of the locomotive, in which was housed the electrical equipment and switchgear. The traction motors – 467hp for the Bo-Bo, and 415hp for the Co-Co – were of the usual axle hung, nose suspended variety, driving the 4ft 2in diameter wheels through spur gears. Electro-pneumatic control equipment was installed in both locomotive types, along with a regenerative braking system. Within the locomotive body, the high tension (HT) compartment housed the main switchgear, in removable frames, for ease of maintenance. The master controllers in the two locomotives differed slightly, with the Bo-Bo design incorporating a series and series-parallel lever, for control of the traction motors, with a third, accelerating lever, combining the function of setting weak field characteristics under motoring conditions. In the larger locomotives, four interlocked handles were provided on the master controller; a removable forward and reverse key, accelerating lever, a regenerative and weak field key, and a fourth lever to select the traction motor combination under regenerative braking conditions. Auxiliary equipment carried included compressors for operating the locomotives' air brakes and control systems, with an exhauster providing vacuum braking functions for train brakes. The two motor generator sets carried, also supplied power for control circuits, and excitation of the traction motors during regeneration.

To absorb the power of these locomotives during regeneration, BTH provided what were believed to be the first railway application of multistage resistance units; electronically controlled four-stage units at the Strafford Crossing, Barnsley Junction and Wharncliffe Wood substations. BTH already had some experience of the design and construction of such equipment, with single stage sets commissioned for use in conjunction with trolleybus networks, as early as 1937.

Further south, the former LNER had prepared plans to electrify the main line from London's Liverpool St. to Shenfield in Essex. Public services began on this route in 1950, although some experimental workings and testing had begun in the previous year. At the time, the majority of electrified routes on British Railways were equipped with third, or conductor rails, energised at 600 to 650V dc, with only the Manchester South Junction & Altrincham lines using the standard 1,500V dc, with overhead catenary. The Shenfield project was the next major route to receive this 1,500V dc

Soon after Nationalisation, British Railways completed the Liverpool Street to Shenfield electrification at 1,500V dc. This early outer suburban electrification was subsequently converted to 25kV ac. Expansion of electric traction on the Eastern Region included the route from Colchester to Clacton and Walton-on-Naze, with BR built multiple units, and English Electric power and control equipment. Class 302, set No. 204 leaves Clacton for Colchester in June, 1959.

(British Rail)

system, with a four-track route running from the Eastern Region's Liverpool Street terminus, through Stratford, Ilford, Romford and Gidea Park, to Shenfield. This route also involved the newly constructed Ilford flyover. Between 1939 and 1949, English Electric provided 92 sets of power and control equipment for three-car trains, the mechanical parts of which were constructed by the Birmingham Railway Carriage & Wagon Co. Interestingly, ventilation for the traction motors was the same as that supplied for some export orders, where cooling air was ducted to the motors from ventilators mounted under the coach roof.

The 1,500V dc electrification was subsequently extended to Southend, and in the 1960s, some early experimental work was carried out with thyristor power control equipment. This latter development was not undertaken until after BR had decided to adopt as standard for electrification schemes, a 25kV ac supply, at the standard industrial frequency of 50Hz. As mentioned in Chapter 5, Hungary was the first country to adopt this frequency for rail electrification work, again, with the heavy commitment of the major partners in the later GEC Traction empire. Following the Second World War, France also undertook some significant work in this field although in fact, in the mid-1930s, the Germans had electrified a 35-mile route through the Black Forest region, with an ac, 50Hz supply; an area which came under French control from 1945.

Another view of these early 25kV Clacton electrics, with the vehicle design based around British Rail's standard suburban stock. The riveted, fabricated bogies seem something of an anachronism considering the essentially 'high tech' nature of electric traction.

(Author's Collection)

Further DC Traction Orders at Home
In addition to the newly formed Southern Region of British Railways, other orders for dc traction equipment came from London Transport for the Northern and Bakerloo Lines' tube stock, and the District and Circle Lines' surface stock. Metropolitan-Vickers were still supplying traction motors to the ageing Liverpool Overhead Railway, along with 180 dual purpose ac/dc motor generator sets for the London, Midland Region's Euston to Watford service. The latter, supplied between 1947 and 1949, also included regulating equipment for the fluorescent lighting installed on this London suburban rolling stock in the late 1940s. Another AEI, later GEC, company, British Thomson-Houston, were the manufacturers involved in a number of improvements to the Watford route at this time, supplying a new generation of steel tank mercury-arc rectifiers.

The Mersey Railway, where Metropolitan-Vickers were responsible for the complete electrification back in 1903, produced further orders for the company in 1953, for 24 sets of power and control equipment, for the Wirral and Mersey section of the LMR. Later equipment for the same lines came from British Thomson-Houston at Rugby. Not far away, in Manchester, or, more precisely, the Manchester to Glossop route, produced orders for eight sets of power equipment for the 1,500V dc multiple unit, trains, between 1939 and 1949. The rolling stock here, consisted of four-car sets, with each of the eight power cars carrying four 185hp GEC designed traction motors, supplied from the company's Witton Works in Birmingham. The London Transport District Line rolling stock, referred to above, included traction motors from both GEC and Metropolitan-Vickers.

One of the final orders for dc traction equipment outside the Southern Region in the 1950s, came again from the

London, Midland, when, in 1958, despite the change of standards in the BR Modernisation Plan, 26 sets of power equipment were supplied by English Electric in 1958. The 141hp traction motors – two per power car – were installed on the two-car sets for the Manchester to Bury services, with power to the conductor rail supplied at 1,200V dc.

AC Traction and The Modernisation Plan

Experience of ac traction equipment in the UK was limited, and examples very few and far between, the most notable of which, at this time, was the short experimental stretch from Lancaster to Morecambe and Heysham. This former Midland Railway route, referred to in an earlier chapter, was energised at 6.6kV ac, 25Hz, with an overhead contact system. English Electric, Siemens Bros, and Metropolitan-Vickers had all provided some equipment for this route, which in 1952-53 was re-equipped by English Electric and BTH, to enable operation at the industrial frequency of 50Hz.

The precursor for the highly successful adoption of 25kV ac 50Hz, electric traction in the UK. Here, the former Midland Railway's Lancaster to Morecambe & Heysham line was a testbed in the early 1950s for the system. The original electrification of this line included equipment from the then major manufacturers, and members of the long list of companies that came under the GEC umbrella in later years.

(British Rail)

Across the English Channel, in France, SNCF, following some experimental work in the region of the French Alps, had decided to electrify the route from Valenciennes to Thionville at 25kV ac, 50Hz. The results of these experiments in France were published in 1951, and prompted the decision to electrify the heavily used route to Valenciennes, against a background of impressive success with 1,500V dc, including the achievement of the world speed record of 207 mph. Influenced by this, the British Transport Commission took the decision to gain experience of the 50Hz system between Lancaster and Morecambe, although its own 1955 Modernisation Plan was set to adopt the 1500V dc standard for impending main line electrification schemes.

In France, the 25kV ac, 50Hz project witnessed outstanding success, which, in turn, influenced BR's decision subsequently, to adopt the same systems in this country. English Electric, from Preston, provided the equipment for the first of the new breed of multiple units, for ac traction on the LMR, with BTH, whose pioneering work in the design of rectification equipment has already been mentioned, were also involved at an early stage. In 1953, BTH successfully tested, in service on the Lancaster to Morecambe line, the world's first semiconductor rectifiers, using germanium. This was a significant advance in the traction world, and resulted in on-board installations that were much less bulky than the mercury-arc rectifiers carried on some locomotives and rolling stock. The air-cooled rectifier in this first instal-

lation was rated at 750kW capacity, and was in regular use on the passenger services operated by these 50-year old multiple units, soon after the refurbishment of the fixed installation.

London Transport Tube and Surface Lines

The London Underground network had produced a number of orders for electrical equipment for almost all members of the later GEC Traction, a trend which continued after WWII. However, it was obvious that due to hostilities, extensive reconstruction would be necessary, and replacement of destroyed and damaged rolling stock. Technical developments too would be accommodated in the post war era, some of which were encouraged by changes in traffic patterns and train operations. A report published in 1944 recommended spending £230 million (1944 prices), on the construction of new lines, with some 100 miles in tunnel, over a period of 30 years. Of four new routes, 'A', 'B', 'C' and 'D', identified in order of construction priority, only route 'C', which became known as the 'Victoria Line', was completed. Some extensions were authorised in the late 1940s, and alternative proposals were put forward, but subsequently abandoned. Route 'C' – the Victoria Line – announced in 1949, was finally sanctioned by Government, 13 years later in 1964, and completed in 1969. From the GEC Traction perspective, and its predecessors, AEI and others, some useful technical innovations were seen here, but still the majority of orders from London Underground tended to be on the basis of maintenance and replacements for existing hardware.

Taking the deep level tube stock as a starting point, hundreds of sets of power equipment were supplied by BTH, Metropolitan-Vickers(AEI) and GEC. The following list, in fact, shows the general extent of former GEC Traction companies' involvement with LT Underground during this period.

Qty	Stock & service	Date ordered
371	R-stock, District Line	1938–1959
246	Surface stock refurbishing	1955–1959
380	1959 Tube stock – Piccadilly Line	1957
12	1960 Tube stock – Central Line (Woodford – Hainault) **	1959
232	A60 and A62 Surface Stock (Metropolitan Lines)	1959–1961
527	1962 Tube Stock – Central Line	1960
158	1967 Tube Stock – Victoria Line **	1965
5	Chopper equipments	1965 & 1968
106	C69 Surface Stock * (Metropolitan & Circle Lines)	1968

** Automatic operation
* One man operation

The difference between 'deep level tube' and 'surface' lines was largely the result of different methods of construction of the right of way. The deep level tubes were bored tunnels, whilst the so-called surface lines were actually constructed where they ran underground, by the cut and cover method. This naturally resulted in differing vehicle profiles, and in most instances alternative forms of power and control equipment. Additionally, both third and fourth rail contact systems were employed, energised at 600V dc. For the power equipment suppliers, the philosophy of rugged, low maintenance equipment has continued from the earliest times, through to the sophisticated equipment installed in modern times.

The design of the tube stock resulted from the use of a 12ft diameter bore for the tunnels, which, in the early part of this century, was felt to be the largest practical size, with the routes following the course of London's streets. This latter restriction no longer applies. A unique characteristic of London's tube network, referred to above, is the use of a fourth rail power supply. Whilst the nominal voltage has been adopted for other urban rail systems, it was adopted in order to avoid any effects which could result from earth return currents passing along the cast iron tunnel lining segments. The power supply system of this type is said to be 'floating' electrically, with, nominally, the side conductor rail carrying +450V dc, and the centre return rail at –150V dc. However, it was also made possible in certain circumstances, for either rail to carry the full 600V potential to earth. An advantage of the arrangement allows a train to be taken out of service, whilst others continue to operate normally, when an earth fault from one of the poles is detected. Other interesting electrical features of the deep level tubes on London Underground are concerned with the evidently more stringent safety requirements; for example, no inter-car power jumper cables are allowed, and there must be a battery backed emergency lighting supply.

Up to 1959, orders from Metropolitan-Vickers and the BTH Co. were separately placed, whilst from 1960, their traction interests were merged in the AEI Traction Division. Most orders for the Piccadilly Line, placed between 1956 and 1959 came under the AEI label, whilst equipment from BTH and Metropolitan-Vickers were ordered in the late 1940s and early 1950s for the Northern Line. The Metropolitan Section, where the unique 'Metadyne' sets had been at work since before the Second World War, saw the replacement in 1960 of this hardware, by AEI Traction, and the installation of electro-pneumatic camshaft control equipment – 114 sets in all. A total of 578 sets of control equipment were supplied to the Metropolitan Section from 1959, by AEI, prior to the arrival of the A60 and A62 Surface stock, and the C69 stock towards the end of the period under review, in 1968.

The Hammersmith & City lines, which also operated 'Metadyne' equipped stock had also seen their replacement by BTH electro-pneumatic control systems, but under the AEI banner from 1959 onwards. The Central, Circle and District Lines ordered almost 1,000 sets of control equipment, including 'Metadyne' conversions between 1946, and the formation of the AEI Traction Division in 1959.

The traditional red colour scheme for Underground trains gave way in the late 1950s to aluminium, or silver colour, as standard. At the same time major orders were placed on vehicle builders Metropolitan-Cammell for the A60 and A62 Surface stock, for which AEI provided the control equipment. The new Victoria Line stock continued a pre-set pattern for Metropolitan-Vickers, BTH and English Electric, who were the suppliers of control and auxiliary equipment. Metropolitan-Vickers and BTH, as AEI, provided the former, along with rheostatic braking equipment, whilst English Electric's contribution was limited to fluorescent lighting and auxiliary motor-alternator sets in the trailer cars. To be precise though, it was BTH style equipment that was manufactured in the Metropolitan-Vickers workshops.

In 1965, AEI provided five sets of 'chopper' control equipment for testing in revenue service on the Underground, similar to equipment supplied to Netherlands Railways on a multiple unit set. Thyristors were used in these first 'chopper' sets for the Underground, with the installations extended following these early experiments. In principle, choppers control the traction motor applied voltage in a series of pulses. The interval between pulses is varied until the motor is operating on its own characteristics. A major advantage of this form of control, which has been exploited very successfully since those early days, is the 'notchless' application of traction power. In addition to performance improvements, use of chopper control removed the need for resistance contactors, or the dissipation of energy through banks of starting resistances.

Completing the period under review, AEI supplied 106 sets of equipment for the C69 surface stock, for the Metropolitan and Circle Lines. These latter introduced a new facet of operations too; the driver only trains, (DOO) although an element of automatic operations had been in use since 1964 on an isolated section of the Central Line. This function was tied to the closing of the train doors, which in addition to giving a start signal, initiated automatic acceleration of the train up to the permitted speed, on receipt of coded signals from the trackside. The train then ran to the next station, where it was stopped entirely automatically, though the doors remained under the control of the train operator. These developments were taken a stage further in the 1970s, under the GEC Traction umbrella, which organisation finally came into being in 1972, after a brief courtship between AEI and English Electric's Traction Divisions.

Major Electrification Projects Overseas

There were really only two major projects begun or completed between 1950 and 1970, with a major order from Poland, as an extension of the pre-war electrification project, in which English Electric, Metropolitan-Vickers and BTH were involved. Oddly perhaps, only one of these projects involved ac electrification, the others extending the dc systems.

The Polish project, which has already been described, was naturally, severely affected by the Second World War, and the 1944 rising in Warsaw. After the end of hostilities, it was found possible to reinstate a form of service over 27 kilometres of route from the capital to Ottwock. The mammoth task of reconstruction in Poland involved restoration of the elec-

In 1959, both EE Co. and AEI received orders from Poland. The former for 20 of these complete, 3,000hp Bo-Bo units and AEI for a similar number of control equipments for Polish State Railways (PKP) Co-Co design. Comparing these to the earlier, box like shape for PKP, the designers in this case have obviously paid more attention to design aesthetics.

(National Galleries & Museums on Merseyside)

trified routes, and resulted in major orders for English Electric and Metropolitan-Vickers. In 1948, Poland ordered six complete sets of power equipment, and a further two sets without traction motors. EE Co. supplied the traction motors, and Metropolitan-Vickers the control equipment.

The following year, continuing the British involvement in the electrification of Polish railways, the Polish Coal Mines Administration placed major orders for 3,000V dc, equipment, ranging from infrastructure to rolling stock. Nine sets of complete electrical equipment, including traction motors and electro-pneumatic control systems were placed on Metropolitan-Vickers, for 2,500hp locomotives, to be constructed in Poland. Substation equipment was also included in this project, and although only a single traction substation was involved, BTH provided the 2,800kW mercury arc rectifiers and transformers, and associated switchgear.

This was not the final Polish order in this period either, since only ten years later, in 1959, the administration requested 20 complete locomotives from English Electric. These latter, known subsequently as Class EU07, were designed by EE Co., and built at that company's Vulcan Foundry plant. They were rated at 3,000hp, and entered service on Poland's 3,000V dc network in 1961/62, and were in fact the last such order from an Eastern Bloc country for the company. Though following delivery of the English Electric locomotives, construction of further units under licence, in Poland, began and later still, an express passenger design and articulated Bo-Bo+Bo–Bo was derived. The original EE Co. units weighed in at 79 tons, and were equipped with four English Electric Type EE541/A motors.

Brazil

1946 was a good year for English Electric Export & Trading Company Ltd, who entered into a contract to electrify the line between Mooca and Jundiai, which included São Paulo, the state capital. The previous two years had been spent surveying the route of the line, which totalled 64km, of 5ft 3in gauge double track, and which included sections of 2.5% gradients. This new 3,000V dc railway connected with the previously electrified Paulista Railway, forming a continuation of the network as far as São Paulo. The catenary was also installed at the extensive freight yards in Mooca under this contract.

The Estrada de Ferro Santos a Jundiai was another example of an electrified route which received its power from a

In South America, English Electric won a contract for the complete electrification of the Estrada de Ferro Santos a Jundai in Brazil. In addition to the infrastructure for this 3,000V dc system English Electric supplied 15 of these 3,000hp, Co-Co locomotives. No. 1000 hauls a 700 ton freight train at Campo Limpo.

hydro-electric scheme, in this case, at 88kV from the São Paulo Light & Power Co. The supply was transformed to 33kV at one of the three substations, which controlled the other two remotely. Steel bulb, pumpless rectifiers at the three substations provided the 3,000V dc supply for the catenary, which was, as in other schemes, the responsibility of British Insulated Callenders Cables. The simple catenary was carried on portal structures, and in places a composite portal/headspan type assembly.

On the rolling stock front, English Electric were contracted to build what were at the time, the most powerful electric locomotives in the UK, and three three-car suburban multiple unit trains. The locomotives, of six-axle layout, had the following main dimensions:

Much closer to home, English Electric supplied these 3,600hp Co-Cos to Spain, in 1952, with the mechanical portions put together at the Vulcan Works. Like South Africa, the preferred system voltage was 3kV dc, and 75 of these locomotives were built for the 5ft 6in gauge.

English Electric 3,000hp Co-Co Locomotives for Brazil

Wheel arrangement	Co-Co
Gauge	5ft 3in
Weight in working order	120 tons
No. of traction motors	6
One hour rating	3,000hp
Control system	electro-pneumatic
Length over buffers	67ft 3in
Balancing speed	60 mph
(with 600 tons trailing load)	
Braking systems	air, vacuum & regenerative

Pakistan

The South American project completed in the early 1950s, and the only major overseas project for a decade, culminated in the award of a contract worth £7.5 million in 1966 for the electrification of a 516km track section of the Pakistan Western Railway. The contract was actually awarded to the British Consortium for Electrification of Pakistan Railways, a group of five UK companies, headed by AEI and English Electric. The initial work covered the 178 route miles from Khanewal to Lahore, and included the provision of power supply equipment, overhead contact systems, signalling and telecommunications. In addition to the installation of 25kV 50Hz contact systems, a fleet of thyristor controlled locomotives was supplied – the world's first export fleet. Whilst British Insulated Callenders Construction Co., and Westinghouse Brake & Signal Co. had been in the forefront of this work for many years, another member of the consortium, Hackbridge & Hewittic Electric Co. Ltd subsequently became English Electric Hewittic Rectifiers.

The infrastructure work included the design, supply and construction of trackside feeder stations, complete with switchgear, transformers and links, at five locations to the then West Pakistan electricity grid. Whilst the initial section was relatively flat and undulating, with a ruling gradient of no more than 0.2%, the proposed extension to Rawalpindi, a distance of 179 miles, introduced gradients of around 1%. With this in mind, the 29 four-axle locomotives were designed for a continuous rating of more than 3,000hp.

The locomotives were ordered and built by the British Rail Traction Group (BRTG), representing the Traction Division of English Electric and AEI Traction Ltd. The mechanical portions of these new generation electric locomotives were sub-contracted to Metropolitan-Cammell of Birmingham, whilst the bogies were supplied by English Electric, and the final erection completed at Washwood Heath. The electrical equipment was supplied jointly by English Electric and AEI, from Preston and Manchester. The leading dimensions of these, then unique, locomotives were as follows:

EE Co./AEI 3,160hp Bo-Bo Locomotives for Pakistan

Wheel arrangement	Bo-Bo
Gauge	5ft 6in
Weight in working order	80 tons
Max. axle load	20 tons
Length over headstocks	51ft 0in
Overall width, over body	10ft 6in
Height to roof from rail	12ft 0in
" to pantograph (down)	14ft 1in
Bogie pivot centre	29ft 0in
Bogie wheelbase	9ft 0in
Wheel diameter (new)	43in
Min. radius curve	560ft
No. of traction motors	4
Continuous rating	3,160hp at 22.5kV
UIC rating	3,650hp at 25kV nominal
Max. starting tractive effort (TE)	56,000lb
Cont. tractive effort (full field)	28,200lb
" " (weak field)	21,000lb
Max. speed	75 mph

The Pakistan Western locomotives saw the first use of thyristor control in a British built locomotive, the design of which was based on the equipment installed in electric multiple units in service on the Eastern and Scottish Regions of British Rail. Also based on a design then in service was the main, or traction transformer, which was similar to that installed in the AL6 (now Class 86) Bo-Bo locomotives of BR's London, Midland Region.

Power was taken from the contact wire through a single roof-mounted pantograph, through an air-blast circuit breaker to the transformer's primary winding. The terminations of the four separate secondary windings were brought out through the side of the tank, with electro-pneumatic contactors mounted directly to the ends of these tappings. The tapping contactors were controlled electronically and connected the transformer's secondary winding to the main rectifier. This latter, consisting of 96 silicon diodes and 32 thyristors, connected together in a bridge formation. The main rectifiers were mounted in two separate cubicles, on box section aluminium heat sinks, with an air cooling system. The throughput of cooling air was then led to the transformer oil coolers at floor level, with the cooling duct incorporating a sand trap. The four 790hp traction motors were series wound force-ventilated machines, and fed from the rectifiers via a single iron cored reactor (fitted to reduce ripple in the rectified power supply to an acceptable level).

These locomotives remain the only 25kV ac types in service with what is now Pakistan Railways, and whilst technical details of the original EE-AEI design made provision for regenerative braking, pending the extension of catenary, the country's political difficulties slowed this progress. The initial scheme from Khanewar to Lahore was energised in 1970, although delivery of the locomotives had been completed the previous year.

The Formation of AEI Traction

In 1959, the final step in the conclusion of the Associated Electrical Industries birth, was announced. AEI it will be recalled, was formed to bring together the interests and activities of British Thomson-Houston and Metropolitan-Vickers back in 1929. Just over 30 years later, the final integration took place.

To be precise, the AEI integration was to create a self-contained AEI Traction Division, to control the railway activities of both M-V and BTH. In addition, the interests of the Metropolitan-Vickers General Railway Signal Co., later to become GEC General Railway Signal, were also included. The newly formed AEI Traction Division established its headquarters, fittingly, at Trafford Park in Manchester, with an interesting product range, as follows:

Complete electric locomotives.
Electrical equipment for electric locomotives.
Complete diesel-electric and gas turbine locomotives.
Diesel-electric and turbo electric equipment for diesel-electric and gas turbine locomotives and motor coaches.
Mechanical parts for electric, gas turbine, and diesel-electric locomotives.
Complete electric motor coach trains.

Electrical equipment for electric motor coach trains.
Tram-car electrical equipments.
Trolleybus electrical equipments.
Complete railway electrification projects.
Trolley mining locomotives.
Electrical equipment for trolley mining locomotives.
Battery mining locomotives and charging equipments.
Electrical equipment for battery mining locomotives.
Traction motors.
Traction gears.
Traction flexible drives.
Traction power and auxiliary motor generators and alternators.
Traction auxiliary motors and generators.
Traction diesel generators.
All items of ac and dc traction control gear.
Traction unbreakable strip and wire resistances.
Traction cast iron resistances.
Traction voltage regulators.
Inductive shunts.
Smoothing chokes.
Ac and dc traction circuit breakers.
Battery vehicles and their electrical equipment.
Power vacuum contactors.

An impressive list perhaps, but of course, AEI's main competition came from English Electric, whose product list was equally lengthy, containing essentially the same equipment. Included in this integration was the Metropolitan-Vickers-Beyer Peacock manufacturing plant at Stockton-on-Tees in the North East. This joint venture was established in 1944, specifically to construct the mechanical portions of locomotives, extending the range of contracts for which Metropolitan-Vickers could tender. English Electric of course had long since acquired the Vulcan Foundry, where the bulk of the mechanical portions of EE locomotives were constructed.

In 1959, AEI's newly formed Traction Division operated from four sites:

Location	Products
Attercliffe Common, Sheffield	Traction motors and machines
Trafford Park, Manchester	Traction control gear
Rugby	Traction control gear Traction machines
Stockton	Mechanical parts of locomotives

The new organisation structure brought in some changes immediately, but others took some time to filter through. It was planned to concentrate on traction machine design at Sheffield, although at the time a significant quantity of generators and other machines were made in the former Motor factory, of the Heavy Plant Division at Rugby.

UK Traction Orders 1955–1970
As referred to earlier, the BR 1955 Modernisation Programme had dramatic implications for electric traction, as indeed it had for diesel traction. Experimental work was already being undertaken with the 25kV ac systems, following the French example, and led the British Transport

Commission to adopt the ac rather than the 1,500V dc system as standard. The BR plans were to have both East and West Coast main lines electrified by the 1960s, requiring massive investment in new locomotives and multiple unit rolling stock – good news for the manufacturers. However, in practice, with escalating costs, and unbridled competition from road transport in particular, only the West Coast Main Line project was successful in the period under review.

The initial plan involved the 'Styal Line', from Manchester to Crewe, linking with Liverpool, and then followed by London to Birmingham, and the Trent Valley route. A series of locomotives were required, based on a four-axle layout, and of two types, 'A' and 'B'. These were for mixed traffic and freight services, respectively. It was also anticipated that an equal number of both types would be required, with their different haulage characteristics. This was not how things turned out, with the slower progress in the adoption of continuous brakes on freight trains, only five of the first 100 locomotives were the freight, type 'B'. Irrespective of type, all the locomotives were rated initially at 3,300hp, and were built mainly by Metropolitan-Vickers and BTH as AEI, and English Electric, with mechanical portions of some constructed at BR's Doncaster Works, and the North British Locomotive Co., in Glasgow. Metropolitan-Vickers, or AEI Manchester, actually supplied the first main line ac locomotive to run in this country, being the conversion of the former gas turbine No. 18100, to a 2,500hp A1A-A1A 25kV ac electric locomotive, for trial running on the Styal Line. Other manufacturers contributed some work to the new fleet of electric locomotives, including Beyer Peacock, and Birmingham Railway Carriage & Wagon Co. English Electric were of course included, with their later subsidiary, Vulcan Foundry constructing the bodies. The list below details the original order from BR to the railway industry, for the 100 new ac electric locomotives.

Main Contractor	Mechanical Parts	Locomotive Type	Class	Later TOPS Class	Qty
AEI/BTH	BRC & W Co.	A	AL1	81	23
AEI/BTH	BRC & W Co.	B	(i)	81	2
AEI/M-V	Beyer Peacock	A	AL2	82	10
EE Co.	Vulcan Foundry	A	AL3	83	12
EE Co.	Vulcan Foundry	B	(ii)	83	3
GEC	NB Loco. Co.	A	AL4	84	10
AEI/BTH	BR (Doncaster)	A	AL5	85	40

(i) Absorbed into Class AL1
(ii) Absorbed into Class AL3

AEI's BTH Rugby Works had by far the lion's share of the orders for electrical equipment, and acted as main contractor on Class AL1 and principal sub-contractor for AL5. The latter, which began to appear from 1960, were constructed at BR's Doncaster Works, and were the first BR electric locomotives to be equipped with the new semiconductor, germanium rectifiers. However, this was not the first proposal to fit semiconductor rectifiers, since English Electric had proposed to BR in 1959, just such a scheme to replace the mercury arc rectifiers being supplied on the Class AL3 locomotives it was building, with silicon semconductors. The BTC agreed to the EE Co. idea on a pair of locomotives, with the proviso that rheostatic braking being included. The latter could not be done since construction was too far advanced on the class as a whole. Simple replacement of the mercury arc with silicon rectifiers was not approved by BR, but one locomotive in the class was chosen to become the

test-bed for a technically more involved project, the fitting of a silicon rectifier/transductor control system.

Continuing the ac traction theme, between 1955 and 1970, English Electric, Metropolitan-Vickers, BTH and GEC were involved with the provision of traction and rolling stock equipment. In addition, tests of the latest technological advances were made on Eastern and Scottish Regions, using existing 25kV ac multiple units as testbeds. Of course, there was the competition in the R&D area to be met, notably from Hawker-Siddeley, in the shape of Brush Electrical Machines, and their *Hawk* experimental locomotive. This prototype, which actually utilised the former NBL GEC-powered Bo-Bo freight locomotive built in the early 1950s, incorporated thyristor based ac drives, powering three-phase ac, squirrel cage traction motors. Brush developed from their experimental work, in conjunction with BR, such devices as solid state voltage regulators, and planned to apply their emerging technology to include alternators driven by diesel engines, in preference to the standard dc traction generator approach. Both AEI and English Electric were moving down this path in the 1960s, naturally, and, in partnership with BR, began to establish a base of more advanced traction control equipment. The early stages sought to eliminate the moving parts in electromagnetic, electromechanical, or pneumatic control systems, using higher powered semiconductor devices, and transistors.

The major ac multiple unit and equipment orders received by AEI and English Electric in the period up to 1970 were as follows:

Quantity	Routes	BR Class	Ordered
112	London–Southend	302(AM2)	1956
91	Glasgow suburban	303(AM3)	1956
45	Crewe-Manchester/ Liverpool *	304(AM4)	1956
74	Enfield/Chingford	305(AM5)	1956
92	Shenfield	306(AM6)	1958
65	GE Outer suburban	307(AM7)	1958
45	Shoeburyness	308(AM8)	1960
23	Clacton express	309(AM9)	1961
50	Euston suburban *	310(AM10)	1964
19	Glasgow suburban	311(AM11)	1969
1	Glasgow suburban (thyristor)	311(AM11)	1969

The AL6 type, Bo-Bos first appeared in 1965, and were the next step forward in British Rail's 25kV electric traction plans. A hundred were built in all, by BR at Doncaster, and by English Electric. Power equipment came from EE Co., AEI and GEC, whilst the type, as Class 86, still survives, it has undergone many modifications. Even in the year of its birth, AEI proposed a Co-Co, 8,000hp version for Channel Tunnel services; this proposal, like the 1960's Channel Tunnel did not materialise.

(Author's Collection)

NB All of the above multiple units, and power equipments were capable of operating on the dual voltage of 6.25kV and 25kV ac, except those marked *. The Classes 304(AM4), and 310(AM10) were equipped for 25kV ac only.

This dual voltage was a requirement specified by the British Transport Commission, due to restricted clearances on some routes, but was later found to be unnecessary.

There were effectively three new standard BR designs for ac multiple units, in either three or four-car sets, but which were connected in multiple to form longer trains. The power equipment was carried in pannier cases, slung from the underframe between the bogies, and which included the main transformer. The power car carried the single arm pantograph, mounted in a roof well, and each of the motor bogies was fitted with standard four-pole dc traction motors, irrespective of whether these came from AEI(Metropolitan-Vickers), GEC, or English Electric. The first of the new generation, as compared with rebuilds, and re-equipment of former dc stock, such as the Shenfield line, were the Glasgow 'Blue Trains', or Class 303(AM3), for suburban services. Metropolitan-Vickers supplied 207hp traction motors and control equipment for this fleet in 1960, whilst in 1967, under the AEI flag, the traction motor rating had increased to 222hp. In appearance, the 1967 order differed little from the 1960 order, and were put into service on the south side of the Clyde, between Glasgow, Gourock and Wemyss Bay. The major equipment difference included silicon rectifiers, instead of the mercury arc installations on Class 303(AM3), with oil cooling. One of the Class 311(AM11) was equipped with thyristor control, replacing the earlier electro-pneumatic systems, whilst another innovation was the provision of fluorescent lighting, also supplied by AEI. Thyristor control circuitry provided smoother and more responsive train and locomotive operation, though the development process was a long one, particularly in the area of thyristor circuits. Here, the rapid switching of on-board high power, and traction control supplies was a potential problem, especially in the

As the 25kV electrification expanded on BR's London, Midland Region, so did its fleet of multiple units. Here, Class AM10/310, set No. 050, with English Electric power and control equipment, waits at Watford Junction with an outer suburban working.

(Author's Collection)

area of interference to adjacent, lineside signalling circuits. It was also well into the 1980s before the high power thyristor devices could be developed to enable the use of such circuits, on a wider scale, and for controlling the high power outputs of modern traction units. Signalling engineers also had to spend some time developing systems to immunise their vital circuits from this major source of interference, in addition to the problems encountered by English Electric, GEC, and AEI producing the 'solid state' control equipments.

The extension and conversion of Eastern Region routes to electric traction produced orders for English Electric and GEC in particular. The former equipped Classes 302 and 308 which were in service on the Fenchurch Street to Shoeburyness services, with 192hp and 200hp traction motors. One of these, as illustrated, was equipped with English Electric's thyristor based control system, for testing on this route. GEC equipped multiple units on the Eastern Region were 305(AM5), 306(AM6), 307(AM7), and 309(AM9). The AM7 units ordered in 1958 were planned for service on the former Great Eastern lines out of Liverpool Street, as the GE Outer Suburban electrification progressed. These were already in service, having been supplied in 1956 as dc units, with GEC power equipment, whilst the replacement ac equipment was ordered from GEC in 1958.

Excluding the changes on the short Lancaster to Morecambe and Heysham line, the LMR's only orders at this time were for use on the Crewe to Manchester/Liverpool electrification, and Euston suburban services. The orders were separated by a period of eight years, and saw significant changes in the appearance and installed equipment on these ac multiple units. The power equipments were supplied by BTH(AEI), and English Electric for Classes 304(AM4) and 310(AM10), respectively. The AM4 order placed in

1956 did not see introduction until 1960, and their use was also extended to the London to Birmingham route, alongside the AM10 units from English Electric. In both cases, the bodies and running gear were constructed in railway workshops. The AM4 sets working out of Manchester Piccadilly initially, were similar in appearance to the dc units on the Manchester to Bury lines, and the Eastern Region's Class AM5 on the GE Outer Suburban scheme. The new AM10, or Class 310 units were very different in appearance as well as traction equipment.

The 50 Class AM10 units were built at BR's Derby Works, and in 1965 were running trials and tests on the LMR from their Rugby base. Having said that the 310s were built for 25kV use only, the transformers were designed with tappings to facilitate use on 6.245kV ac if this was later found necessary, and enabled them to be used anywhere on BR's ac electrified lines. All the power equipment supplied by EE Co. was naturally cooled, or self-ventilated, reducing the quantity of auxiliary hardware required to service the power equipment. The rectifier design included a 'first', where, for the purposes of conducting the heat generated by the silicon diodes, these were mounted on beryllium oxide bases, in turn connected to cooling fins mounted on the equipment case. These fins actually formed a part of the equipment case, and enabled the unit to be sealed completely, preventing any contamination by dirt. All the under-car equipment cases were mounted on slides, except for the main transformer and inductor, to enable ease of removal and maintenance, by fork lift truck, for example. Four traction motors were provided, of 270hp, and each carried on the two-motor bogies of the power car. The train's acceleration was designed to be completely automatic, using current limiting relays in two of the motor control circuits, and two rates of acceleration were provided, depending on whether or not the master controller was put directly into the weak field position. This arrangement meant that the unit's operation was independent of load or driving technique.

Whilst English Electric were busy with developments in train control, so too were AEI, announcing in 1966, their oil-

Here again, an English Electric powered 4-car Class AM10/310 multiple unit set No. 067, is seen at work on the London, Midland Region, heading for Euston in April 1966.

(Author's Collection)

The third generation of 25kV locomotive arrived in 1973, from the newly constituted GEC Traction, the last of which included the first thyristor controlled example, numbered 87101 and named *Stephenson*. BR and GEC Traction had raised the installed power in an 80 ton, Bo-Bo design, which was basically the same in this example, as it was in the Class 81 which dated back to 1959, from 3,000 to more than 5,000hp.

(Author's Collection)

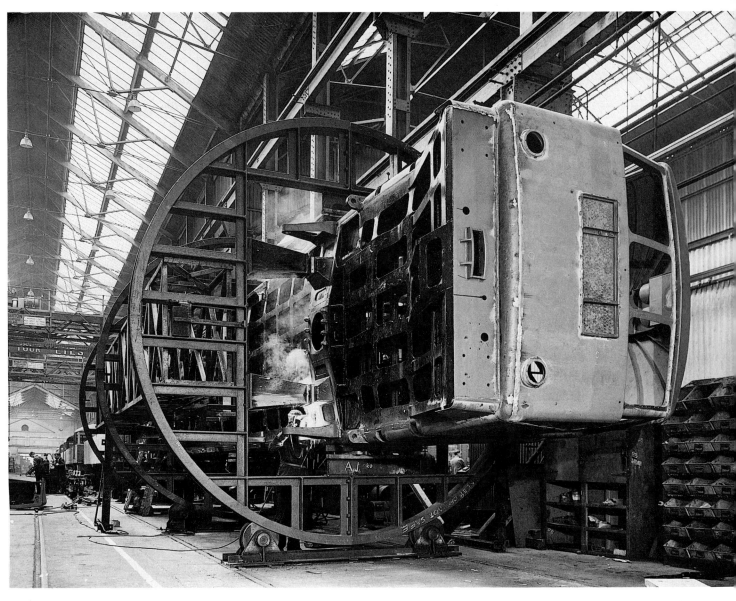

The English Electric portion of the order for 100 Class AL6 (86) electric locomotives' mechanical parts were fabricated at EE Co.'s Vulcan Works. Here, a welder works on the underframe of one of the class, in a specially designed manipulator.

(Author's Collection)

cooled thyristor rectifier, referred to earlier, and installed in one of the new Glasgow suburban sets. Prior to these developments, diesel electric locomotives, electric locomotives, and multiple units with dc traction motors regulated the motor supplies by tap change mechanisms on the main transformer. On dc systems, variation of traction motor power supplies was, and indeed for some, still is, achieved by modification of the arrangement of traction/braking resistances in series with the motors themselves. The thyristor, which is essentially a controlled rectifier, enabled the use of a variable voltage below that of the line/supply voltage on dc systems, or the secondary output of the transformer for ac systems to be fed directly to the traction motors, with a much smoother, notchless control of motor speed. The idea, compared with more traditional control systems, was commercially very attractive, and offered significant operating cost benefits to the railway operator. Amongst the advantages were reduced starting losses, no risk of overheating control equipment, no moving parts to break down, simplified and more compact means of providing rheostatic braking, and ultimately, reduced maintenance costs.

The AEI installation on the Class AM11 unit replaced the low tension tap changer mechanism and mercury arc rectifier, with oil-cooled semiconductor rectifier housing both diodes

and thyristors. Two separate transformer secondary tappings were led to a pair of traction motors, through the rectifier bridge, with one of the three arms containing thyristors; the remaining three arms housing diodes. Variation of the traction motor applied voltage was by the 'cycle selection' technique in which the required mean voltage is obtained by acceptance/rejection of complete half cycles. This was unconventional by comparison with the 'phase angle' technique used by EE Co., where the firing angle of the thyristors was varied to give the required mean voltage. The 'cycle selection' technique caused serious problems however, introducing excessive harmonics into the supply, and was quickly dropped.

Having mentioned the 'phase angle' technique used by English Electric, this was adopted in the hardware installed by the company in one of the Colchester line's multiple units on the Eastern Region. Most of the conventional equipment was retained in the test unit, except for a completely new rectifier case, with modifications to the main transformer, and surge protection. The transformer provided secondary tappings in two sections, one of which was used up to half voltage, with the two in series at up to full voltage. The main bridge rectifier included no fewer than 32 silicon diodes, and two thyristor arms, the output from the rectifier being connected in parallel to the four 192hp traction motors. In operation, the transformer midpoint supply was connected to the thyristors, which were fully retarded (firing angle 180 degrees). This firing angle was gradually reduced to zero, until full midpoint voltage was reached, progressively increasing the dc voltage from zero. At this point the connection from the transformer was switched to the diode arms, reducing the thyristor firing angle again, fully, with no disturbance to motor voltage. The transformer's full output was then connected to the thyristor arms, then again reducing the thyristor firing angle to zero, the full voltage then being progressively applied to the traction motors. Another new idea introduced on this test unit, and one of the London, Midland Region's fleet, was a logic unit to control the transformer tapping contactors.

DC Traction Equipment

Whilst ac electrification traction equipment and progress was taking the limelight on BR at this time, further orders and extensions to dc networks were still providing orders for GEC, English Electric and AEI. Obviously most dc orders were still coming from the Southern Region, which included some 630 sets of 'standard' power equipments between 1955 and 1964, and later, equipment for the Bournemouth extension, Brighton, and Central Division rolling stock. In addition there was an order for 237 sets of motorcoach equipment between 1964 and 1970, covering the REP, VEP, BIG, and CIG units. There were additional/replacement equipments ordered for the Euston suburban, Manchester to Bury, and of course, the GE Outer Suburban units, which have already been mentioned, and which were later the subject of conversion to ac.

The major dc traction equipment orders between 1955 and 1970 are noted in the table.

A unique compromise for BR were these 'electro-diesel' locomotives, used by the Southern Region. This particular example, No. E6021 of Class 73, was the second such design, also with English Electric power equipment. The latter included a 4-cylinder, 600hp diesel engine, as well as collecting power at 750V dc from the third rail.

Quantity	Routes	BR Class	Ordered
57	Euston–Watford	501	1955
65	GE Outer Suburban	307	1956
26	Manchester–Bury (1,200V)	504	1958
630	Southern Region		1955–64
22	Waterloo–Bournemouth (tractor units)	4REP	1964
20	Waterloo–Bournemouth	4VEP	1964
35	Brighton Section	4VEP	1966
50	Southern Reg. Central Divn.	4VEP	1969
110	Southern Reg. Central Divn.	4VEP 4REP 4BIG 4CIG	1969/70
2	Post Office Railway *	—	1961

*The Post Office Tube Railway was electrified at 440V dc. The figures referred to in the quantity column relates to the number of sets of motorcoach power equipment supplied. The type of equipment supplied would include; traction motors, control equipment, master controllers, resistances, etc.

On the Southern Region, July 1967 saw the introduction of express services on the newly commissioned Bournemouth/Weymouth extension, with 4REP and 4VEP multiple units. English Electric supplied their type EE546 traction motors, rated at 395hp, on the units' type JA bogie, which itself was interchangeable with the bogies supplied for the

unique electro-diesel locomotives built that same year. The 4VEP sets featured English Electric's type EE507 260hp traction motors, and all were equipped with the standard Southern/English Electric control equipment.

The electro-diesel locomotives came in two varieties, one built, or rather converted from electric locomotives manufactured by Doncaster Workshops, and one from English Electric's Vulcan Foundry plant. The latter were those that took to the rails in 1967, with the Bournemouth/Weymouth services. They were a 1,600/600hp, dual rated locomotive, but were of lower power than the Doncaster built locomotives, converted from straight electric Bo-Bos of 2,552hp, introduced in 1958. These 1958 locomotives, which acquired a classification of 71 in later BR days, were equipped with a pantograph, in addition to the conventional third rail collector shoes, for picking up the 750V dc supply from an overhead contact system in some Southern yards. These 24 locomotives were fitted with English Electric built power equipment, which incorporated a motor-generator set, and four 638hp spring borne traction motors, driving the wheels through an SLM (Swiss Locomotive & Machine Works) drive. The principle of operation was essentially similar, insofar as the motor generator sets were concerned, to that of the existing Southern electric locomotives of Class CC, described earlier in this book.

The Class 73 as it became known, from English Electric, actually took to the rails in 1962, at least the six Type JA locomotives did, whilst the more numerous Type JB did not materialise until 1964. The electro-diesels were fitted with a four-cylinder EE type 4SRKT diesel engine, and rated at

The Southern Region of BR produced yet another hybrid 'Electro-Diesel' type, with, in this case, the assistance of English Electric power and control equipment, and a 650hp Paxman diesel engine. In this case, the locomotives were converted from an earlier, Doncaster built, EE Co. equipped design, but minus the original pantograph for current collection in yards. No. E6101 started life as electric locomotive No. E5015, was rebuilt at BR Crewe Works and later renumbered 74001. All the rebuilt locomotives were withdrawn by the end of 1977 – none survive.

(Author's Collection)

600hp, was directly connected to a 387kW main generator, supplying power to four 395hp traction motors. The main dimensions of these electro-diesel locomotives are shown in the accompanying table.

English Electric Type JB Electro-Diesel Locomotives

Overall length	53ft 8in
Overall height	12ft 5$\frac{7}{16}$in
Overall width	8ft 8in
Bogie pivot centres	32ft 0in
Bogie wheelbase	8ft 9in
Bogie wheel diameter	3ft 4in
Wheel arrangement	Bo-Bo
Power rating – diesel	600hp at 850 rpm
– electric	1,600hp
Max. tractive effort	42,000lb
Nominal supply voltage	675V dc
Weight in working order	75 tons
Max service speed	90 mph

Mechanically, these were uncomplicated locomotives, with a fabricated body frame, covered in sheet steel panels, with removable translucent roof panels, and extensive use was made of aluminium in the engine compartment. Glass fibre was used for the cab roof mouldings, and to insulate the cab from the engine compartments, whilst the bogies were interchangeable with those used on the newly acquired multiple units of the 4REP type.

Further Overseas Orders

Between 1955 and 1970, the overseas orders secured by all the members of the GEC Traction fold were predominantly for dc systems, although in India especially, some 25kV orders were received. In Europe, the orders came from Denmark, Holland, Poland and Spain, whilst further east, various Indian railways were supplied, and in Australasia, New Zealand and Australia were still being equipped with English Electric-AEI Traction equipment. For AEI especially, the South African Railways were the most important dc traction market, with the company supplying both complete locomotives and multiple units, or, the power

Obviously in Australia, with Sydney Harbour Bridge in the background, these Australian-built suburban multiple units were fitted with control equipment from Metropolitan-Vickers.

equipments, with the mechanical portions being constructed by Union Carriage & Wagon Co. AEI laid claim with the South African orders, to designing and installing the most powerful traction motor for the 3ft 6in gauge. In fact, looking at a list of GEC Traction's machine types in the 1980s, the type 283, with a rating of 324hp continuously, was the single most powerful motor in the range.

In Australia, power equipments were the order of the day, with, in New South Wales, the double deck motorcoaches, and 'interurban' cars being powered by AEI traction motors, and control systems. However, these were a total of only eight sets, ordered in 1967 and 1968, for NSW's 1,500V overhead dc system. The equipment was manufactured at the AEI Engineering Pty Ltd works in New South Wales, although some control equipment and auxiliary machinery was built at the Trafford Park plant, and the traction motor works at Attercliffe Common, Sheffield. Similar PCM type control equipment had been supplied to the Central Line underground route in London, and Toronto in Canada. Regenerative braking was standard on other New South Wales stock, but in the 1967/68 equipment, braking was controlled electronically. The extension of electrification on Victoria's broad gauge network produced rather larger orders for AEI, which included substation equipment in the mid-1950s, but between 1954 and 1958, some 190 sets of power equipment had been ordered.

So far as main line electric traction was concerned, these were the only orders from Australia at this time. Neighbouring New Zealand produced even less, and in fact, the only equipment ordered was from BTH, and consisted of power equipment for diesel locomotives.

India meanwhile was engaged on the suburban electrification of lines around Calcutta, for which AEI supplied steel tank rectifiers for the substation equipment, in addition to 36 complete sets of multiple unit equipment. Also for the Eastern Railway, 1956 saw the order placed for twelve complete 3,120hp Co-Co locomotives. Six years later, following a decision to convert to ac traction, in 1962, an order was placed with AEI to supply motorcoach power and conversion equipment. The Western Railway too was extending electrification, and placed orders on English Electric and AEI, and also, as Indian Railways progressed towards self-sufficiency, on Bharat Heavy Electricals (BHEL) and Calcutta Locomotive Works (CLW). For the most part, between 1955 and 1970, 1,500V dc traction equipment predominated. Mainly multiple unit rolling stock and equipment was supplied, although the Great Indian Peninsula Railway, which had pioneered electrification with the assistance of English Electric, GEC and others, ordered 29 new 3,600hp Co-Co locomotives between 1954 and 1961.

The Heavy Electricals factory was opened at Bhopal in 1962, and AEI were appointed technical consultants, supplying the initial designs for traction equipment built at the plant. By the late 1960s, the BHEL factory was constructing some of the most complex electrical equipment for traction use, but some specialist hardware was still being supplied from the UK.

English Electric had had a long association with Danish State Railways, dating back to 1933, and which resulted in a series of orders for 1,500V dc equipment. Four orders had been placed prior to, and including 1960, for traction motors and camshaft control equipment, supplied from Preston, and totalling 117 sets. Between 1965 and the end of 1970, a further seven orders were placed for a total of 233 sets of power and control equipment. Not all of these were manufactured in this country, some traction motors for instance were made

New South Wales was also proceeding with electrification at 1,500V dc after the second world war. This resulted in an order for 40 of these 3,820hp 46 class Co-Co locomotives. The locomotives, from Metropolitan-Vickers were hailed, in 1950, as being the most powerful built in Great Britain.

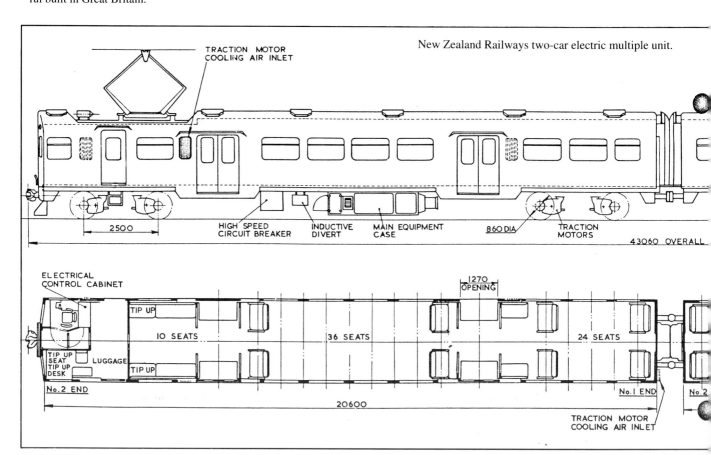

New Zealand Railways two-car electric multiple unit.

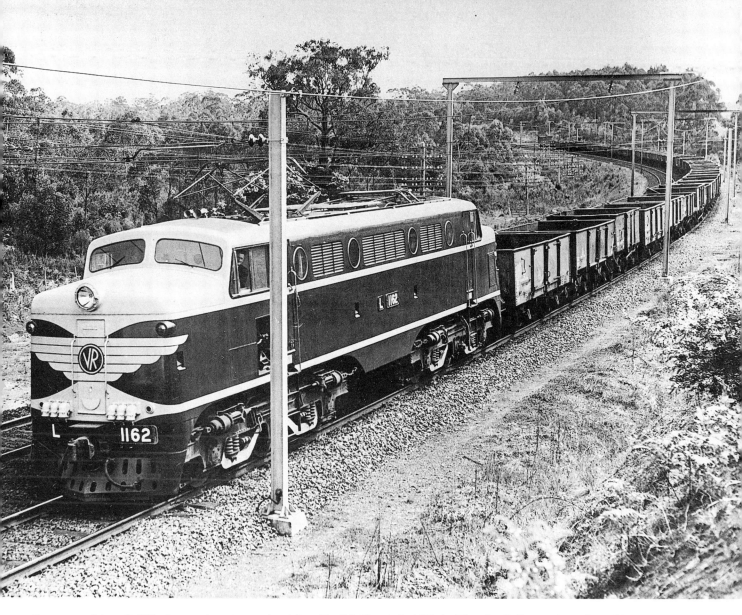

Seventeen of these 2,400hp locomotives were ordered from English Electric in 1950, by Victorian Railways, Australia. Taking power at 1,500V dc, they weighed in at 96 tons, and were built at the Preston Works. They were set to work on Victorian Railways' 5ft 3in gauge line from Melbourne to Gippsland.

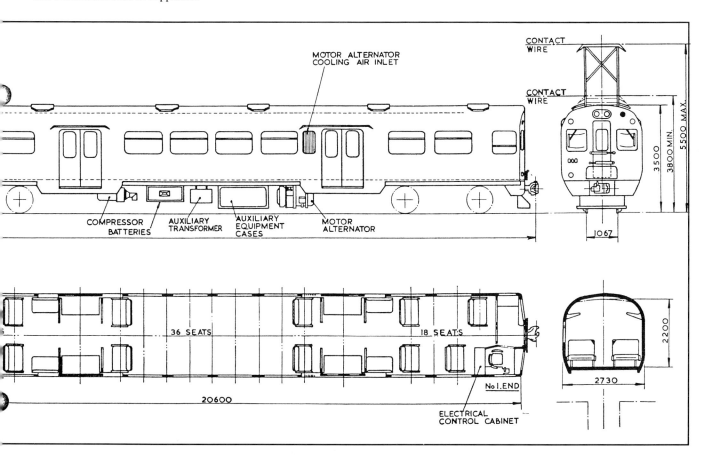

Between 1954 and 1958 Victorian Railways ordered some 190 sets of power equipment from English Electric, for these seven-car sets, built in Australia.

(Author's Collection)

in Denmark under licence. The two-car sets powered by English Electric were set to work on suburban services around Copenhagen, and the equipment supplied consisted of motor generator sets, motor and trailer coach control gear, traction motors, and final drive gears.

Neighbouring Holland also adopted 1,500V dc overhead contact systems for its electrification work, but orders for hardware were placed with Metropolitan-Vickers, and later, AEI Traction. In the 1950s, various plans were adopted to develop the electrification and restore the country's transport system following the end of the Second World War. From AEI, the following was supplied up to 1970:

Netherlands Railways

Ordered	Qty	Equipment	Plan
1956	192	Traction motor resilient gears	'G'
1956	106	Inductive shunts and resistors	'G'
1957	30	Inductive diverters and resistors	'M'
1957	2	Sets of main resistors	'M'
1957	60	Sets of resilient gears	'M'
1958/9	104	Inductive diverters and resistors	'P'
1958/9	32	Sets of main resistors	'P'
1958/9	208	Sets of resilient gears	'P'
1959	64	Traction motors – type 139	'U'
1959	64	Sets of resilient gears	'U'
1960	46	Inductive diverters and resistors	'Q'

Ordered	Qty	Equipment	Plan
1960	23	Sets of main resistors	'Q'
1960	92	Sets of resilient gears	'Q'
1960	2	Motor-alternators, type MG53	'TT'
1960	4	Inductive diverters and resistors	'TT'
1960	10	Sets of resilient gears	'TT'
1960	10	Traction motors – type 139	'TT'

This was not all the equipment orders received in the period, since further hardware was provided in 1962, and in 1967 and 1968, the provision of thyristor and 'chopper' control equipment followed. In fact, Netherlands Railways had converted a 1924 postal motorcoach to accept the latest 'chopper' equipment from AEI in 1967, which, following successful completion of trials was followed by the award of an order for more chopper control equipment for their 1,500V dc stock. At the same time, AEI also had a test installation on a London Underground vehicle, which was also followed by orders for further control equipment, initially for test, but later, in production service.

Elsewhere in Europe, English Electric and AEI had been involved with the electrification of Polish Railways in the 1930s, and in 1959, electrical equipment was supplied to Poland for 20 new, 3,000hp Co-Co electric types. An even bigger order had materialised in 1957, from Spain, for similar 3,000V dc locomotives, totalling 75 in number, and supplied by English Electric. Neighbouring Portugal's Estoril Railway had also placed orders, but for multiple unit equipment, in 1958 and 1968, for what was in many countries, the standard 1,500V dc contact system.

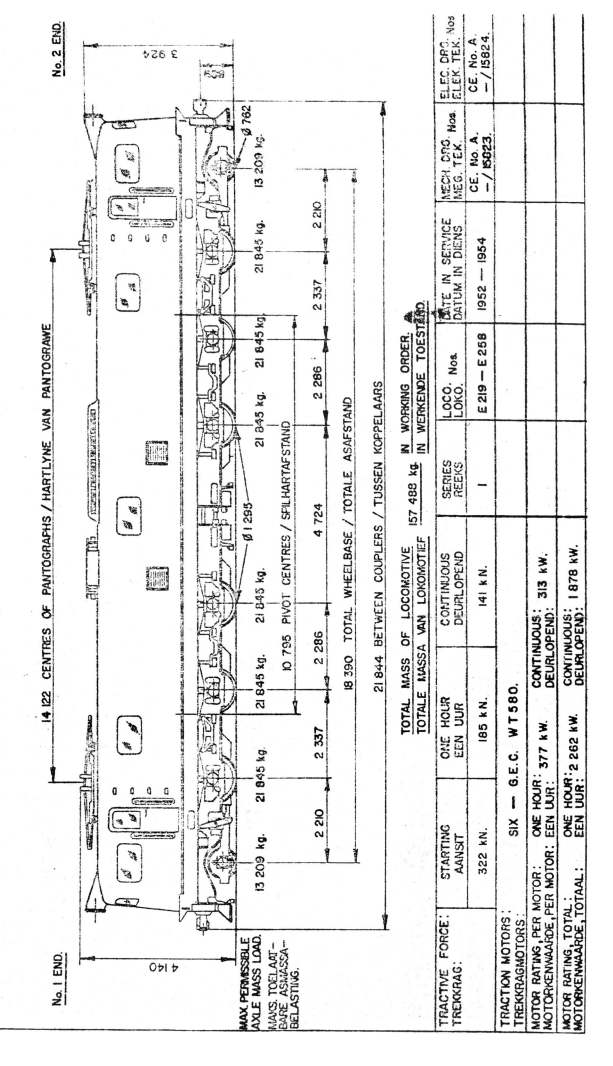

South African Railways Class 4E.

The South African Orders

Unquestionably the most fruitful area for AEI, and Metropolitan-Vickers during this period, was the supply of complete locomotives, power equipment, and multiple unit rolling stock and power equipment for South African Railways. For the mechanical portions of the main orders during the 1950s and early 1960s, until the Union Carriage & Wagon Co.'s facilities at Nigel in the Transvaal came into production, Metropolitan-Cammell of Birmingham were main sub-contractors. With the exception of some 50kV and a smaller section of 25kV ac, discussed later, almost all of the SAR systems were 3,000V dc, running on the 3ft 6in gauge.

Dealing with the locomotives first, five classes were constructed, and powered by AEI electrical equipment between 1950 and 1970, namely, the Class 4E, 5E, 5E1, 6E and 6E1. In 1951 however, North British Locomotive Co. and GEC entered the SAR field, supplying 40 Class 4E 1Co-Co1 locomotives, of 3,000hp. These locomotives remained until 1970, when the Class 6E Bo-Bo arrived, the most powerful units at work on SAR. They were not so successful however, and were later modified to a Co-Co wheel arrangement. In 1955, SAR took delivery of the first of Class 5E, an 82-ton locomotive, developing 2,021hp, and produced by AEI's main rival, English Electric. In all, 160 of these locomotives were delivered by 1956, each of Bo-Bo wheel arrangement, and fitted with four EE type 529 traction motors. Although Metropolitan-Vickers were responsible for the next development, the Class 5E1, both the Class 5E and 5E1 were prod-

Metropolitan-Vickers and the North British Locomotive Co. teamed up to supply these 3,030hp 1Co-Co1 Class 4E locomotives to the 3ft 6in gauge South African Railways, ordered in 1954, and set to work in 1956.

ucts of the English Electric-AEI traction brand, with the 5E1 eventually totalling no less than 690 locomotives. Of these, only 135 were built in the UK, at Metropolitan-Cammell's Saltley, Birmingham works, the remainder coming from Union Carriage & Wagon, in the Transvaal. The change in policy, where most of SAR's motive power was home-built took place in 1962, after completion of UCW's Nigel plant, and which, subsequently constructed 500 of Class 6E and 6E1 locomotives, in addition to the 555 of Class 5E1. SAR was progressing well with its electrified routes in the 1950s and 1960s, which had begun with the Natal, and Reef areas, and expanded to include the main lines out of Cape Town, on the Cape Western section. Whilst the 3kV dc was essentially standard for South Africa, and which occupied three major areas of the network, developments in the 1970s saw a shift towards ac systems. The 6E and 6E1 classes were ordered in 1969, including 80 of the former and 420 of the latter, with more orders from SAR to GEC Traction following, for this successful design. The first 6E1 appeared later in 1969. Essentially, there was little difference in appearance and layout between Classes 5E, 5E1, 6E and 6E1, although power output had risen from 2,021, through 2,600, to 3,340hp in Class 6E1.

All these locomotives were double ended, with a full width body and Bo-Bo wheel arrangement equipment was arranged internally, almost symmetrically about a central gangway. On either side of this gangway, compartments housed the HT switch groups, motor alternators and resistance banks. A novel development with the 6E1s, was the provision of external links between the body, inclined to attachments on the lower edges of the bogie frame. These traction links were designed to lower the bogie pivot centre height to almost rail level, and intended to eliminate weight transfer within the bogie. The accompanying table details the Classes 4E to 6E1.

Above: Straight out of the box, this fine view of a Class 5E1 2,380hp Bo-Bo, demonstrates the attractive lines of this design. The photograph was taken in 1960, at Metropolitan-Cammell Carriage & Wagon's Saltley Works, in Birmingham and shows No. E464.

(Author's Collection)

Below: South African Railways Class 5E1 Bo-Bo No. E919. These locomotives numbered 635 in all, and were ordered from Metropolitan-Vickers between 1962 and 1968. Metropolitan-Cammell of Birmingham were subcontracted to supply the mechanical parts. The 5E1 series were the last complete locomotives to be shipped out to South Africa, since Union Carriage & Wagon were poised to provide a major manufacturing base in the republic.

(South African Railways)

The overwhelming similarity in appearance of the Class 6E1 locomotive shown in this photograph, and its predecessors is obvious. Detail changes in design were few, but included the long inclined traction links seen in this view. These links were intended to further reduce the centre of gravity of the locomotive. Union Carriage & Wagon manufactured the mechanical portions of the more than 900 built, and rated at 3,340hp, sported the world's most powerful traction motor on the 3ft 6in gauge.

Technical Details of SAR Locomotives – Classes 4E to 6E1

Class	Built	Wheel arrgt.	Length o/a	Wt. (tons)	No. in class	Output (hp)	Mech. parts	Elect. eqp.
4E	1952	Co-Co	71' 8"	155	40	3032	NBL	GEC
5E	1955	Bo-Bo	50' 10"	82	160	2021	EE	EE
5E1	1959	Bo-Bo	50' 10"	82	690	2600	M-V (135) UCW (555)	M-V & AEI
6E	1970	Bo-Bo	50' 10"	87.5	80	3340	UCW	AEI
6E1	1969	Bo-Bo	50' 10"	87.5	420	3340	UCW	AEI

M-V   Metropolitan-Vickers
AEI   Associated Electrical Industries
EE   English Electric
UCW   Union Carriage & Wagon Co.

On the multiple unit front, literally hundreds of vehicles were constructed during the 1950s and 1960s, although the last of the imported vehicles was supplied in 1958 to the Reef area. From 1958, UCW constructed the mechanical portions, with the electrical equipment coming from the UK, from AEI, and in 1961, UCW built the first all-steel electric multiple unit.

Between 1950 and 1970, no fewer than twelve separate orders for motorcoach equipments were placed with Metropolitan-Vickers, and later AEI, and English Electric-AEI Traction. The motorcoach equipments supplied included traction motors, electro-pneumatic or resistance camshaft control systems from the Metropolitan-Vickers stable. This continued even after UCW had taken on responsibility for the mechanical portions, into the 1960s, and beyond. In 1970, in common with the Netherlands, and BR, SAR began experimenting with the use of thyristor control, and two sets of chopper equipments were ordered in 1970.

The basic layout of the multiple units typical of the 1950s seated 68 first class, with the H.T. and driving compartments at the leading end of the vehicle – the 60ft 6in long coaches were carried on 8ft 6in bogies. Some later UCW built units adopted a 9ft 0in wheelbase bogie. The driver's position was located on the left side of the 'cab', and on the motorcoaches, separated from the end door gangway by a lattice steel gate. A tip up seat was provided for the guard, on the right hand side. Passenger accommodation was normally arranged 3 and 2, either side of the central gangway, and a five-seater bench was fitted with its back to the HT compartment on motor coaches. The external design of the body was fairly simple, generally slab sided, with rectangular windows and four access doors on either side. Substantial footsteps were provided, with long grab rails from waist level almost down to the solebars, with, normally, a large diameter headlight fitted over the end gangway doors.

Union Carriage & Wagon produced the first all-steel sets in the 1960s, from home produced steel, and incorporated a number of detail improvements and modifications in design and layout. Although to all intents and purposes they were similar to earlier, Metro-Cammell built vehicles, and incorporated only minor changes to body styling. Fibreglass thermal and sound insulation was fitted, as were the standard 3ft 0in wide droplights in the bodysides, which were interchangeable with those on any other vehicle, as self-contained units. The top hung sliding doors were aluminium, and air-operated by the guard, with two pairs on either side of the coach.

When UCW began to build the sets in South Africa, AEI South Africa (Pty) Ltd were actually awarded the first contract, although, most of the electrical equipment was constructed in England, at Attercliffe Common, Sheffield. Some electrical equipment was made by an AEI associate company, the First Electric Corporation, in South Africa. The list details the multiple unit stock built by Metro-Cammell for SAR:

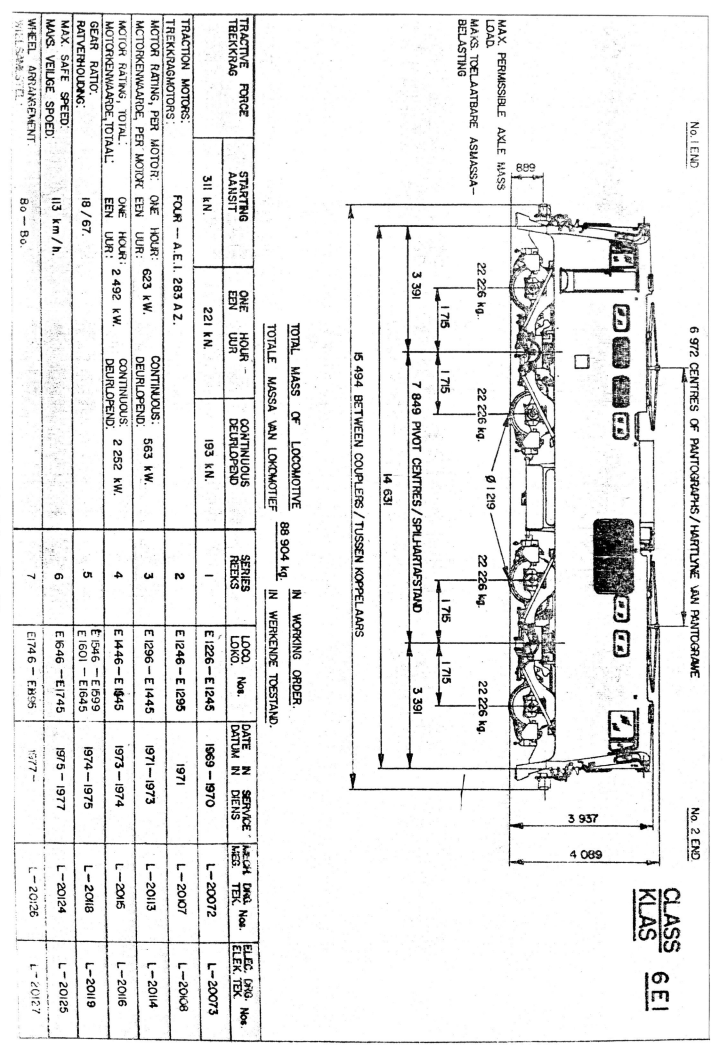

No. I END

No. 2 END

6 972 CENTRES OF PANTOGRAPHS / HARTLYNE VAN PANTOGRAWE

CLASS
KLAS

6 E1

MAX. PERMISSIBLE AXLE MASS LOAD.
MAKS. TOELAATBARE ASMASSA-BELASTING

889

3 391

22 226 kg.

175

175

22 226 kg.

Ø 1 219

7 849 PIVOT CENTRES / SPILHARTAFSTAND

22 226 kg.

175

175

22 226 kg.

3 391

15 494 BETWEEN COUPLERS / TUSSEN KOPPELAARS

14 631

3 937

4 089

TOTAL MASS OF LOCOMOTIVE
TOTALE MASSA VAN LOKOMOTIEF
IN WORKING ORDER.
IN WERKENDE TOESTAND.
88 904 kg.

		SERIES REEKS	LOCO. Nos. LOKO. Nos.	DATE IN SERVICE DATUM IN DIENS	MECH. DRG. Nos. MEG. TEK.	ELEC. DRG. Nos. ELEK. TEK.
TRACTIVE FORCE TREKKRAG	STARTING AANSIT	1	E 1226 — E 1245	1969 — 1970	L — 20072	L — 20073
	311 kN.					
	ONE HOUR EEN UUR	2	E 1246 — E 1295	1971	L — 20107	L — 20108
	221 kN.					
	CONTINUOUS DEURLOPEND	3	E 1296 — E 1445	1971 — 1973	L — 20113	L — 20114
	193 kN.					
TRACTION MOTORS: TREKKRAGMOTORS:	FOUR — A.E.I. 283 A Z.	4	E 1446 — E 1545	1973 — 1974	L — 20115	L — 20116
MOTOR RATING, PER MOTOR: MOTORKENWAARDE, PER MOTOR EEN:	ONE HOUR UUR: 623 kW. CONTINUOUS DEURLOPEND: 563 kW.	5	E 1546 — E 1599 E 1601 — E 1645	1974 — 1975	L — 20118	L — 20119
MOTOR RATING, TOTAL: MOTORKENWAARDE, TOTAAL:	ONE HOUR EEN UUR: 2 492 kW. CONTINUOUS DEURLOPEND: 2 252 kW.	6	E 1646 — E 1745	1975 — 1977	L — 20124	L — 20125
GEAR RATIO: RATVERHOUDING:	18 / 67.	7	E 1746 — E 1895	1977 —	L — 20126	L — 20127
MAX. SAFE SPEED: MAKS. VEILIGE SPOED:	113 km / h.					
WHEEL ARRANGEMENT: WIELSAMESTEL:	Bo — Bo.					

South African Railways Class 6E1.

Many hundreds of motor coaches, and trailer cars were supplied to South African Railways between 1927 and the 1980s, all of which like this typical suburban set, collected power at 3,000V, from the standard SAR overhead contact system.

(South African Railways)

Metropolitan-Cammell Rolling Stock Produced for South Africa

Order No.	Description	Ordered	Built
OP 11850	14 1st class motorcoaches	9/2/1944	1948/49
OP 11851	15 3rd class motorcoaches	9/2/1944	1948
M 15175	17 motorcoaches and 4 bogies	22/4/1949	1953/54
M 15939	2 motor bogies	30/1/1951	1954
M 18041	60 1st class motorcoaches	1/7/1955	1957–59
	10 2nd class motorcoaches	1/7/1955	1957–59
M 18042	90 2nd class trailer coaches	1/7/1955	1957–59
M 18043/4	386 bogies for orders M18041 & M18042	1/7/1955	1957–59

English Electric-AEI Traction

During the period between 1957 and 1961, the members of the AEI Group were gradually becoming more interlaced, although the separate trading names of Metropolitan-Vickers and BTH were still used. From 1961, AEI Traction were effectively a single trading organisation, and in fact, the former Metropolitan-Vickers plant at Attercliffe Common, Sheffield had been constructing traction equipment for BTH

for some time. There was little active involvement in the rail traction industry by GEC during this period, with the market dominated by English Electric and AEI. In 1967, AEI had received the distinction of being granted a Queen's Award To Industry, for export achievements.

The company had achieved sales totalling £6 million in 1966, 70% of which was destined for export, with the main markets in South Africa and Australia, and the major consultancy work with the establishment of the Heavy Electrical Works at Bhopal, India. Continuing the long tradition of close co-operation with English Electric, as a member of the British Rail Traction Group, the electrification of the Pakistan Western Railway was an important project.

In 1969, GEC re-entered the railway traction arena, by courtesy of its involvement in the merger of English Electric and AEI, to form the English Electric-AEI Traction Division. GEC's involvement was essentially at board level, having nothing like the same manufacturing base as the two principal members of the team. This was not to be the final move in this merger period, as three years later, in 1972, GEC Traction was formed. The period of English Electric-AEI Traction naturally saw the emergence of some inter company rivalry between the Trafford Park and Preston sites in particular, although none that impacted the railway business, and was very largely the good natured rivalry that inevitably stems from such changes. It was perhaps inevitable, with GEC in the driving seat, a more obvious, and permanent change should subsequently take place in the company structures.

8
Surburban and Rapid Transit Systems

The present day GEC Traction has become one of the world's successful suppliers of conventional rail traction equipment and systems. It also has a history – a very extensive history – of design, development and provision of urban transport systems, ranging from trams and trolley buses, to the modern equivalent, the light rapid, or mass transit systems.

It is important at this point to define what is meant by rapid transit. There are a number of possible 'definitions', and an obvious overlap, or at least, a 'grey' area, with road transport. For the purposes of this study, a useful definition of these systems, which in their present form are a relatively recent arrival, can be taken as providing a rail-based, guided transport system, for the rapid movement of large volumes of people in urban areas. There seems still to be no clear definition, and in the recent past, rail borne urban networks have been, and are, seen as either light rail, mass rapid transit, light rapid transit, and a variety of similar combinations.

If the definition is vague and uncertain, then to attempt to isolate a 'first appearance' of the rapid transit system is even more difficult. Indeed a standard gauge rail network itself can in many circumstances be construed as a rapid transit network. It is obvious that at least part of the web of rail routes, in major urban connurbations, form a part of the definition. However, examples of such urban transport systems as the London Underground, or the Paris Metro, provide perhaps the most obvious representations of a mass rapid transit network. These may not be the systems that nowadays spring to mind as serving that definition, and will not be looked at here. It is interesting to reflect that if we are more liberal with the definition of a rapid transit system, then one of GEC Traction's

predecessors, Dick, Kerr & Co., of Preston, were in at the birth of that very first system, the London Underground. They were also very much involved with the numerous electrified tramway systems that were being proposed, and installed, towards the end of the 19th century.

For the modern rapid transit network, a common perception is of a railway on standard, or narrower gauge tracks, electrically powered and controlled, and in some cases operated automatically by some very sophisticated technology. They are predominantly, indeed all modern systems operate multiple unit rolling stock, with either overhead, or conductor rail contact systems. Commonly they are formed into two or four-car units, and carried on either a pair of bogies per vehicle, or an articulation system, and are capable of rapid acceleration from rest, maintaining the required, tight, point to point schedules. The nature of rapid transit system is such that the rate of acceleration from stops is an area of vital importance, as are the braking and control systems provided, to meet the expected traffic requirements. With the arrival of more sophisticated computer technology, the operation of fast services, at frequent intervals, with numerous, closely spaced stations, can be accomplished more easily with either one person, or automated control.

Having said that the definition of a rapid transit system may not be easy, there is, of even more recent date, a further 'complication'. These are the new generation of so called light rail systems, being proposed for many towns and cities in the UK alone, as well as some already in service, and expanding in Europe and elsewhere. These LRT networks represent essentially, in a number of cases, the re-introduction of trams and tramways, which the motor vehicle ousted from city centre streets many years ago. Of course, we have learned an important lesson from the dramatic congestion apparent in these urban areas, clogging up streets, and other transport arteries. Some of the proposals for light rail systems are very close to those, erstwhile tramways, hence the use of the term 'supertrams' for some such examples. It is in this area where problems of distinction arise, between railways, and other guided transport systems. The fact that there is the essential steel wheel on steel rail con-

Outside London, these Liverpool to Southport multiple units, using third rail contact systems at 660V dc, were a regional contender in the UK mass transit stakes. Seen here at Meols Cop depot, some 30 years on, after their entry into service in the 1930s, these units were originally ordered by the LMSR as replacements for even older mass transit stock ordered by the Lancashire & Yorkshire Railway, with Dick, Kerr & Co. power equipment. Classified as 502 by BR, the chimney was *not* part of the equipment.

To demonstrate the difficulty of giving an accurate definition of 'mass rapid transit', this Calcutta prototype 25kV multiple unit would easily be considered as a candidate in that category. But, definitely not as a light rail system! In 1962, AEI supplied the power equipment to convert these 3,000V dc units to ac operation, for the Eastern Railway's Calcutta electrification.

tact does lend some weight to the railway definition, but then, the rubber tyred Paris Metro system is a railway; or is it? There will always be a grey area where definitions are concerned, and with the changing technology comes some need to revise definitions for both railway, and rapid transit networks – and then, there are the magnetic levitation systems, large and small! For the purposes of this study, and GEC Traction's involvement, we will take as a starting point, the proposal, design, and construction, of the Tyne & Wear Metro, in the early 1970s. This modern rapid transit system is now almost 20 years old, and initiated some standards which have been, and are being adopted by a number of other schemes.

United Kingdom Projects
GEC Traction had been formed for just two years, from the merged English Electric-AEI Traction divisions, when the North East of England provided yet another 'first' in the railway industry. Under the guidance of the Tyneside PTE, a new metro system was proposed and constructed to serve the Tyneside area. The route chosen ran from South Shields, through Jarrow and Gateshead, crossing the Tyne to run in a closed loop through Long Benton to Monkseaton, Tynemouth and Wallsend, and then back to Newcastle city centre. Electric traction for urban transport was certainly not new to this area, above ground at least, although the earlier Tyneside electrification had used third rail, side contact systems, where the new metro was designed for 1,500V dc, overhead.

Running on standard gauge lines around Newcastle, the Tyneside metro was provided with twin-car, articulated vehicles, which were built by Metropolitan-Cammell in Birmingham. GEC's part in the order consisted of the

supply of power and control equipment, with the first vehicle delivered in August 1978. The whole scheme, for which early planning had begun in 1973, was comparatively inexpensive, at £65.5 million, which worked out at £2 million per mile – less than half the cost of urban motorway construction. This particular metro scheme was an opportune development, coming along at a time when the star of rapid transit was beginning to rise all around Europe, and there was at least a perception of export potential, some of which was later capitalised upon by GEC Traction.

In terms of the equipment supplied by the company, there was an international 'feel' to it, since the camshaft control system was the same design as that supplied to Denmark for multiple units in service there. Although on Denmark's suburban networks, 1,500V dc was the chosen power supply, this 'standard' camshaft control gear was available in a 750V dc version, for the Southern Region of British Rail. The traction motors on the Tyneside vehicles were based on a standard Siemens design, which were fitted to many Duwag monomotor type bogies in use all over Europe. They were, indeed, are, four-pole, self-ventilated machines, wound for 750V dc operation, but insulated for 1,500V to ground, for service on the 1,500V dc system. In practice the motors were designed for connection permanently in series, during motoring.

The selection of a 1,500V dc overhead contact system provided useful cost savings on the Tyne & Wear metro, since only half the number of trackside substations that would be provided on a 750V installation, were needed. Whilst the lack of series-parallel transformation in the control of traction motors, could have been seen as being wasteful of energy, in the original installation, the motor characteristics were carefully designed, with a calculated energy saving of 3.5% for 1,500V dc, as compared with 1,000V dc systems. The electrical equipment was designed to be carried equally, distributed between the two halves of the articulated vehicles. The control equipment carried below the two cars, distributed between the two units, was arranged primarily to reduce the number of inter-car connections required. Heating of the passenger saloons was by means of a waste heat recovery

Hard to miss the reason for this photograph, the opening of the first true, modern rapid transit system in the UK. These articulated sets, collecting power from an overhead catenary, at 1,500V dc, provided orders for GEC Traction in 1974 and 1976. The Tyne & Wear Metro marked the beginning of the modern rapid transit era in the UK.

(Tyne & Wear PTE)

A closer view of the first of the Tyne & Wear cars No. 4001, showing the clean, light, and attractive design of the new generation of rapid transit rolling stock.

(Tyne & Wear PTE)

Railway workshops are a much cleaner place nowadays, as this view of the Tyneside workshops at Gosforth ably demonstrates.
(Tyne & Wear PTE)

system, also distributed between the two cars, to ensure continuity of supply. Auxiliary power supplies are fed from a single motor-alternator set on each articulated car, of GEC design, and rated at 10kW, with 415V three-phase output selected, to enable the use of 50Hz, industrial lighting units. GEC also supplied the motor used to drive the Westinghouse air compressor – required for the braking system, and door operation – which was mounted on an extension of the compressor shaft.

The metro cars were designed to be controlled from one of two driving positions, at either end of the twin unit, through the air/oil camshafts, on the driver's master controller. The traction and braking resistances served two purposes, with, in addition to normal function, such as the dissipation of surplus electrical energy, the heat generated being ducted through a waste heat recovery system, into the passenger

saloons. Two items which demonstrated the contrast of new with old technology on these vehicles, was the use of a slightly modified, standard tramway, single-arm pantograph, and the inclusion of electronic wheelslip/slide, detection equipment. This latter feature measures the speed of each axle by counting the rate at which gear teeth pass a probe, with the cab mounted speedometer driven from the axle units. In operation, the equipment compares signals during acceleration from the two powered axles, with signals from the non-powered axles. When a preset difference is exceeded, the current breakers trip, and the camshaft controller returns to the 'off' position, with notching commencing again automatically. During braking, instead of comparing speeds, the rate of change of speed is compared, to detect slide, and if present, the air brake on one half-car is released, and sand applied, until sliding ceases, when brakes are then re-applied. More sophisticated arrangements of this slip/slide detection equipment were fitted to other, and current GEC Traction products.

The Tyne & Wear metro cars, built by Metropolitan-Cammell in Birmingham, were constructed using a combination of materials, including steel and aluminium, in a lightweight welded and riveted structure. With passenger access by means of four pairs of power operated plug doors on each half-car, the vehicles were turned out in a striking yellow and white livery, and sporting the Tyne & Wear PTE logo on the bodysides. With a maximum intended service speed of 80km/h, the original specification provided for acceleration of up to 1 metre/sec/sec, and braking of 1.3 metre/sec/sec. In emergencies however, with the additional effects of the magnetic track brakes, the braking effort could rise to 2.32 metres/sec/sec.

Next on the list of UK developments was the complete refurbishment of the Glasgow Underground, whose physical dimensions placed it in a category amongst the smallest passenger tube railways in the world. The system had been built just before the turn of the century, in 1897, as a cable hauled railway, and was converted to electric traction in the 1930s. At that time, the original cable hauled vehicles were retained, with Metropolitan-Vickers supplying the 22 sets of electrical equipment, ordered in 1934. In 1977, when the order for 33 new vehicles was placed with Metro-Cammell, GEC Traction were awarded the contract for the power systems. The circular route of the Glasgow Tube placed some constraints on the designers too, since because of the use of a track gauge of 4 feet (1,220mm), standard gauge type traction motors could not be used. The tunnel diameter, at only 11 feet (3,353 mm), required a car of very small cross sectional area, but which had to be reduced still further, because of doubts over the profile, or envelope, of the tunnel, since some misalignments were possible from the original construction. The combination of narrow track gauge, 50

This interesting view shows the dark and gloomy station interiors before the refurbishment of the Glasgow Underground, and gives some impression of the small size of the tunnels and rolling stock; seen here on the right. *(Strathclyde PTE)*

The new cars for the 4ft gauge Glasgow Underground ordered from GEC Traction in 1977, numbered 33 in all, and replaced stock dating back to 1933, and this was rebuilt from the original stock of 1896! Here, No. 117, one of the new sets for Glasgow's 600V dc system waits at Govan Station.

(Strathclyde PTE)

metre radius curves, 12.75 metres long cars, and requirements for single unit operation made the inclusion of all the appropriate hardware on board a difficult proposition. The overall height above rail level of the cars was only 2.652 metres, and a width of 2.34 metres. These cars were then driven through tunnels whose section was much less than that considered normal for a tube railway.

The vehicles themselves were constructed from aluminium on steel frames, and carried on a pair of bogies, whose design followed, to a degree, that adopted by London Transport, for the London Underground, as also was the control equipment. All axles were powered, and equipped with GEC's type G312AZ traction motor, which is self-ventilated 300V machine, mounted on a roller bearing suspension sleeve, fitted around the axle, and supplied with a resilient, rubber nose suspension unit. The drive to the wheels was through spur gears, enclosed in an aluminium gearcase. Including the gear case, and 'U' tube suspension, the traction motor measures only 908mm from end to end, and is rated at 35.5kW (46hp), continuously, at 1,740 rpm.

The conventional control equipment was, as mentioned, of the type developed, and used by London Underground tube trains, with a high degree of reliability over many years, and many millions of miles of operation. The twin camshafts, driven by air/oil engines were used for series, and parallel notching, respectively, with both in operation during motoring and braking, and were mounted in a steel case, with fibreglass covers. in order to improve the control, and smoothness of operation, a static notching relay, referencing signals from dc current transformers in the motor circuits, was used to control the camshafts, in place of the electro-magnetic relay preferred by London Transport. Auxiliary power was taken from a motor alternator set, as used by London Transport, whilst extensive use was made of electronics in the automatic train operation, and other control systems. Automation for the new Glasgow Underground trains was taken to the extent of not having a driver on board, only a guard, and has proved highly successful. The vehicles for Glasgow's new underground were delivered in 1979, and in keeping with an emerging trend, particularly for systems supported by the passenger transport executives, a distinctive, bright colour scheme was adopted.

Whilst the orange cars of the new Glasgow Underground were a significant step forward for that city, it was seven years after that order was placed, when, in 1984, the most important development at home was announced. The development was of course, the Docklands Light Railway (DLR), which in addition to bringing a new railway into the heart of London, saw important changes in the technology of the train too. It was to be a fully automatic railway, with minimal human intervention in the day to day operation. There were important changes in the contractual arrangements too, since this was indeed a composite contract, with the GEC-Mowlem organisation tasked with designing, building, and handing over to the DLR, a fully operational railway, and within a cash limit of £60 million. The scheme was funded equally by the Department of Transport, through London Regional Transport, and the Department of the Environment through the London Docklands Development Corporation. The DLR project resulted from the LDDC's task to improve public transport in the London Docklands, through a massive ten-year investment programme, of inner city restoration.

In 1984 GEC Traction received an order for eleven articulated vehicles for the new Docklands Light Railway in London. GEC also joined forces with John Mowlem to complete this integrated project. This photograph clearly shows the twin, articulated units, from the side, but in model form.

The Isle of Dogs, centre of this redevelopment area, included some very grand schemes, ranging from the Canary Wharf development, to the successful establishment of new homes, office space, and many other projects, was the site of the DLR's initial railway. Whilst it is also true to say that the DLR was essentially an entirely new construction, extensive use was made of former British Rail lines, since the railway was to be built to standard gauge. In particular, in phase one, the route of the old London & Blackwall Railway was followed for some of its route, and even in the early stages, plans were already in preparation for expansion, especially the City and Beckton extensions, passing, and serving the London City Airport.

Trains for the initial railway were twin-car articulated units, 28 metres long, 2.65 metres wide, and 3.4 metres high, with the bodies supplied by Linke-Hoffman-Busch, and powered by GEC Traction. The Germans won the order for the bodies, to a degree, on their strength, and reputation in the rapid transit market, since here in the UK there was little experience in the home base.

The vehicles themselves pick up power at 750V dc from a bottom contact conductor rail, insulated from accidental contact on the top and two sides. A single substation was located initially, at Poplar, with further substations installed at Royal Mint Street, Crossharbour and Bow, to cope with the power required for the additional traffic generated by the extensions to the railway. The conductor rail, of aluminium, is steel faced, to reduce wear from the under-running contact shoe, and the contact systems were supplied by Brecknell Willis, another company associated with GEC in other projects. The power systems installed on the DLR cars were choppers with GTO thyristors, a development which reduced the need for costly and bulky commutation circuits for the thyristor equipments. The two motors themselves, fed from a common chopper, drove the wheels of the two powered bogies on each articulated unit, through two right angled gearboxes and flexible couplings. Rheostatic braking systems were installed, with the heat generated being dissipated in banks of resistors slung underneath the vehicle bodies.

A second, GTO thyristor based convertor, provided auxiliary supplies for control and battery charging, whilst the train's automatic operation used two systems. These two, Automatic Train Protection (ATP), and Automatic Train Operation (ATO), are actually independent systems, but serve to control and operate the railway. The ATO computer stores the timetables for the railway at the Operation and Maintenance Centre, and as the controller calls the train into service each day, the on-board systems are connected to the ATO computer by means of a Data Docking Link (DDL), where following safety checks, the ATO computer instructs the DLR train to proceed to its first station. During operation, the ATO computer can communicate with the train's on-board computers by means of a DDL at each station, and update the train computers. The ATP system serves two purposes, on the one hand it ensures trains observe speed limits and on the other, to prevent unsafe train movements. Train speeds are regulated by the rate at which transponders are crossed on the trackbed, with appropriate regulatory control being taken.

For this initial railway, other GEC companies were directly involved, including GEC Transmission &

Distribution Projects, GEC Telecommunications, etc. Whilst the growing railway has brought in other suppliers for its extensions, notably, on the power equipment/traction side, Brush Electrical Machines, the original GEC-Mowlem scheme has certainly proved successful. This has demonstrated the way forward for a number of other projects, with variations on the DLR schemes being presented at the 'Project Light Rail' exhibition in Manchester. The latter city is now pressing ahead rapidly with its own LRT project, the Metro Link, the first sections of which opened in stages throughout 1992.

Project Light Rail was held in Gorton, an area of Manchester noted for its past railway connections, with Beyer Peacock, and the one time Great Central Railway. In 1987, a DLR set was brought to Manchester, fitted with a pantograph, collecting dc from an overhead contact wire, with the objective of demonstrating the advantages of light rail to the people of Manchester, and local and national government representatives. A short section of track, 2km in length was used to operate the DLR vehicle, taking passengers for trips. This was car No.11, which was also selected to carry the Queen, on return to the DLR in London, for the official opening ceremony. The whole Project Light Rail event, at which GEC products were displayed, was an example of co-operation between the various competitors in the railway industry, and certainly contributed to the growth in interest in light rail systems around the country. Excluding the DLR, there are now more than 20 light rail/rapid transit schemes in progress, or in an advanced planning stage for the UK.

Leaving the developments in the home light rail market, we must at least refer to the interesting and unique, Birmingham Maglev project. Having said it is unique, it is at least true within the UK, since both the Germans and the Japanese have working test tracks considerably longer than Birmingham's Maglev. There are also some proposals for various high speed Maglev systems/routes in the USA, and other locations, but so far at least, none of these have materialised in practical form.

In Birmingham, the Maglev project was the culmination, if not the result of experimental work on wheel-less guided transport systems, dating back to the 1950s. GEC Transportation Projects involvement, as part of the People Mover Group, included overall project management and systems engineering. The system itself consists of four main components; track, suspension, propulsion and control, with GEC TPL engineering the power supply system. Metro-Cammell, a long time associate of GEC, built the cars, whilst a major rail industry competitor, Brush designed and supplied the propulsion system.

The infrastructure comprises of an elevated concrete guideway, 620 metres long, with two curves of 50 metres radius, and gradient of 1.5%, with a removable section, to allow cars to be taken off the track. In fact, two parallel tracks are installed, separated by a central walkway with steel support rails carried on concrete crossbeams. The aluminium conductor rails are energised at 600V dc, with the linear motor reaction rail in between. Cable loops are installed for data links to the vehicle's on-board systems, whilst the suspension rails are laminated to ensure adequate lift.

Power supplies are taken from Birmingham Airport's main switchboard, with a single substation located to the midpoint of the track. The incoming 11kV supply is stepped down, and supplied to the track and the extruded conductor rails, through two oil-filled transformers and rectifiers – one for each track. This arrangement means that in the event of the failure of supplies to one track, the other remains operational.

The cars themselves, designed to accommodate 40 passengers, are 6 metres long, and weigh 5 tonnes, and with due regard to the fact that they are 'flying', have been designed to a degree at least, along the principles used in aviation. The 'flying' actually consists of a 15mm air gap between the four groups of six levitation magnets, and the steel suspension rails. Propulsion is achieved with a linear induction motor mounted in the centre of the vehicle, below floor level, interacting with the reaction rail fixed to the guideway. This motor is powered from a computer controlled, three phase, variable frequency supply, the design and provision of which was the responsibility of Brush Electrical Machines. The suspension and guidance systems were designed and provided by another GEC company, GEC Transmission & Distribution Projects Ltd, including the magnets, sensors, and a power transistor based chopper control system. Again, the automatic operation of the Maglev was achieved with similar ATP and ATO systems to that adopted for the DLR. The prototype Maglev vehicle, built and tested at Derby by BR's R&D unit was controlled manually, whilst the automatic control systems on the Birmingham installation were provided by GEC General Signal. The Maglev however, even as a peoplemover system remains a one off venture, with other systems preferring the use of rubber tyred vehicles, though still on guided tracks.

Overseas Rapid Transit Projects

In the export market, what may be considered as the first major project, and success for GEC Traction, or subsequently GEC Transportation Projects Ltd, was the Hong Kong Metro. The first contracts on the Modified Initial System were placed in 1976, almost ten years after a report published by the Hong Kong Government had resolved to pursue the transport question further, as a result of the problems of road traffic congestion. In 1969, consulting engineers were appointed to review the options for the underground rail system, proposed in the 1967 report. The following year, 1970, saw the submission of a study to the Hong Kong Government which recommended the building of the Initial System, to be subsequently expanded to the full system, including four separate lines, with a total length of 52 route km. The four routes of the full Hong Kong Metro as proposed were:

(i) Kong Kow Line – Chater Station to Ma Yau Tong Station.
(ii) Tsuen Wan Line – Prince Edward Station to Tsuen Wan West Station.
(iii) Island Line – Kennedy Station to Chai Wen Central Station.
(iv) East Kowloon Line – Rumsey Station to Diamond Hill Station.

It was two years later before the Hong Kong Government decided to go ahead with the Initial System, and proceeded to attempt to negotiate a single fixed price contract, although the Government subsequently abandoned this idea after one of the consortia withdrew from the negotiations. Subsequently, a Modified Initial System was proposed, involving part of the Kong Kow Line, 15.6km in length, and running between Chater station and Kwun Tong, of which 12.8km was to be underground, and the remainder on elevated tracks. A maintenance depot was included, and constructed at Kowloon Bay, whilst the second line, from Prince Edward station to Tsuen Wan – the Tsuen Wan Extension was progressed rapidly, and no less than 470 sets of power equipment were ordered from GEC between 1976 and 1982. The MRT was electrified at 1,500V dc, with an overhead contact system, and power obtained at 33kV from the China Power and Hong Kong Electric Companies, with system distribution at 11kV, ac. Some consideration was given to using a third rail contact system, but problems with ensuring adequate safety margins, even with a shrouded contact rail, precluded this approach.

At the time, the MRT cars were believed to have the highest capacity of any metro car in the world, with each being just over 22 metres in length and three metres wide. With a capacity for 330 standing (under maximum load), and 48 seated passengers, getting passengers on and off required the provision of five pairs of sliding doors on each side of the car. With the generous internal spaces for passenger movement along vehicles, and in the standing room provided, eight car trains were planned to carry some 3,000 passengers at peak periods. Three years after the Hong Kong MRT contracts were awarded, GEC Traction again tendered successfully for power equipments, for new trains to run on the neighbouring, and electrified, Kowloon to Canton Railway. This is reviewed in more detail in the next chapter. There were some similarities with the MRT cars, and the railway itself started alongside the MRT along Hong Kong's waterfront at Kowloon, with the route then taking it to the border with the People's Republic of China, in Canton.

The initial £11 multi-contract was awarded to GEC Traction, shared between the MRTC, GEC Traction and Metro-Cammell. The work necessitated close co-operation between the three organisations for the supply and installation of the electrical and mechanical equipment. GEC Traction, in addition to the sub-contractor's role, supplying the traction power equipments, were also tasked to undertake a power systems study, and separately, an interference study, whilst Metro-Cammell co-ordinated the installation work. For the MIS, there were nine main electrical hardware contracts, as follows:

Hong Kong Mass Rapid Transit Corpn. – Electrical Contracts

E1 Multiple unit trains
E2 Signalling and control systems
E3 Telecommunications
E4 Power supply fixed equipment
E5 Escalators and lifts
E6 Automatic fare collection equipment
E7 Environmental control systems
E8 Station and tunnel auxiliary equipment
E9 Kowloon Bay depot equipment

The power systems study was largely intended to cover the high and medium power distribution networks, determining the adequacy of cables, circuit breakers, ac and dc systems, and auxiliary and traction supplies. Operation of trains under conditions of abnormal loading/operations, earthing methods, and establishing power flow levels. The data obtained was used to establish the affects on signalling and telecommunications systems, cables and equipment, and emphasising the need to protect the integrity of these vital systems. Following the theoretical work, the calculations arrived at were tested on the Tyne & Wear Metro, where the first Hong Kong MRT cars were sent for trials on the Tyneside system's test track, prior to dispatch to the Far East.

The MRT cars, ultimately in eight-car formations were required to operate at 90 seconds headway between trains, and a two-minute interval with ATO (Automatic Train Operation) in use. Acceleration rates were of the order of 1.3 metres/sec/sec, with all the axles motored, although this was

increased in practice, because many of the stations along the route were constructed on 'humps'. Propulsion and control equipment from GEC Traction was conventional, and included camshaft control of the same type as that supplied to Denmark and other systems. The traction motors, of type G313, were fitted to all axles, and were derived from those used on British Rail's Great Northern Suburban electrification. They were, indeed are, four pole, self-ventilated machines, with groups of four connected permanently in series, across the supply. Each car also carried a motor alternator set for the usual auxiliary supplies, including the air conditioning systems, necessary on Hong Kong's MRT system due to the wide variation of temperatures experienced. The climate is such in Hong Kong that the vehicles, and their passengers, are expected to withstand extremes of temperature, from 0 to 40 degrees C., up to 100% humidity, and may even be required to run through flood water in some sections, as a result of the impact of typhoons. It will be recalled that almost 60 years previously, multiple unit stock powered by English Electric had to suffer similar, harsh, climatic conditions in India. The protection of traction equipment in such circumstances was thus certainly not a new phenomenon to the collective GEC Traction experience. The MIS for Hong Kong was swiftly followed by the Tsuen Wan Extension, with the obvious demand for more rolling stock, and by 1982, GEC Traction had supplied more than 400 sets to the MRT Corporation.

That same year, two very different systems on opposite sides of the world ordered power equipment from GEC Traction. These were, on the one hand, the Seoul Subway in South Korea, and in Brazil, the extensive suburban electrification of 20km of route in Recife. The Brazilian connection is a long established one, with, in 1935, Metropolitan-Vickers securing the contract for the first complete electrification scheme, for suburban routes around Rio De Janeiro. The Recife project, which, for GEC was a composite contract, requiring the company to provide for complete electrification of 21 route km of previously narrow gauge railway, operated by diesel multiple units. The Brazilian standard 3,000V dc was selected as the supply, with an overhead contact system, with GEC Transportation Projects Ltd responsible for overhead catenary, track switching cabins, a signalling centre, and train installations for automatic train control. Each trainset, design and construction, for the first three four-car sets at least, was undertaken by MAN of West Germany, and fitted with GEC Traction power equipment. Vehicle construction was gradually transferred to Brazil and carried out under licence by Comphania Industrial Santa Matilde who completed the mechanical portions, while Villares SA built electrical control and other equipment under licence from GEC Traction. This gradual transfer of expertise, from GEC Traction's perspective meant that, for the Recife contract, half of the equipment was manufactured and supplied from the UK, with the other half produced in Brazil.

Each four-car set consisted of two driving motor cars, and two non-driving trailers, with the bodies constructed entirely of stainless steel, to minimise corrosion, with a tare weight of each four-car unit, in working order, coming in at 187 tonnes. The GEC power equipment consisted of four type G418AZ, 248kW traction motors, auxiliary motor alternators, and control systems. The traction motors–four pole, wave wound machines–were self-ventilated, with air ducted from inside the passenger saloon to the motor, and exhausted at the drive end. Hung from the axle through white metal bearings, the motors were fitted with a rubber sandwich nose suspension unit, and drove the wheels through single reduction spur gears.

Recife Metro Cars – Technical Data

Nominal operating voltage	3,000V dc
Track gauge	1,600mm
Weight of 4-car train	177 tonnes
Crush loaded weight	294 tonnes
Passengers carried at crush load	1,800/train
Initial acceleration	0.8m/sec/sec
Maximum speed	90/100km/hr
Length of 4-car train	90.35 metres
Height	2.977 metres
Height – pantograph lowered	4.6 metres
Height – pantograph raised	6.4 metres
Traction motors, 4 type G418AZ	248kW
Motor alternator set type	70kW

The power control system adopted rheostatic control of acceleration and braking, with an air/oil driven camshaft controller mounted in each car, controlling the four motors on that car. Wheelslip protection is also included, with speed detection from an inductive probe on each gearbox, and the method of operation is the same, essentially, as that described earlier, and fitted to the then latest generation of multiple unit rolling stock at home and abroad. The 70kW motor alternators are installed on the trailer cars, with each unit supplying power for the main air compressor, lighting, saloon ventilation, saloon air-conditioning, destination indicators, headlights, and of course, battery charging.

In South Korea, GEC Transportation Projects, GEC TPL, were contracted to the Seoul Metropolitan Subway Corporation, to supply 402 cars, and infrastructure equipment for lines 3 and 4 of the Seoul system. The Seoul suburban rail plan actually dates back to 1971, but GEC Traction's involvement, through GEC TPL, came about for the expansion of the network with the construction of lines 3 and 4, supplying 134 three-car trains, with chopper control. Each train, or formation, consists of two motor cars and a trailer vehicle equipped with four traction motors, collecting power from the 1,500V dc from a single pantograph mounted on top of one of the motor cars. The unmotored trailer car possesses a full width driving cab at one end, whilst generally, the appearance of the new trains is completely different to the earlier series, with smoother profiles. Some revision of the undercar layout was required in order to accommodate the chopper equipment, which was not carried on the emu's running on lines 1 and 2. Perhaps with the exception of the thyristor choppers, the electrical equipment supplied was essentially standard GEC Traction manufacture, although having said that, by the mid-1980s, thyristors, and chopper control was fast becoming standard on multiple unit vehicles. The 'standard' wheelslip/slide protection equipment was installed, along with automatic cab signalling, and automatic train protection. The main purpose of such systems, was, and is, to ensure that the train's speed is controlled in accordance with speed commands transmitted to the on-board systems, from the railway's signalling system.

Control of the propulsion is by means of two thyristor

GEC Traction provided these three-car sets for the Seoul Subway, in South Korea, collecting 1,500V dc from the overhead contact system, and fitted with a regenerative braking system. Compare the attractive front end of these units with those illustrated elsewhere, on this same system.

GEC Traction's success in the rapid transit market included the chopper control systems on these three-car trains. The customer in this case was the Seoul Subway in South Korea, with the mechanical portions supplied from Japan.

The spacious interior of one of the Seoul cars demonstrates the typical layout of modern mass transit cars.

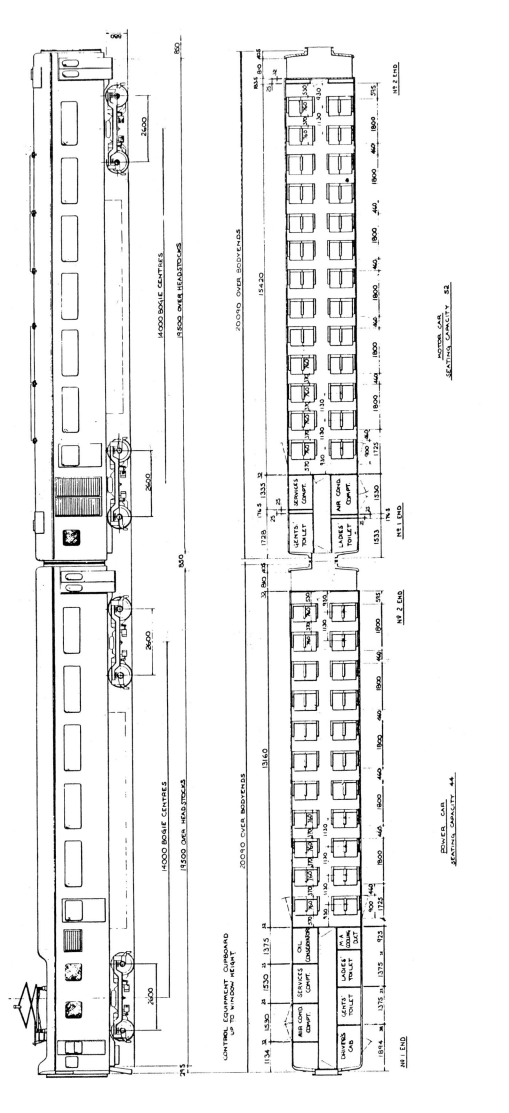

MOTOR CAR
SEATING CAPACITY 52

POWER CAR
SEATING CAPACITY 44

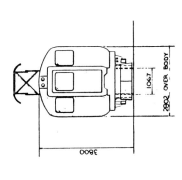

Express multiple units for the 25kV ac, Taiwan Electrification.

choppers, one on each of the two motor cars, controlling four traction motors. Power is taken from the roof-mounted pantographs, through a fuse protecting the cable, and line breakers isolating the choppers, whilst the four motors are connected in series, permanently, and employ two stages of field weakening. The latter is provided by field divert resistors. The motors themselves are actually mounted on the bogie transom, and drive the wheels through spur gears in the conventional manner, with each rated at 147kW, operating at 90% full field. The Seoul Subway specified frame-mounted motors, although axle hung versions were offered, since the previous trains already had this arrangement. The auxiliary equipment supplied, including motor alternators, required two separate auxiliary supplies, one dc and one ac, with the former used for control circuits, and the latter for air-conditioning, lighting, and other systems.

Before the equipments were shipped out to South Korea, they underwent testing on GEC Traction's then recently commissioned combined test rig at Preston, where a series of trials evaluated the performance of the equipment under service conditions. To make the tests as realistic as possible, the major components, choppers, traction motors, motor alternator set, battery, air compressor and brake cylinders were connected together, just as they would have been in service on the vehicle. Eight traction motors were connected to machines that could operate as either generators or motors, to ensure that the chopper control units were put through their paces effectively. Computers were then used to simulate various loading conditions and track gradients, in order to simulate a journey over a particular route profile as accurately as possible. The tests produced a considerable amount of useful information relating to the performance of the equipment, enabling 'fine tuning' of equipment design, and more accurate tailoring to customer/railway route requirements. However, despite comprehensive equipment testing, nature still had a hand in the design of railway hardware, and despite consideration of air temperatures that can fall to –25 degrees Centigrade, operation in service did reveal a need to tighten up on some details of the design of pneumatic equipment such as warning horns and contactors. For comparison with contemporary designs, the Seoul units main features are noted below:

Seoul Subway Trains – Technical Data

Nominal operating voltage	1,500V dc
Maximum gradient (main lines)	3.5%
Maximum gradient (depots)	4.5%
Ambient temperature range	–25 to +40C
Length of cars	20 metres
Overall height	3.75 metres
Overall width	3.16 metres
Wheel diameter	860mm
Weight of three-car train	117 tonnes
Minimum curve radius (main line)	180 metres
Minimum curve radius (depots)	76 metres

The Seoul Subway was the latest major overseas rapid transit type contract for GEC TPL, and during 1988 further orders were received for 14 more three-car trains, with identical power equipments from GEC Traction. Here again, Daewoo Industries were the main sub-contractor for mechanical parts, as they had been on the first 134 trains, with all electrical equipment from GEC Traction.

The period of expansion of the rapid transit and light rail systems has recently begun to achieve greater momentum, and consequently, this area cannot be studied to conclusion. Further orders have been placed with the company for new, and replacement parts for vehicles and equipment on existing systems, such as 19 further sets of control equipment for Hong Kong's metro. Again, Metro-Cammell were awarded a contract for 19 new trains, with GEC Traction as main sub-contractor for electrical equipment, but, unlike the previous hardware, this time, in 1987, the almost standard GEC thyristor chopper systems were being supplied. In fact, 1987 was a popular year for thyristor control systems from GEC, who had, by then been able to employ, effectively, high power gate turn off (GTO) devices, with the resultant savings on equipment bulk, and costs. In addition to Hong Kong, for instance, British Rail had chosen the equipment for the Class 319 'Thameslink' trains, and similar hardware was being provided for Danish State Railways, for evaluation. The most recent developments are to some degree still in the planning stages, with many contracts continuing to be out to tender, for which GEC Traction will undoubtedly maintain its high success rate.

But, perhaps the most notable successes of the company now well known as GEC Traction, have been in the heavy rail sector, extending the frontiers of rail technology, most notably in electric traction. The latest developments, and the general progress of the company between 1972 and the present time are explored in the final chapter.

9
GEC Traction from 1972

GEC Traction, as a company was formed in 1972, as part of the GEC Power Engineering Group, and followed a succession of company developments/changes, which began in 1959. Perhaps the most controversial of those moves took place in 1968, when the AEI Group of companies, and its Traction Division, were acquired by the General Electric Co. GEC had not been directly involved with rail traction for a number of years, whereas AEI, like English Electric, had maintained and developed its long tradition of association with that industry, providing some of the earliest forms of non-steam traction in this country, and many others around the world. Resulting from the 1968 move, the GEC/AEI combination set out to take over the prestigious English Electric Group, which had perhaps the longest history of all in the non-steam traction market.

English Electric's long history of progress, innovation and development in the railway field, dates back to Dick, Kerr & Co., Siemens Bros, and even included the Vulcan Foundry Co., of Newton-le-Willows. The name English Electric, as discussed in the opening chapter, first appeared early in this century and was effectively an extension of the Preston Works of Dick, Kerr & Co. However, both English Electric and AEI Traction, which of course included BTH and Metropolitan-Vickers, also had a history of close co-operation on major projects, in addition to their rivalry, particularly in overseas markets, and a logical development was the formation of the English Electric-AEI Traction organisation. A recent development emphasising that co-operation was the

foundation of the British Rail Traction Group, which, in the late 1960s, successfully exported traction equipment to South Africa and Pakistan. With GEC in the driving seat of the AEI portion of the merged organisation, some changes were likely to follow, and the merger period of 1969 to 1972 brought controversy, investigations at official levels, bids, and counter bids, as GEC attempted to secure overall control of English Electric. The moves even attracted the attention of the national press – a rare event for the railway industry – but, by 1972, the die was cast, and GEC Traction came to be, and with the amalgamations and mergers that had taken place, more than 150 years association with the railway industry was claimed by the new company. That claim stretched back to 1823, and the establishment of Robert Stephenson's locomotive works in Newcastle – which company had only recently been fully acquired by English Electric. With works that stretched the experience of GEC Traction from British Thomson-Houston's Rugby Works, through Paxman's Colchester based diesel engine works, through the giant Manchester and Preston plants, to Metropolitan-Vickers, Sheffield Works, and English

Now rated at 2,000hp, and carrying reconditioned 16SVT engines, from former British Rail Class 40 locomotives is National Railways of Zimbabwe Class DE2, (No. 1212). Originally these locomotives were ordered from English Electric for Rhodesian Railways in 1955/56, and totalled 35 in the class.

(National Railways of Zimbabwe)

Electric's Bradford factory – once the home of the old Phoenix Dynamo Co., the new organisation could provide for every aspect of rail traction. Later, a reorganisation in the 1970s brought in GEC Transportation Projects Ltd, based at the Trafford Park headquarters of GEC Traction, but with responsibility for project management, particularly important for the large, integrated projects that had been secured by the individual companies in the past, and would soon arrive again. The company, both as GEC Traction and as GEC Transportation, has continued the innovation, progress and development that were the hallmark of their illustrious predecessors, throughout the 20 years history since that formation in 1972. In the 1970s and 1980s, orders for diesel and electric traction continued to come, although the diesel sphere has not been so prominent as electric traction because of the worldwide trend towards electrification which has contributed towards that seemingly diminishing market. For electric traction though, the opposite is undoubtedly true, and more lately, the pace of growth in that market has increased, in both main line, suburban and rapid transit systems.

Diesel Traction – Home and Abroad – 1973 to 1988

In general terms, the home market produced quite a number of orders for industrial locomotives, notably for British Steel and the former National Coal Board, but for British Rail, major contracts were few, although they included traction equipment for the High Speed Trains. Ruston Paxman Diesels, under the GEC Diesels flag had also secured orders for the engines to be fitted into the new Class 58 freight locomotive, and a prototype dmu, of Class 210 was equipped with a a six-cylinder Paxman engine.

At the time GEC Traction came into being, English Electric-AEI Traction were supplying ten of the Class 70 locomotives to East African Railways, ordered in 1970. EAR had actually undertaken some reclassification of its locomotive fleet, and the Class 91 1Bo-Bo1, to which the new Class 72 was similar, had been operating as Class 71. The Class 91s were an English Electric design, dating from 1966/67, of 1,240hp, and the Class 72 development incorporated the same eight-cylinder English Electric 8CSVT diesel engine, uprated to 1,350hp. The Class 72 locomotives were intended for branch line and light main line work, with the same wheel arrangement as their predecessors. A slightly heavier axle load was permitted in the new locomotives, following investigations into track behaviour, whilst the traction motors, final drive gears, and wheel and axle assemblies were fully interchangeable with the earlier designs supplied to EAR. Some detail improvements were made, as a result of the operating experiences with the Class 71 and 87 (formerly 91, and 90, respectively), with the major change including alterations to the dynamic braking equipment and hydrostatically controlled radiator fans, with an electrically driven, rather than mechanical air compressor. Various changes were also made to the footplate crews' welfare, with filtered water supplies, a toilet, and increased output from the cab heater.

An interesting, perhaps unique modification to a diesel locomotive built in this country, was made on the Class 72. This included the provision of strengthening to the light-

The second order from Malaya for diesel traction came in 1970, and was placed soon after the English Electric-AEI Traction organisation was established. Here, No. 22102, the second of forty 1,760/1,710 diesel electric locomotives is seen under construction at the Saltley (Birmingham) Works, of Metropolitan-Cammell Ltd, who provided the mechanical parts, whilst Metropolitan-Vickers in Manchester supplied the power equipment.

weight superstructure by the fitting of footsteps at the four corners, to minimse the effects of damage in collision with the larger species of wild animals! Other, more conventional alterations added to that stengthening, included the fitting of lifting lugs and separate lifting bars, carried as part of the breakdown equipment, when lifting of the locomotive at one end, whilst still attched to its bogie(s). The first locomotives were delivered in mid-1972, with two of their number dispatched for working the EAR's Tanzanian Section.

Another contract in the process of completion at this time, was the Malayan order for no less than 40 1,760hp diesel electrics, also equipped with the English Electric type 8CSVT engine. The co-operation between English Electric and AEI was emphasised in this Co-Co design, since English Electric, in addition to the diesel engine, also provided the traction and auxiliary generators, whilst AEI supplied the traction motors. The locomotives were constructed entirely in this country, with the mechanical portions built at Metropolitan-Cammell's Saltley Works in Birmingham. Their principal dimensions were as follows:

Class 22 Locomotives for Malayan Railways

Wheel arrangement	Co-Co
Weight in working order	83.8 tonnes
Diesel engine	8CSVT (Mark III)
Rating	1,760hp
Gauge	1.0 metre
Length over headstocks	12.192m
Overall width	2.75m
Overall height	3.68m
Max axle load	14.22 tonnes
Wheel diameter	919mm
Max tractive effort	26,468kg
Cont tractive effort	18,296kg
Brakes (train)	vacuum
(locomotive)	air
Max speed	96.5km/hr
Fuel capacity	800 galls

The Mark III engine installed in the Malayan locomotives, produced some 17% more power, in its turbo charged form, than the 12-cylinder predecessors, built 15 years earlier. Attached to the engine, was the EE Co. type 822 10-pole generator, and overhung auxiliary generator, providing power for battery charging, control, and a variety of other circuits. The traction generator supplied the six AEI type 253 traction motors – four pole, self-ventilated machines, of which, at that time, more than 4,000 were in service around the world. A conventional camshaft control arrangement was installed, with the traction motors connected in three parallel strings across the generator, with each string comprising two pairs of motors connected permanently in series.

1973 saw the delivery of six locomotives, ordered in 1970, by GKN Contractors Ltd, for service on the metre gauge Upper Zaire Great African Lakes Railway. These locomotives were based on the Co-Co locomotives built for Malaya, but using the name Ruston Paxman for the 8CSVT engine developed by English Electric, and installed in this order, which in this case, was rated at 1,650hp. The mechanical portions were, perhaps naturally, in view of the Malayan order, built by Metropolitan-Cammell, in Birmingham. The same combination of electrical power and control equipment was also installed in these locomotives.

Nearer to home, and on a much smaller scale, in 1972, the Industrial Locomotives Division of GEC Traction, won an order to supply twelve diesel locomotives to the UNINSA steel works of Gijon in Spain. The design was similar to the 'Stephenson' type, which had already been successful at home, and included a 620hp Dorman diesel engine, and which were constructed in association with Companhia Auxiliar de Ferrocarriles de Beasain. Other industrial

With the vehicle bodies built by BREL at Derby, GEC Traction supplied eight sets of 600hp power equipment to Northern Ireland Railways in 1972.

associations at that time included the Ruston Paxman engines fitted into Andrew Barclay locomotives for the Benguela Railway in Africa, and similar 0-6-0 types for East Africa, equipped with the Paxman 8RPHL engine, also by Andrew Barclay.

British Rail Engineering Ltd, the manufacturing arm of British Rail, formed as a subsidiary to manage the railway workshops and much of the construction work for British Rail, won a £1.4 million order in 1973, to build diesel multiple units for Northern Ireland Railways. The mechanical portions of the three-car sets were constructed at BREL's York and Derby Litchurch Lane Works, but with some interior works completed in Northern Ireland. The order included the engines, traction motors, auxiliary and control gear from GEC Traction, with manufacturing split between the company's Preston, Manchester and Sheffield works. Earlier, in 1964, similar equipment had been supplied to Northern Ireland for the first diesel electric trains to run on the NIR system. For this order, Ruston Paxman Diesels were supplying the 4SRKT engine, a former English Electric design, rated at 560/600hp, with a GEC type 824/6E main generator coupled on a common shaft. The two GEC type 538/4A traction motors were fitted to the inner bogie on each motor car, driving the wheels through conventional spur gearing. In total, nine sets of power equipment were supplied to BREL, for the completion of the 1973 order.

Backtracking a little to 1972, a major development was taking place on British Rail, with the prototype High Speed Train, intended originally as a stopgap until completion of the Advanced Passenger Train Project. The power cars were constructed at BREL's Crewe Works, and equipped with the Ruston Paxman Valenta engine with Brush power and control systems. The 12-cylinder 'Valenta' series engines were manufactured by Ruston Paxman Diesel Ltd, and produced 2,025hp, driving Brush main and auxiliary generators and traction motors. Ruston Paxman Diesels Ltd were formed in 1970, as a management company for English Electric Diesels, with headquarters at Newton-le-Willows. English Electric had absorbed Ruston & Hornsby it will be recalled, in 1966, who had themselves taken over Davey Paxman of Colchester in 1940, and in 1972, English Electric Diesels Ltd changed its name to GEC Diesels Ltd. During the lifespan of the orders from BR for the Paxman 'Valenta' design for the HSTs, Ruston Paxman built the engines at Colchester, whilst their headquarters were at the Vulcan Works, along with GEC Diesels Ltd. In 1975 Ruston Diesels Ltd became a separate company within GEC Diesels Ltd.

Whilst the HST, and its Paxman 'Valenta' engines were on the verge of becoming the most successful high speed form of passenger train on BR, another design of motive power was achieving new records in its successful history. The English Electric 'Deltics' had been the mainstay, and a remarkably successful mainstay at that, of the Eastern Region's principal express services, since their introduction, and in 1973 the class of 22 locomotives had notched up more than 64 million kilometres in service. One member of the class had established an individual record of 3.2 million kilometres since entry into service in 1961. Their useful lives only came to an end following the expansion of HST operations, as the production designs were introduced on the Eastern and Western Region main lines. In fact, the 'Deltics' had another eight years left, being finally withdrawn, officially, at the end of 1981, after 20 years in the 'top link' bracket.

The first orders from British Rail for HST sets came in 1974, and Ruston Paxman Diesels Ltd secured a £2.5 million contract to supply 54, 2,250hp 'Valenta' engines. The engines were of course supplied from Colchester, and incor-

porated only minor modifications to the prototype engines, affecting the turbochargers, and an increased size of radiator. The first production HST's went into service on the Western Region's main line between London (Paddington) and Bristol/South Wales, along with a new design of BREL built passenger coach, the Mark III.

The home market saw some fairly regular orders from the industrial scene, and in 1975 the British Steel Corporation asked for ten 650hp 'Stephenson' type 0-6-0s. BSC ordered five for service at Llanwern Steelworks in South Wales, and five for Lackenby on Teesside. The power equipment consisted of a Dorman 12QT diesel from the recently acquired Dorman Diesels Ltd, then incorporated as the Dorman Division of GEC Diesels Ltd, with the locomotives all built at the Vulcan Works. However, the 'Stephenson' range was essentially a diesel-hydraulic design, and the new locomotives in this order were diesel-electric, and extended the 'Stephenson' range into that area. The Dorman 12QT engine for the BSC 0-6-0s drove former English Electric designs of generator and traction motors, with the final drive to the locomotive's wheels through double reduction spur gearing.

Metrication was overtaking the railway industry at home too, and the EE506 traction motors were a metricated form of this traditional design. Automatic wheelslip control was provided, along with air brakes and sanding, and giving the 47 tonne locomotives a maximum tractive effort of 21,150kg. In 1977 GEC Traction received a further order from BSC, for seven more diesel electric locomotives, but of a much smaller design, with an 0-4-0 wheel arrangement, weighing in at 26 tonnes, and built by Baguley Drewry at Burton-on-Trent. These locomotives, for hauling sinter or coke cars at Scunthorpe, were equipped with a Rolls-Royce diesel engine, six-pole GEC type RTB6032AZ traction generator, and a single four-pole type RTA5041AZ traction motor. Here too, the final drive to the wheels was by means of double reduction spur gearing, with a maximum tractive effort of 7,200kg. Scunthorpe already had a fleet of 'Janus' type 0-6-0 locomotives, fitted with British Thomson-Houston transmissions, and which formed the basis of the 1977 order, at least in some of the basic design aspects, for the new 0-4-0 locomotives.

In 1978 British Rail were developing the Class 210 diesel multiple unit, intended to replace the ageing diesel multiple unit fleets introduced during the Modernisation Plan of the 1950s. The Class 210 was a new generation dmu, but one which would make considerable use of available technology, notably the Mark III coach superstructure, and various other components, pressings, etc. to exploit economies of scale in manufacture. The new dmus were also to adopt a new design of bogie, with air bag secondary suspension, and rubber primary, but developed from the standard design of bogie for suburban use. The most interesting development, though not new, as the English Electric powered sets for the Southern Region bear testimony, was the decision to include a body-mounted diesel engine, with electric transmission. This was in direct contrast to the underfloor power systems already in widespread use, and meant to allow inclusion of diesel engines in a cleaner environment, with the power to meet the more arduous demands of modern timings.

For this prototype, indeed there were two prototype sets, both GEC Traction, and their main rivals, Brush, were to install the electrical equipment. GEC were able to draw on their own diesel engine manufacturing division, for the provision of the 1,104hp diesel engine, whilst in the Brush equipped example, the West German M.T.U. company provided the prime mover. For GEC, Ruston Paxman Diesels supplied a six-cylinder variant of the HST power plant, designated type 6RP200L, which had been developed jointly

with British Rail. To this engine, an alternator was fitted, not a generator, the output from which was rectified and supplied to conventional dc traction motors. As it turned out, the 210 project was dropped in favour of the 'Sprinter' designs, which maintained the underfloor power train design, with more modern underfloor mounted engines from the likes of Cummins, but with hydraulic, and mechanical transmissions.

The following year, 1979, British Rail decided to order a further 18 HST, or InterCity 125 sets, for use on North East to South West routes, following the successful expansion of HST services. The same power plants were to be installed, but for this order, BR decided to award GEC Traction the contract for some of the electrical equipment, although Brush continued to supply the main and auxiliary generators. The further GEC element in the HST order included traction motors and final drives only, with Brush providing the control systems.

1979 saw the formation of GEC Industrial Locomotives as a separate trading organisation, formed from the Industrial Locomotives Division, but based at the Newton-le-Willows, Vulcan Works. In announcing the formation of the new company, GEC Traction claimed that 90% of the products of the Vulcan Works, for industrial traction, could be supplied from within the overall GEC organisation. The 'Stephenson' range of locomotives continued to be built, at the Newton-le-Willows plant, appropriately perhaps, since that works could trace, directly, links to Robert Stephenson, and his original partnership, for locomotive manufacture, with Charles Tayleur, in 1830.

In 1981, as GEC Transportation Projects Ltd, GEC Traction was contracted to supply electrical power for a fleet of 45 980hp diesel shunting locomotives for Turkish State Railways. The first ten of these were actually built in Germany by Krauss-Maffei, whilst the remainder were shipped to Turkey, in completely knocked down (CKD) form, and reassembled there. The locomotives were put to work between Istanbul and the Bulgarian border initially, but later employed around Izmir and Ankara. The same year that

In 1983, at the same time as GEC were busy tendering for the prestigious BR Class 91 order at home, 45 sets of power equipment for these freight locomotives for Turkey were supplied.

the order for Turkey was placed, GEC received a major order for diesel traction from British Rail, in the form of the Class 58 Co-Co diesel electrics.

The new Railfreight Sector locomotives, the first of which was completed at Doncaster Works in December 1982, were built on a modular principle and incorporated a Ruston Paxman 12-cylinder 12RKCT engine, rated at 3,300hp. Brush Electrical equipment was installed, as it had been on the earlier Class 56 freight locomotives, which entered service in 1976, and which also had the benefit of a Ruston Paxman diesel engine – the 16-cylinder RK, rated at 3,250hp. The Class 58 was intended to supersede the 56, and did not include the full width body, as had been the case on BR diesels, freight and passenger, since the 1960s. The initial order for Class 58 was only 35 locomotives.

Class 56 and 58 Freight Locomotives for BR

	Class 56	Class 58
Wheel arrangement	Co-Co	Co-Co
Mechanical parts	Electroputere/ Brush/BREL	BREL
Electrical	Brush	Brush
Diesel Engine	GEC Diesels 16RK3CT	GEC-Ruston 12RK3ACT
Rating	3,250hp	3,300hp
Weight	126 tonnes	130 tonnes
Max. tractive effort	61,800lb	60,000lb
Max. speed	80 mph	80 mph

Completing the diesel traction overview, in 1984 and 1985, a program of 'life extension', or refurbishment of former English Electric built locomotives for East African Railways (then Kenya Railways), and the Sudan, was undertaken. Deliveries of the refurbished locomotives, or rather,

139

the equipment from GEC Traction to support the project, was begun in 1985, with the first refurbished unit handed over to Kenya Railways by the then British Foreign Secretary, Sir Geoffery Howe.

The locomotives were taken out of service during the program, with their engines overhauled in the railway workshops, with the spares supplied from the UK. The electrical equipment, traction motors and generators, were returned to the UK, and were rewound, and refurbished in this country. In Kenya, the program included some of the 44 Class 87 locomotives, which carried the same power plant as the 309 British Rail Class 37 locomotives, which themselves were the subject of a life extension programme during the early 1980s. Also in 1984, as the famine in the north east corner of Africa – Ethiopia, and the Sudan – was reaching the front pages of newspapers around the world, GEC Traction was assisting the relief effort by aiding the necessary improvements to transport in the region. In fact, as part of a £6 million programme funded by the European Community, massive upgrading and overhaul of the Sudan Railways links with the famine stricken region were being carried out. Sudan Railways bought a fleet of 65 1,850hp Co-Co locomotives from English Electric between 1959 and 1968, but many of the locomotives were out of service through lack of spares or accident damage. Ten of the fleet were almost renewed completely by GEC Traction in 1985; refurbishing the traction motors, just as it was for Kenya, and supplying the much needed spares.

Whilst there have been steady orders for industrial locomotives in the 1980s, there have been few orders for main line diesel traction for British Rail. The most recent order, for a replacement freight locomotive, the Class 60, has actually been won by one of GEC's main competitors of many years standing, Brush Electrical Machines. Similarly, little development has been seen in the export market too, leaving GEC Traction and GEC Transportation Projects Ltd room to make some major strides forward in the electric traction field. This latter is particularly true for British Rail.

Electric Traction – Home and Abroad 1973 to 1988

In the field of electric traction, at the time that GEC Traction was formed, at home, design work had recently begun on the Great Northern Suburban electrification, and grants totalling £52 million had been approved for work on the London Underground. South African Railways continued to provide a great deal of work with the expansion of their 3kV systems, whilst major changes were being considered, including experiments with 25kV ac, and 50kV ac systems. In fact, in 1972, GEC Traction received orders worth £8.5 million, for equipment for South Africa, Denmark and British Rail Southern Region. The greater proportion of this, an order for £6.8 million, came from SAR, and comprised power equipment for the Class 6E1 Bo-Bo electric locomotives. The order was placed with GEC-English Electric of South Africa (Pty) Ltd, and included traction motors, gears, auxiliary machinery and current collection equipment, with some hardware made in South Africa at the Benoni Works of GEC-English Electric. In the UK, manufacture was undertaken at Preston, Manchester and Sheffield, with Union Carriage & Wagon building the locomotives at its works at Nigel in the Transvaal.

Like South Africa, Denmark had a long association with GEC and its predecessors, which dates back to 1932, and the first suburban electrification for Copenhagen. In 1972 a twelfth order for traction equipment, for 1,500V dc multiple units was placed, which resulted in the supply of 24 sets of power equipment for two-car units, including traction motors, motor-generator sets, control systems and gears.

Here at home, rounding the year off for GEC Traction, new 4VEP four-car trains were being built by BREL, for the Southern Region, and were fitted with GEC Traction's standard traction motors, motor-generator sets, control gear, and auxiliary systems, in an order worth some £1.2 million.

At this juncture, it is as well to point out that the 25kV ac electrification of the London, Midland Region's West Coast Main Line was rapidly being extended to Scotland, and which was due for completion in 1974. This project had had important implications for GEC Traction, since they had been contracted to supply the power equipment for the new British Rail 5,200hp Class 87 locomotives, the first of which emerged from BREL's Crewe Works in 1973. No fewer than 35 of the new design were constructed, and their main characteristics were as follows;

British Rail Class 87 Locomotives

Overall Length	17,830mm
Wheelbase	13,159mm
Wheel arrangement	Bo-Bo
Bogie pivot centres	9,982mm
Bogie wheelbase	3,280mm
Wheel diameter	1,150mm
Weight in working order	80 tons
Axle load	20 tons
Max speed	176km/hr
Max permitted speed (original)	160km/hr
Rating	3750kw
	(5,200hp)
Max. tractive effort	58000lb

In original form, the new flagships of BR's 25kv ac fleet were broadly similar to their predecessors – notably the Class 86 series, although the obvious external differences resolved to the twin windscreen layout for the cab. They were intended for the Anglo-Scottish expresses, and geared for 100 mile/h working initially, although subsequent modifications have raised this to 118 mile/h (190 km/h), and were planned to haul Freightliner trains too. The Bo-Bo wheel arrangement was maintained, with an all up weight of around 80 tons, though the experiments with 'flexicoil' secondary suspension on other designs, resulted in that arrangement being fitted from new to the 87s. The original GEC crossed arm pantograph has disappeared in recent times too, being replaced by the proven performance of the Brecknell Willis 'Highspeed' design, with its single arm, low mass arrangement. In addition to the modified suspension, the bogie frames in the new design carried the traction motors, compared with the long standing tradition of using axle hung types.

The GEC type G412AZ dc motors were four pole, series wound machines, force-ventilated, and rated at 950kW, with a hollow armature shaft. The power train included a gear type coupling at one end of the armature shaft, connected to a cardan shaft running through the armature, to a resilient rubber coupling on the driving pinion. The arrangement enabled a reduction of the unsprung mass on the axle, by allowing the motors to be frame mounted. Roof-mounted vacuum circuit breakers developed by GEC Traction were also introduced to six of the original locomotives, whilst the transformer and tap changer assemblies were essentially the same design as the Class 86, but with an increased rating, in keeping with the required power output.

The Class 87 were BR's flagship until 1988, when the Class 90 emerged, also from the BREL/GEC Traction stable. One of their number, designated No. 87101, was to become the 'testbed' for the first application of thyristor control systems on a main locomotive in this country. This prototype 25kV locomotive was delivered in 1976, and whilst con-

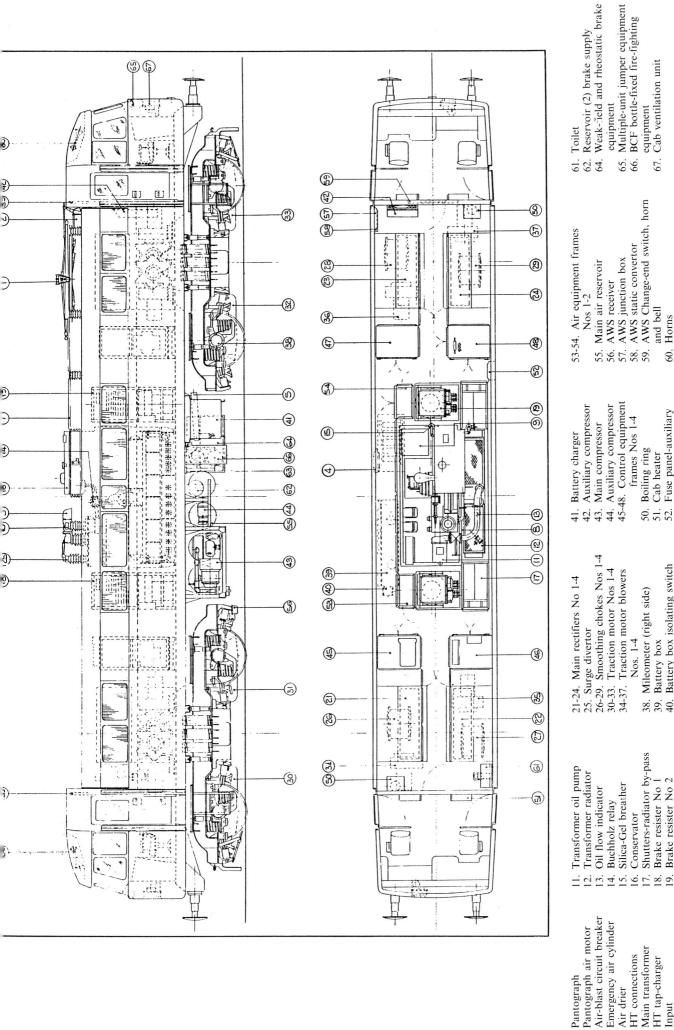

1. Pantograph
2. Pantograph air motor
3. Air-blast circuit breaker
4. Emergency air cylinder
5. Air drier
7. HT connections
8. Main transformer
9. HT tap-charger
10. Input

11. Transformer oil pump
12. Transformer radiator
13. Oil flow indicator
14. Buchholz relay
15. Silica-Gel breather
16. Conservator
17. Shutters-radiator by-pass
18. Brake resister No 1
19. Brake resister No 2

21-24. Main rectifiers No 1-4
25. Surge divertor
26-29. Smoothing chokes Nos 1-4
30-33. Traction motor Nos 1-4
34-37. Traction motor blowers
　　　Nos. 1-4
38. Mileometer (right side)
39. Battery box
40. Battery box isolating switch

41. Battery charger
42. Auxiliary compressor
43. Main compressor
44. Auxiliary compressor
45-48. Control equipment
　　　frames Nos 1-4
50. Boiling ring
51. Cab heater
52. Fuse panel-auxiliary

53-54. Air equipment frames
　　　Nos 1-2
55. Main air reservoir
56. AWS receiver
57. AWS junction box
58. AWS static convertor
59. AWS Change-end switch, horn
　　　and bell
60. Horns

61. Toilet
62. Reservoir (2) brake supply
64. Weak-field and rheostatic brake
　　　equipment
65. Multiple-unit jumper equipment
66. BCF bottle-fixed fire-fighting
　　　equipment
67. Cab ventilation unit

British Rail Class 87 Bo-Bo 25kV locomotive for express passenger duties.

A clean, uncluttered driving cab may not always have been the outcome of the construction of some diesel and electric locomotives, but this is the driver's view of a BR Class 87.

forming in almost all other aspects to the main Class 87 design, the bulky, electro-mechanical tapchanging equipment was conspicuous by its absence. In the thyristor locomotive, each traction motor armature circuit is supplied from two rectifier bridges, in series, with each bridge comprising two thyristor arms and two diode arms. The voltage applied to each traction motor circuit depends on the firing angle of the thyristor, with each thyristor group's firing advanced until 'free' firing is reached. At this point, the second bridge's fully retarded thyristors are advanced, adding that voltage to the first, until, as the firing angles of the thyristors are gradually advanced, full motor voltage is achieved. Any further increases to the locomotive's speed are achieved by retarding the firing angle of the thyristors controlling the motor field windings, giving weak field running. This locomotive is still in service with British Rail and carries the name *Stephenson*.

The trend of 'firsts' begun by English Electric, Metropolitan-Vickers, and others in the GEC Traction domain was continued, and indeed does to this day.

The continuing expansion in the export successes achieved by GEC Traction proceeded unabated, as South Africa ordered power equipment for 76 motor coaches, and 215 trailer vehicles. The contract worth some £3 million was for power equipment only, the vehicles actually being built by Union Carriage & Wagon, and even some electrical hardware was manufactured in the republic, at Benoni, by GEC's South African arm, and the Knights Works of First Electric Corporation. GEC had also supplied control equipment for SAR multiple units, using thyristor choppers, on their 3kV dc network, which was then under evaluation on Reef Area services, as it was in Holland, in similar multiple units, but operating at 1,500V dc

The following year, 1974, witnessed the award of a significantly important contract from SAR to GEC Traction, since it was equipment, to include some chopper control, on 119 motor coaches, and 360 trailer vehicles, for the Cape

In its original guise, with GEC's crossed arm pantograph design, 30 of these Class 87 locomotives began to appear in 1973. The triple windshield layout was replaced by the two-screen version, whilst for the majority, on load tap changers were still preferred for power control. No. 87005 later named *City of London*, is seen here approaching Preston with a Euston to Glasgow express.

Western electrification. In fact, 24 of the motor coaches were to be fitted with thyristor choppers, enabling notchless control of traction motors and the elimination of energy dissipation in accelerating resistances. The chopper equipped sets were planned to operate in multiple with contactor equipped units too, using a system of common control wires. The tests on the two trial units had shown that savings on electrical energy consumption of the order of 15% were possible, with chopper equipment. In addition to the sophisticated control technology, the 1974 order for Cape Western power equipment, worth £6.7 million, also included motor alternator sets, compared with the previously standard motor generator sets, for auxiliary power supplies.

For the extension of the electrification, involving the GE suburban routes out of London's Liverpool Street terminus, GEC were awarded a contract to supply transformers (naturally cooled), and inductors for 19 new Class 312 trains. The four-car sets were built by BREL, and were essentially the same layout at least as the Class 310, or AM10 series built for the London, Midland Region's suburban, and outer suburban services.

The mid-1970s were a developing time for London Underground too, as the Northern and Piccadilly lines were adding new stock, and extending their routes, respectively. The Piccadilly line extension was of course to Heathrow Airport, and required 175 three-car sets, with 350 sets of motor alternator and control equipment from GEC Traction. The Northern Line order was for traction control equipment only, with traction motors being supplied by Brush. At the same time, BREL had constructed eleven battery locomotives, for departmental/maintenance service, which could operate either from the 630V line, or from the on-board batteries. Traction motors and control equipment were supplied by GEC Traction, with the locomotives initially being put to work on the new Piccadilly Line extension. The same route saw the testing of thyristor based control equipment on the London Underground, with rheostatic/regenerative braking. The system was chosen carefully, to ensure that the performance characteristics made the most effective use of regenerative braking. This particular set of GEC Traction equipment was intended to be the prototype for further builds of Underground equipment, likely to include automated operations, and included the development of filter circuits to reduce interference levels from chopper equipment, which had begun in 1964. Since for automated operation, the system relied on signals from a range of signalling frequencies, it was obviously important to ensure that the new generation of sophisticated control equipment did not interfere with its safe operation.

By far the most important development in 1975 was the winning of a contract from the Taiwan Railway Administration, placed with GEC Transportation Projects Ltd, which was the complete electrification of 494 kilometres of route. The electrification was to be carried out at 25kV ac, and involved work that occupied GEC Traction, and its associated companies, over a period of five years. Essentially, this composite project required GEC to act as project manager for the design, supply, and installation, including catenary, substations, telecommunications, locomotives, and luxury multiple unit express trains. So far as GEC Traction were concerned, this represented, basically, 20 2,840hp, thyristor controlled locomotives and 13, five-car multiple unit trains, for operation on a 25kV ac, 60Hz supply.

The Taiwan electrification came about as a result of the increasingly heavy traffic between the northern port of Kee-

Eight years after the Pakistan Western Railway provided GEC with an order for the world's first production fleet of thyristor locomotives in 1966, Taiwan placed an order for a complete electrification scheme. The 25kV ac project included 20 of these 2,840hp thyristor controlled locomotives.

Lung, and the southern port of Kao-Hsiung. The track – a 3ft 6in gauge installation – was also being upgraded at the same time, to take heavier axle loads, with renewed signalling, and of course, the electrification infrastructure. This itself was drawing heavily on the features in use with British Rail, adopting a sagged, simple catenary, but supporting masts varied from steel portal structures on concrete masts, or steel/concrete cantilever masts over single track sections. In addition, it was obviously necessary to build in protection, or the ability to withstand typhoon conditions, and preservation against salt laden sea spray by zinc coating, and bitumastically painting all the steelwork.

The locomotives were for mixed traffic service, with a Bo-Bo wheel arrangement, and rated at 2,100kW. Whilst designed by GEC Traction in the UK, they were actually built by Union Carriage & Wagon in South Africa, before shipment to Taiwan during 1977. The locomotives went into service on both coastal and mountain routes, hauling trailing loads of between 1,250 and 2,000 tonnes. The latter was achieved by two units in multiple, and the capacity was limited only by the strength of the drawgear. General construction principles aimed at keeping the locomotive's weight to a minimum, assisted by the adoption of thyristor control, which of itself eliminated the need for bulky tapchanging equipment, made use of aluminium alloys in conduits, air reservoirs, and the transformer tank. The main details of these locomotives are listed below:

Taiwan Railways Administration – Thyristor Locomotives

Wheel arrangement	Bo-Bo
Track gauge	1 metre
Max. service speed	110 km/hr
Weight in working order	72 tonnes
Axle load	18 tonnes
Line voltage	25kV, 60Hz
Length over buffer beams	14,050 mm
Height to cab roof	3,720 mm
Width over body	2,820 mm
Bogie wheelbase	3,430 mm
Bogie pivot centres	7,250 mm
Wheel diameter (new)	1,219 mm
Min. radius curve (running lines)	300 metres
Min. radius curve (yards)	100 metres
Final drive gear ratio	18/67
Brakes – locomotives	air
– train	air

In common with essentially standard practice, the roof-mounted GEC crossed arm pantograph supplied traction current from the contact wire, by way of vacuum circuit breakers, to the centrally mounted main transformer. The latter was designed and built by GEC Transformers Ltd, whilst, of course, GEC Traction supplied the four G413AZ traction motors, which themselves were an adaptation of the GEC/AEI 283AY design. These were, and are, the same traction motors, thousands of which were installed on South African Railways locomotives, in particular, on the Class 6E1 design. In this case, the motors were provided with separately excited field coils, which permitted more responsive control of adhesion, by controlling the motor speeds individually under conditions of high tractive effort, and low creep values.

The 13, luxury, multiple unit trainsets ordered at the same time, were planned to cover the whole north to south journey in four hours, with passengers carried along in air-conditioned comfort. They were normally coupled in five-car formations, consisting of a driving power car, a motor car, a pair of plain trailer cars, and a driving trailer. For these north to south services, three five-car sets were marshalled together in a 15-coach formation. There was considerable UK involvement in the production of these units, and whilst the main contract was awarded to GEC Traction, BREL con-

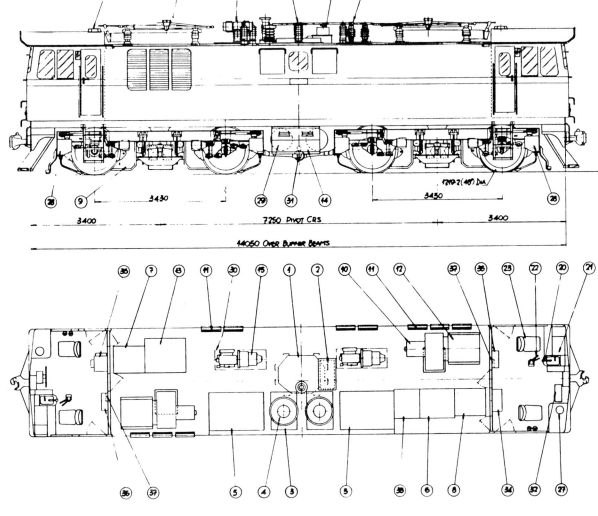

General arrangement of the Taiwan Railways 2100 kW thyristor-controlled locomotive: 1. Transformer; 2 Conservator; 3. Radiator; 4. Fan & Motor; 5. Main rectifier; 6. Electronics control cubicle; 7. Equipment frame No 1 end HT; 8. Equipment frame No 2 end HT; 9. Traction motor; 10. Traction motor blower; 11. Air filters; 12. Smoothing choke; 13. LT equipment frame; 14. Battery; 15. Air compressor; 16. Isolating switch; 17. Pantograph; 18. Vacuum circuit breaker; 19. Input bushing; 20. Master controller; 21. Instrument panel; 22. Brake valves; 23. Seat; 27. Boiling ring; 28. Sandbox; 29. Air reservoirs; 30. Brake equipment; 31. Inter-bogie spring coupling; 32. ATC equipment; 33. Aux & battery charger; 34. Clothes locker; 35. Cupboard; 36. Water cooler; 37. Cab heater 1 kW, and 38. Cab roof ventilator.

Taiwan Railways Thyristor Locomotive.

structed the mechanical portions, the design of the body at least, being developed from the then current Mark II coach design for British Rail. The power equipment from GEC consisted of the main transformer, underframe mounted, traction motors, auxiliary power supplies, and control systems. The main transformer was the largest underframe mounted design then installed, and supplied from a single roof-mounted pantograph, by way of GEC's vacuum circuit breakers, on each five-car train. The traction motors in this instance were not sep-ex type, and were series wound G414AZ four-pole machines, because the additional cost of the separately excited machines could not be justified on the multiple units. The motors were mounted on the BREL designed and constructed bogies, driving the wheels through resilient gears, and because of the restricted space in the bogie, force ventilation was used.

Control of the Taiwan express multiple units adopted thyristors in two asymmetric bridges, each bridge controlling a pair of traction motors. Two motors were connected in parallel because of the reduced tendency to 'run away' under wheelslip conditions, the latter being detected/controlled by the emerging standard arrangement installed on other GEC Traction orders. The non-driving power cars also carried the motor-alternators for auxiliary supplies, with each of the two bogies sporting a pair of traction motors. Another 'high tech'

development was the simplified driver's control, with only one handle used normally, except when coming to a standstill, or during emergency braking, when the separate Westinghouse supplied air-brake controller was used. The driver's controller was provided with an 'off', 'inch', or 'shunt' position, followed by speed graduations up to the maximum speed of 120 km/hr. In operation, the driver would select forward, or reverse, then move the controller handle to the desired speed position, the train would then be automatically, and progressively accelerated to that level. Rheostatic braking used in normal conditions was included as an integral part of the speed control system, and as the control handle was notched back, the greater the speed reduction required, the greater the braking effort applied, automatically. Approaching the speed level indicated by the controller position, the effort required for both rheostatic and air brakes was reduced.

The initial order for 13 five-car trains was followed in 1985 by a second order, for power equipment, for a new series of three-car trains. These differed from the first order, by increasing the number of motored axles, on this occasion, eight traction motors were installed, with a single, central power car, and two driving vehicles.

At home, 1977 saw the announcement of a major electrification scheme – the St Pancras to Bedford line – and the arrival of the new Class 313 multiple units. The latter were

When BR decided to press ahead with the Bedford to St Pancras, or Midland Suburban, electrification in 1979, 48 sets of thyristor controlled power equipments were ordered from GEC. In this view, a Class 317 unit, No. 317303, is on a driver training run just north of Radlett.

Dual voltage 25kV ac/750V dc was the order of the day for the King's Cross Inner Suburban lines on British Rail's Eastern Region. No less than 128 sets of power equipment were ordered from GEC Traction in 1973, incorporating traditional camshaft control.

intended to be the standard British Rail outer suburban design, and as dual voltage – 25kV ac and 750V dc – units, were built by BREL at York. The power equipment came from GEC Traction, and included 'standard' G310AZ traction motors fitted to all axles, with vacuum circuit breakers installed in 25kV operation for the first time in production multiple units. In the first orders, standard camshaft control equipment was used, carried in a single undercar pannier case. Subsequently, vehicles of this type were used to test the performance of thyristor control systems on BR multiple unit stock. In general, the traction equipment installed on these units was based on the hardware fitted to the prototype electric multiple units supplied to British Rail's Southern Region, of the 4-PEP design, a little earlier. Switching from operation on the Great Northern suburban 25kV ac lines to 750V dc, and tunnel operation required little more than a push button changeover on the driver's control panel. However, regulations in place on tunnel services meant that it was not possible to use a power bus-line between the vehicles in a train, and accordingly, each car was equipped with its own collector shoes, on the third rail. The 25kV ac bus lines were isolated following the changeover between supplies. Sixty-four of the Great Northern units were put into service in 1977, with a maximum speed of 120 km/hr, and a maximum capacity in the three-car train of 232 seated passengers.

The following year saw the placement of an order for ten thyristor equipments for the new Class 314 units, intended for service on newly electrified lines in the Glasgow area. The electrification under the Clyderail banner was supported by the Greater Glasgow PTE, with 16 three-car trains ordered. The remaining power equipments, for six trains were supplied by Brush Electrical Machines. This particular order followed

on from a British Railways Board decision in 1975, that all future stock would use thyristor control, compared with the traditional tapchanger methods. In the Clyderail Class 314, the 25kV ac supply was fed to the main transformer, and then, by way of a centre tapping on the secondary windings, to the thyristor bridges, controlling the traction motor voltage supply. The same phase angle control of the thyristor firing angles was adopted, as used successfully on export orders, and then seeing gradual adoption on BR.

Further multiple unit traction equipment orders from BR were received during the late 1970s, as suburban electrification schemes on the Eastern Region were progressed. On the Southern, a new breed of emus began to appear in the shape of the Class 508, which was derived from the prototype vehicles that had undergone extensive testing on the region. The 1970s drew to a close with GEC Traction winning a contract to supply the power equipment for 48 four-car multiple units, Class 317, for the Bedford to St Pancras electrification, in an order worth £7 million. Here again, BREL were the mechanical parts contractors, with the traction equipment similar to that installed in the Clyderail Class 314, and Liverpool Street to Shenfield Class 315 units. A difference in layout included the fitting of all the power equipment under the floor of the centre car, instead of the two motor cars, as adopted in the earlier sets. The traction motors, still series wound dc, conventionally fitted, were designated type G315, and were

In 1977, BR Southern Region ordered 48 sets of camshaft control and power equipment for these Class 508 inner suburban multiple units. The following year, two sets of chopper control equipment were ordered for a Class 508; the first such hardware for the Southern from GEC. In the early 1980s all the Class 508s were transferred north for use on the Merseyrail system.

GEC continued to supply control equipment to the Southern Region of BR, including these Class 455 units, dating from 1982/1983.

(British Rail)

essentially the same as those fitted to the prototype Class 210 diesel multiple units, then being tried out by BR.

The gradually developing use of thyristor choppers, many of the GEC design being in service on other railways around the world, including Denmark, Australia, and South Africa, was not the only interesting development at the time. Although, like the APT, the proposed Tubular Axle Induction Motor (TAIM), whose roots could be traced to a British Rail Research project, with GEC support, did not, ultimately, take off. The TAIM idea required the use of on-board variable voltage/frequency static inverters, supplied by GEC Rectifiers. The arrangement was essentially an inside out, squirrel cage induction motor, with the rotor forming part of the inside of the axle tube linking the wheels, and rotating about a central stator. The arrangement eliminated transmission problems such as mechanical linkages between motor and wheels, resilient gears, and the like, and, additionally, offered twice as much power for the same physical size, and without commutator or brushgear, as that provided by the GEC G350 design. This latter was installed on the TAIM fitted test units, and utilised the same frame design as the G310AZ motor, powering the Class 313, and later variants. The TAIM idea promised a great deal, but was not pursued, to a degree based on the complications of fitting static inverter power conditioning systems in production use with BR. There were, and indeed are, perhaps more practical, and effective ways of developing the use of ac motor drives.

In the export market, GEC Traction were awarded a contract in 1975 for 25 complete locomotives, collecting power at 50kV ac, and for use on the 864kM Sishen to Saldanha line of the South African Iron & Steel Industrial Corporation (ISCOR). The 1975 ISCOR order was Class 9E, 168 tonne, 5,000hp thyristor controlled locomotives, with a Co-Co wheel arrangement. The locomotives were once again constructed by Union Carriage & Wagon in South Africa, but with the power equipment coming from GEC's UK factories. GEC's 'first' on this occasion, was a 'first' fleet of 50kV 50Hz locomotives, and which were complemented in 1980, by a second order for six more, but designated Class 9E1. 50kV was selected by ISCOR because it reduced significantly the number, and hence the cost, of traction substations required, and under the worst emergency conditions if line voltage fell to 25kV, the locomotives would still be able to operate, albeit at reduced speed. Generally, the Class 9E was a single ended design, with a full width body, with the roof lowered at the No.2 end, for about half the locomotive's length, to accommodate the required clearances for 50kV equipment mounted on the roof. The basic characteristics of these locomotives are as follows:

South African (ISCOR) – Thyristor Locomotives

Wheel arrangement	Co-Co
Track gauge	1,065 mm
Overall length	20,120 mm
Overall height	3,900 mm
Overall width	2,900 mm
Max service speed	90 km/hr
Weight in working order	168 tonnes
Axle load	28 tonnes

The first 50kV main line electric locomotive was equipped with GEC Traction power and control equipment, and put to work on the Sishen to Saldanha line in South Africa, hauling some of the heaviest freight trains in the world. The mechanical parts were constructed by Union Carriage & Wagon, in the Transvaal and rated at 5,000hp, with 31 of these Class 9Es being built for the 3ft 6in gauge.

(South African Railways)

Another view of the 5,000hp thyristor-controlled Class 9E locomotive, showing the reduced height of the rear section, to maintain clearances for working under the 50kV catenary.

(South African Railways)

Line voltage	55-25kV ac
Bogie wheelbase	3,940 mm
Bogie pivot centres	12,700 mm
Wheel diameter (new)	1,220 mm
Ma. tractive effort	55,440 kg
Cont. tractive effort	39,040 kg
Rating (continuous)	3,696 kW
Brakes – locomotives	air
– train	air

The 50kV supply is collected from the contact wire by means of a GEC designed diamond frame pantograph, through vacuum circuit breakers. The VCB used on the Class

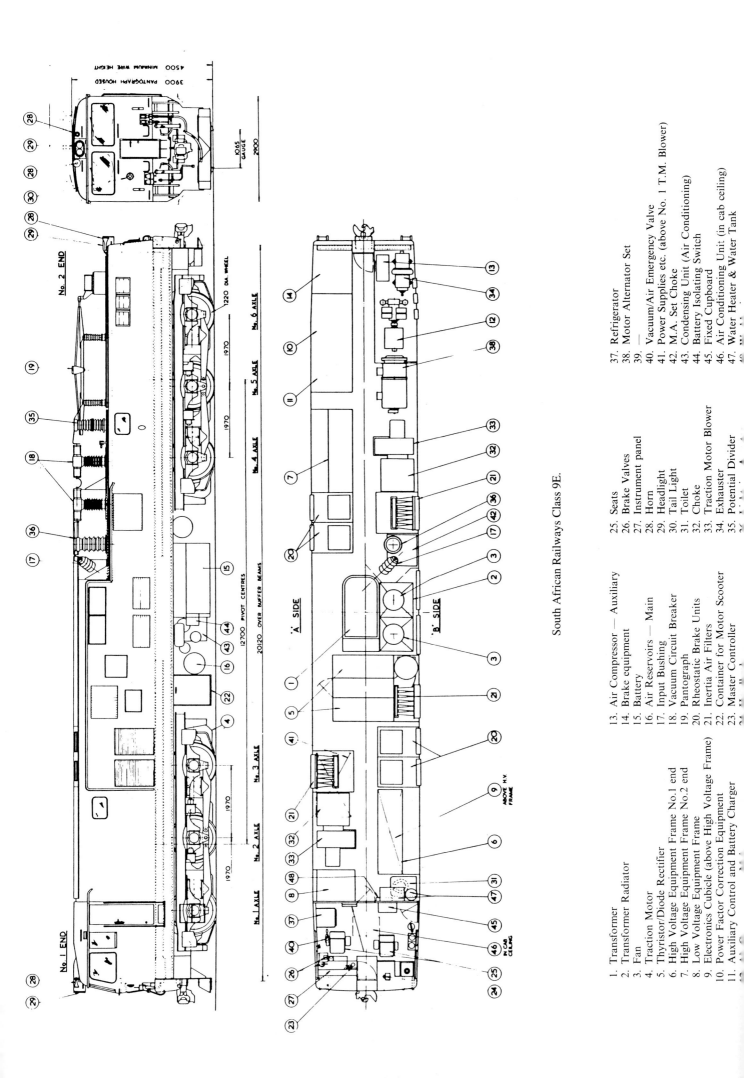

South African Railways Class 9E.

1. Transformer
2. Transformer Radiator
3. Fan
4. Traction Motor
5. Thyristor/Diode Rectifier
6. High Voltage Equipment Frame No.1 end
7. High Voltage Equipment Frame No.2 end
8. Low Voltage Equipment Frame
9. Electronics Cubicle (above High Voltage Frame)
10. Power Factor Correction Equipment
11. Auxiliary Control and Battery Charger

13. Air Compressor — Auxiliary
14. Brake equipment
15. Battery
16. Air Reservoirs — Main
17. Input Bushing
18. Vacuum Circuit Breaker
19. Pantograph
20. Rheostatic Brake Units
21. Inertia Air Filters
22. Container for Motor Scooter
23. Master Controller

25. Seats
26. Brake Valves
27. Instrument panel
28. Horn
29. Headlight
30. Tail Light
31. Toilet
32. Choke
33. Traction Motor Blower
34. Exhauster
35. Potential Divider

37. Refrigerator
38. Motor Alternator Set
39. —
40. Vacuum/Air Emergency Valve
41. Power Supplies etc. (above No. 1 T.M. Blower)
42. M.A. Set Choke
43. Condensing Unit (Air Conditioning)
44. Battery Isolating Switch
45. Fixed Cupboard
46. Air Conditioning Unit (in cab ceiling)
47. Water Heater & Water Tank

9E, was based on the type adopted by BR, for 25kV, which used a pair of vacuum interrupters, and which in the 50kV design was modified, and included four interrupters. The main transformer was built by GEC Transformers Ltd at Stafford, with the rectifier cubicle housing the four traction motor thyristor bridges, six motor field bridges, and the motor alternator set bridges. The traction motors themselves, designated type G415AZ, were a significantly modified and uprated version of the 283AY design, which was in service with South African Railways on, amongst others, the 3kV Class 6E1 locomotives. The 9E1 motors were force-ventilated, separately excited machines, axle hung, and nose suspended, driving the wheels through a single reduction spur gear. Whilst with sep-ex motors, wheelslip is inherently more controllable, and 'self-correcting', wheelslip detection and correction equipment is fitted to protect against prolonged wheelslip situations. Here again, as in a number of other applications, the arrangement included an inductive probe, mounted in the gearcase, sensing the passage of gear teeth, on the main gearwheel. The ISCOR locomotives were designed to work in multiples of three units, hauling 202 four-axle wagons, with a gross trailing weight of no less than 20,200 tonnes. This feat has has been exceeded in service, with Class 10Es hauling loads of more than 70,800 tonnes! The general conditions of service expected were equally as demanding on the locomotive's performance, with frequent dust storms and electrical storms, on a route through largely semi-desert, scrub country. In addition to the ISCOR locomotives, GEC Traction received further orders for Class 6E1 locomotives between 1972 and 1982, totalling 760 sets of power equipment, along with orders for power equipment for five Class 12E locomotives, and the latest order, for 50 power equipments for Class 10E1 Co-Co locomotives was placed in 1984. The 10E1 locomotives were 50 in number, and the order valued at £35 million, which included state of the art technology, with a continuous rating of 3,000kW, for freight service anywhere on the South African Railways 3kV network. In addition to thyristor chopper control, the 10E1 design features microprocessor control systems, with the digital control providing fast, effective response, especially to correction of wheelslip not corrected automatically by the separately excited traction motors. The on board computers (microprocessors) also allow multiple unit operation between GEC equipped and other manufacturers' locomotives – though in South Africa these were very few in number. The thyristor choppers installed in the 10E1 featured GTO (Gate Turn Off) devices. This was a new development, since previously, such devices had been used primarily for auxiliary services. The choppers also enable more efficient use of energy, and in combination with the microprocessor controls, a regenerative braking system allowed surplus energy to be returned to the line, for use by other locomotives and trains. Everything about the 10E1, using modular design and construction methods in the electronics, combined with diagnosis and fault logging facilities was aimed at reducing downtime and maintenance costs. The first of the latest GEC Traction powered locomotives for SAR was delivered, and entered service in 1986.

On the multiple unit front, SAR's 3kV systems were still expanding, and between 1972 and 1980, no less than 668 sets of power equipment were supplied, in six orders. South Africa was not the only export success for GEC Traction during the 1980s and in Hong Kong for instance, where the Mass Rapid transit Corporation – already discussed in the previous chapter – was taking GEC power into service, while

Equally high tech, this artist's impression illustrates the designer's view of the latest offering for South African Railways provides another example of the application of the thyristor based control systems from GEC Traction.

Four of the Class 10E locomotives in service on South African Railways' metals, representing the latest technology from GEC Traction.

(GEC Traction)

the Kowloon to Canton Railway was being electrified.

The Kowloon – Canton line, running from Hong Kong harbour to the Chinese border, was originally a single track line, then being doubled, electrified, and signalled by UK companies. The electrification adopted a 25kV ac contact system, based on the standard British Rail Mark IIIb catenary, installed by Balfour-Beatty's Traction & General Division. In three orders, placed between 1979 and 1985, GEC supplied a total of 86 motorcoach power equipments, with the final order including 25 sets of thyristor control systems. The three-car outer suburban trains were manufactured by Metro-Cammell, and were similar in appearance to the MRTC cars for Hong Kong, being supplied during this period, but with different passenger accommodation. Of course, the contact arrangement included a single roof-mounted pantograph, on the central motor car, flanked by two driving trailers. The equipment was similar to components fitted to the then current BR multiple units, including the underfloor transformers, rectifiers, and traction motors. In fact, the rectifiers were identical to those installed on British Rail's Class 312 emus, whilst the motors were type G315AZ71, and similar to the motors fitted to BR's Class 317 units, and on the KCR vehicles were frame mounted.

Also on the multiple unit front, GEC Traction had received an order from New Zealand Railways in 1979, for 44 sets of multiple unit power equipment, for their 1,500V dc system. This order continued a tradition of association with New Zealand, which dated back to the first electrification scheme there in 1921, and for which English Electric were a main contractor. In fact, English Electric had also supplied trains to the Wellington suburban system in 1937 and 1942. The 1979 contracts related to the extension of 1,500V dc electrification to Paraparaumu from Paekakariki, with Ganz Mavag of Hungary supplying the mechanical portion, and GEC Traction the power equipment. From the electrical view, the New Zealand multiple units were certainly a conventional design, with the two-car units driven by four traction motors of the same basic design as the G310AZ type used by BR, but modified to suit New Zealand's, (3ft 6in, 1067 mm) gauge. Nearer to home, in the Republic of Ireland, GEC were selected to supply the power systems for Dublin's new suburban multiple units, with the mechanical portions constructed by Linke-Hoffman-Busch. This 1,500V dc scheme was very much in the GEC Traction field, and based around a two-car unit, included the popular thyristor chopper control, which, by 1983 was either on test, or in productive service on a number of railways. Both regenerative/rheostatic braking was adopted on these first 40 units, with the four nose suspended, axle hung motors – type G314BY – developing 130kW on the motor car. Whilst the initial Howth–Bray line has a ruling gradient of no more than 1%, likely extensions could see

Perhaps this should really have been included in the previous chapter, as the Dublin area's own 'rapid transit system'. GEC, through predecessors, in particular Metro-Vick, had an association with Irish Railways dating back some 40 years. In this case GEC Traction supplied the power and control equipments, once again using thyristors for the 40 sets, which collected power from the 1,500V dc overhead contact system.

steeper gradients, and as a consequence, the traction equipment has been designed to take this into account.

The early 1980s, and 1981 in particular, saw an upsurge of interest in the extension of 25kV ac electrification on British Rail, whilst, perhaps curiously, at the same time, some extensions were made to the Southern Region's extensive dc network. However, the ac network has attracted most orders for GEC Traction and GEC Transportation Projects Ltd, with the St Pancras–Bedford, King's Cross Outer Suburban, and Thameslink schemes being completed. The 1981 proposals for the wider extension of 25kV electrification included the Western Region and East Coast Main Lines, along with North-East to South-West routes, and Strathclyde and Glasgow to Edinburgh routes in the various options. Of these various proposals, the East Coast Main Line project has now been completed, together with Strathclyde and the East Anglian routes now have a 25kV network. The Western Region though, still awaits the wires.

For the £400 million ECML project, GEC Traction secured the order for the new Class 91 'Electra' locomotives, which are paired with a new generation of coaches, and included the current traction technology. At the same time, the company won orders for a new fleet of locomotives for the West Coast route, and the dual voltage Class 319 multiple units for the 'Thameslink' project. In each case, mechanical portions are the preserve of BREL and Metro-Cammell, and whilst the Class 91 is undoubtedly the star of British Rail's electric traction fleet, there are plans to introduce more sophisticated technology still, in the shape of three-phase ac drive systems. These latter are presently under test on multiple unit rolling stock, although there is an intention to include a test installation on one of the new InterCity flagships.

Thirty-one Class 91 'Electra' locomotives were ordered by BR, along with 50 of the Class 90 (formerly known as 87/2), and 86 sets of power equipment for the Class 319 multiple units. All these orders feature thyristor control, with more extensive use of microprocessors, and, for the locomotives, separately excited (sep-ex), dc traction motors. Considering the suitability, and effectiveness of chopper control, the later order, for the new Network SouthEast Sector's Class 421 'Wessex Electrics', it may seem surprising that these were equipped with camshaft control. However, this was a commercially sound move, since the power equipment

GEC Traction were amongst the forefront of those in the railway industry to support the 'green' lobby, perhaps? The Class 442, or 'Wessex Electrics', despite their futuristic appearance, made use of recovered camshaft control equipment supplied by English Electric to the Southern Region some years earlier, together with refurbished traction motors.

No. 2407 passes through Upwey on a 'down' working to Weymouth on 16th February 1992.

(Peter Nicholson)

This photograph of the model Class 91 for British Rail shows how closely the design of the production version, of the real thing, matched the designer's ideas. Things were not always the case with prototypes, production versions, and artist's impressions. GEC Traction were the main contractors for these high tech locomotives, employing BREL as sub-contractors for the mechanical parts.

(British Rail)

was essentially recovered from older multiple units (former Southern Region 4-REP stock, of 1967 vintage), refurbished, and re-used with great success in the new units.

Completing this review of the latest equipment supplied from GEC Traction, the major characteristics of the Class 91 are detailed below:

British Rail Class 91 'Electra' Locomotives

Wheel arrangement	Bo-Bo
Track gauge	standard
Overall length	19,400 mm
Overall height	3,757 mm
Overall width	2,740 mm

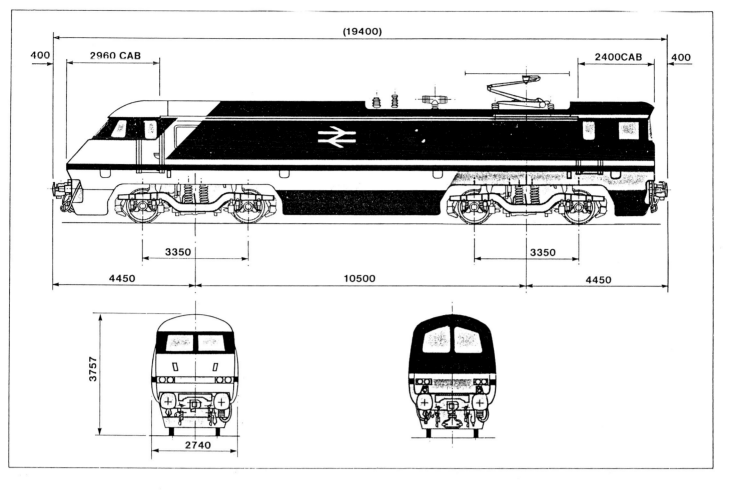

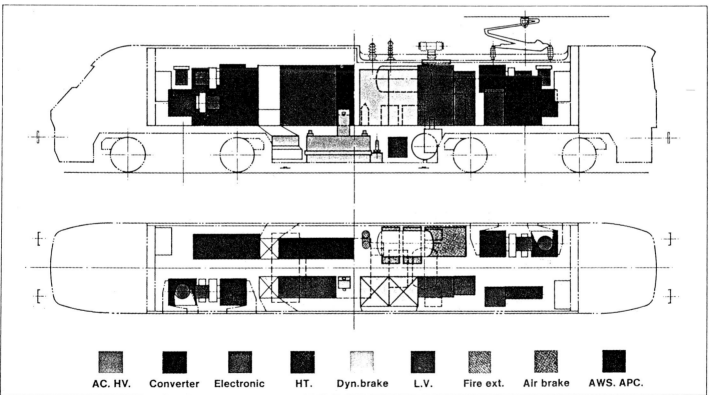

| AC. HV. | Converter | Electronic | HT. | Dyn. brake | L.V. | Fire ext. | Air brake | AWS. APC. |

Equipment layout.

British Rail Class 91 'Electra' 25kV locomotive for the East Coast Main Line electrification.

Max. service speed ....240 km/hr
Weight in working order........................80 tonnes
Unsprung mass per axle........................1.7 tonnes
Line voltage ....25kV ac
Bogie wheelbase ....3,350 mm
Bogie pivot centres ....10,500 mm
Wheel diameter (new)..........................1,220 mm
Max. tractive effort ....55,440 kg

Cont. tractive effort ....39,040 kg
Max. power at rail ....4,700 kW
Continuous power ....4,530 kW
Brakes – locomotives..air
          – train ....air

The Bo-Bo wheel arrangement was not the original option
for the new ECML units, and indeed, the early indications of

British Rail's new motive power were that a Co-Co layout would be the preferred design, exemplified by the Class 89 locomotive from Brush Electrical Machines.

The Class 91 order was for 31 locomotives, with an option for a further 25, and featured a double ended design, but with only the No.1 end having any degree of aerodynamic styling. In normal service, during the day, the streamlined end would normally be at the end of the train, pulling when running in one direction, and pushing, when running in the opposite direction. When pushing, control signals are transmitted to the Driving Van Trailer (DVT) attached to the opposite end of the train, by means of Time Division Multiplex (TDM) signals, sent along train wires, on board. The No.2 end cab is flat faced, and a profile that matches the profile of the adjoining coaches was adopted. The non-streamlined end would be used normally when the locomotives were running semi-fast, sleeper services, or other non-high speed duties.

The electrical equipment includes sep-ex dc traction motors, oil cooled traction converters – featuring GTO thyristor components – and, microprocessor control. The main transformer is located below the body, between the bogies, lowering the centre of gravity, and assisting in the reduction of body roll, and relative pantograph movement. The traction motors are body-mounted, but slung below the floor, in the bogie space, which in turn, has enabled a more or less conventional layout of equipment on board. The transmission features a coupling arrangement patented by GEC Traction, with the motors driving the wheel sets through a right angle gearbox, and bevel gears. The hollow output shaft of the gearbox drives the wheels through a rubber bushed link coupling, isolating the drive from relative radial and lateral movement of the wheel sets imparted by the primary suspension. Each traction motor is fitted with a ventilated disc brake at the inboard end.

Microprocessor control systems are based around a single Intel 8086 16-bit chip, with the control programme stored in an Eraseable Programmable Read Only Memory (EPROM), with data held in Random Access Memory (RAM). The armature and field control converters are under the direct digital control of these microprocessors, which also include diagnostic and fault recording functions. An advantage of the use of microprocessors has been the simplification of the overall locomotive design, by reducing the number of mechanical interlocks, with the following contributing to the success of this form of control:

— good load sharing between individual traction motors and bogie groups
— closed loop control of armature and field circuits
— compensation for bogie weight transfer
— wheelslip and slide detection and correction by measurement of acceleration/deceleration speed difference, voltage difference, and current balance
— wheel creep control in conjunction with track speed measurement by doppler radar
— tractive effort control in both motoring and braking within limiting performance envelopes
— automatic speed limitation
— protection against over voltage, under voltage, and overload, in addition to limitation of motor voltage when the line voltage exceeds 25kV
— interfacing with the TDM (remote control) system as well as with the air-brake system, and the various safety systems

Interestingly, the Class 91 has been designed for a 35 year working life, averaging 420,000km per year. GEC's Combined Test Facility at Preston was used to good effect when testing the various components and the combination of components in the Class 91 installation.

GEC Traction to GEC-Alsthom
Today's GEC Traction has effectively two manufacturing bases in the UK, and despite the acquisition of Metro-Cammell in Birmingham, is still very largely a company based in the North, and indeed North West of England. The main sites are still Trafford Park in Manchester and Strand Road, in Preston.

BR Class 90 No. 90024 at Bounds Green depot on 30th December 1991.

(Peter Nicholson)

Former works of course have gradually disappeared, at least from the traction view, such as the old English Electric works in Bradford, Robert Stephenson & Hawthorns in Newcastle, and Metropolitan-Vickers-Beyer Peacock's plant in Stockton-on-Tees.

GEC Traction was, until very recently (1989), an autonomous member of the GEC Group, within which there are nearly 200 specialist companies dealing with every conceivable kind of electrical engineering product. The company's claim that it is probably unique in the world, whereby its resources are purely devoted to producing equipment for the railway industry, does indeed stand up to some examination. *All* its plants are engaged on rail traction work, and the company continues to produce innovative solutions to conventional rail systems, and in some areas has continued the pioneering trends established by its illustrious predecessors. The company's history can certainly be traced back to the days of steam, and Robert Stephenson's early works in Newcastle, and for non-steam, they were undoubtedly in at the birth of both electric and diesel traction. They have been very active in the field of industrial traction too, both diesel and electric, although this has purposely, not been covered in any significant detail in this study. The current GEC Traction sites are responsible for the following areas:

Manchester – the company's headquarters, where the administrative, commercial, and accounting functions are undertaken. Here too, are the principal design and development departments, with allied workshops and laboratories. Out in the works – the overall character of which is still essentially Metropolitan-Vickers — components, and control equipment is manufactured.

Preston – here, GEC Traction, on the site of the former English Electric, and indeed Dick, Kerr works, maintain their largest manufacturing base. At Preston, production includes control equipment assemblies, rotating machines, the Machine Design Department, and the Materials and Insulation Laboratory. Here too, is located the Combined Test Facility, which has proved an invaluable addition to the testing of traction power systems in recent times.

Perhaps the most significant development has been the acquisition of long time partners on railway contracts, Metro-Cammell of Birmingham. GEC Traction now have the specialist vehicle builders in the group, and their Saltley Works, adds further breadth to the range of activities that the GEC Traction of the 1990s can accomplish, with an interweaving of activities. More recently still, a commercial relationship with Alsthom of France has blossomed into a full scale partnership. The new company, trading as GEC-Alsthom follows in the wake of other international partnerships, such as that between Asea of Sweden, and Brown Boveri. GEC-Alsthom's traction activities have a very considerable depth and span of experience, from the heaviest diesel and electric traction, through suburban and mass transit systems, to light rail and urban tramways. With the removal of international trade barriers, and the creation of the single European market, this latest move certainly bodes well for the future of the GEC Traction heritage.

The Class 465 is the very latest multiple unit design to be powered with equipment from the GEC Traction stable, and now operating on British Rail's Network SouthEast Sector.

(BR Network SouthEast)

Appendix I

GEC Traction Ltd — Constituent Companies

Location	Company	Established
Newcastle upon Tyne	Robert Stephenson & Co.	1823
	R. & W. Hawthorn, Leslie & Co.	1883
	Robert Stephenson & Hawthorns Ltd	1937
Stockton	Metropolitan-Vickers-Beyer Peacock Ltd	1949
Darlington	Robert Stephenson & Hawthorns Ltd	1937
Manchester	British Westinghouse Co. Ltd	1899
	Metropolitan-Vickers Electrical Manufacturing Co. Ltd	1919
	Associated Electrical Industries Ltd	1929
	English Electric-AEI Traction Ltd	1969
	GEC Traction Ltd	1972
Preston	Dick, Kerr & Co.	1883
	Electric Railway, Tramway & Carriage Works Ltd	1898
	English Electric Manufacturing Co.	1900
	United Electric Car Co.	1905
Newton-le-Willows	Charles Tayleur & Co.	1830
	The Vulcan Foundry Co.	1847
	Vulcan Foundry Ltd	1898
Stafford	W. G. Bagnall & Co.	1870
	Siemens Bros & Co. Ltd	1901
Rugby	British Thomson-Houston	1896
	Willans & Robinson	1880
Thames Ditton	Willans & Robinson	1880
Lincoln	Ruston Proctor	1857
	Ruston & Hornsby Ltd	1918
Kilmarnock	Dick, Kerr & Co.	1883
Bradford	Phoenix Dynamo Manufacturing Co. Ltd	1903
London	English Electric Co. Ltd	1918 (offices)
	Associated Electrical Industries Ltd	1929 (offices)
	Siemens Bros UK Ltd	1850
	General Electric Co.	1889

Appendix II

Operators of GEC Traction Equipped Electric Locomotives

Country	Operator	Power Supply		Track Gauge (Metres)	Number Supplied
		Voltage	Frequency		
UK	British Rail, London, Midland Region	25kV	50Hz	1.435	236
	British Rail, Eastern Region	1500	dc	1.435	76
	British Rail, Southern Region	6.6kV	25Hz	1.435	21
	British Rail, Southern Region	600/750	dc	1.435	29
	British Rail, Southern Region (Electro-Diesel)	600/750 &	diesel	1.435	49
	London Transport (Tube lines)	600 &	battery	1.435	63
	London Transport (Surface lines)	600	dc	1.435	42
	Post Office Railway	400	dc	0.610	150
Australia	New South Wales GR	1500	dc	1.435	41
	Victoria GR	1500	dc	1.60	25
Brazil	EF Santos a Jundai	3000	dc	1.60	15
	Paulista	3000	dc	1.60	1
	Rede Mineira de Vianca	3000	dc	1.00	14
	Rede Mineira de Vianca	1500	dc	1.00	5
	Parana–Santa Catarina	3000	dc	1.00	10
Canada	Montreal Harbour Commission	2400	dc	1.435	9
	Canadian National	600	dc	1.435	2
Czechoslovakia	State Railway	1500	dc	1.435	2
France	CF Du Midi	1500	dc	1.435	140
Hungary	State Railways	16kV	50Hz	1.435	26
Italy	State Railways	3000	dc	1.435	3
India	Central	1500	dc	1.676	93
	Southern	1500	dc	1.00	4
	Eastern	3000	dc	1.676	12
	Eastern	1500	dc	1.676	57
	Eastern (dual voltage)	1500/25kV	ac/dc	1.676	34
Japan	Imperial Government Railways	600	dc	1.067	2
	Others	1500	dc	1.067	57
Morocco	National Railways	3000	dc	1.435	26
New Zealand	Government Railways	1500	dc	1.067	29
Norway	Thamshaven–Lokken	6600	25Hz	1.435	3
Pakistan	Western Railway	25kV	50Hz	1.676	29
Poland	State Railways (& Mines)	3000	dc	1.435	43
South Africa	SAR	3000	dc	1.067	1610
	Industrial Operators	3000	dc	1.067	4
Spain	RENFE	3000	dc	1.668	75
Taiwan	TRA	25kV	60Hz	1.067	20
Zambia	Selection Trust	1500	dc	1.067	2

Appendix III

Operators of GEC Traction Equipped Diesel Electric Locomotives

Country	Operator	Track Gauge (Metres)	No. Supplied at 1/1975	No. of Orders
UK	British Rail	1.435	3,125	74
	Northern Ireland Railways	1.60	28	3
	Miscellaneous Industrial	1.435	540	numerous
Australia	New South Wales GR	1.435	230	8
	Victoria GR	1.60/1.435	16	2
	Australian Iron & Steel	1.435	45	9
	Commonwealth Railways	1.067	13	4
	Queensland GR	1.067	170	20
	South Australian Railways	1.067/1.60	103	10
	Tasmania GR	1.067	48	8
	Western Australian GR	1.067/1.435	102	9
	Miscellaneous		16	5
Argentina	State Railways	1.00	32	3
Bangladesh	Bangladesh Railways	1.00	26	1
Brazil	Eastern & Northeast	1.00	16	2
East Africa	East African Railways	1.00	65	7
Egypt	Egyptian Republic Railways	1.435	57	4
Eire	Coras Iompair Eireann (CIE)	1.60	108	6
Ghana	Railways & Ports Administration	1.067	53	5
India	Government Railways	1.00/1.676	400+	numerous
	Miscellaneous Industrial	1.00/1.676	40	3
Jamaica	Government Railway	1.435	15	4
Malaya	Malayan Railway	1.00	86	5
Malawi	Malawi Railways	1.067	10	2
Mozambique	Trans Zambesia Railways	1.067	10	3
Netherlands	Nederlandse Spoorwegen (NS)	1.435	115	4
New Zealand	Government Railways	1.067	142	8
Nigeria	Railway Corporation	1.067	39	3
Peru	Central & Southern Railways	1.067	19	3
Portugal	State Railways (CP)	1.665	77	4
Rhodesia	Rhodesian Railways	1.067	55	5
Sierra Leone	Development Corporation	1.067	1	1
Sri Lanka	Government Railway	1.676	27	3
South Africa	Miscellaneous	1.067	40	19
Sudan	Sudan Railways	1.067	72	6
Sweden	State Railways (SJ)	1.435	2	1
Zaire	Upper Congo–Great Lakes Railway	1.067	6	1
Zambia	Zambia Railways	1.067	7	3

Appendix IV

English Electric Co. Ltd: Works List

Works No.	Builder	Date	Type	HP	Gauge	Customer	Notes
511	DK	1920	4w BE		Std	Blackburn Corporation Electricity Dept., Whitbirk Power Station, Lancs.	To British Electricity Authority
512	DK	1920	4w BE	60	Std	A. Reyrolle & Co. Ltd, Hebburn, Co. Durham	
513-4	DK	1921	4w BE		2'6"	Cia Carbonifera e Industria de Lota (Chile)	
515	DK	1921	4w BE		2'6"	Edward Lloyd Ltd, Sittingbourne, Kent	To Bowaters Lloyd Pulp & Paper Mills Ltd
516	DK	1921	4w BE		3'6"	Anglo Chilian Nitrate & Rly Co., Tocopilla, Chile	
517	DK	1921	4w BE		5'3"	Harland & Wolff Ltd, Queen's Island Shipyard, Belfast	
518-9	DK	1921	4w BE	60	Std	Wallsend & Hebburn Coal Co. Ltd, Hebburn Colliery, Co. Durham	
520	DK	1921	4w BE		Std	City of Glasgow Electricity Supply Co., Dalmarnock Power Station, Lanarks	Sold to Aberdeen Corporation Electricity Dept.
521	DK	1922	BoBo BE	200	3'6"	New Zealand Rlys	
522	DK	1922	4w		3'6"	New Zealand Rlys	Battery tender for No. 521
523-7	DK	1922	BoBo WE		3'6"	New Zealand Rlys	
528	DK	1922				Mitchell Conveyor	
529-30	DK	1921				Yamanoto (Japan)	
531-2	DK	1922				Walker & Co.	
533	DK	1922	Bo BE	38	Std	Ministry of Munitions, Bramley Depot, Hants	To Sinfin Lane Depot, Derby, then to Chilwell Depot, Notts. Sold to Ind Coope & Allsopp Ltd, Burton-on-Trent, Staffs
534-50	NBL	1922	BoBo WE		3'6"	Imperial Govt Rlys of Japan	Nos 1040-5 (later ED50.1-17)
551-9	NBL	1922			3'6"	Imperial Govt Rlys of Japan	Nos 6000-8 (later ED51.1-9)
560-7	NBL	1923	2CoCo2 WE		3'6"	Imperial Govt Rlys of Japan	Nos 8000-7
568-9	NBL	1923	BoBo WE		3'6"	Kobe Rly (Japan)	
570	DK	1923	Bo BE	60	Std	Wallsend & Hebburn Coal Co. Ltd, Hebburn Colliery, Co. Durham	
571	DK	1923	Bo BE	52	Std	Ministry of Munitions, Bramley Depot, Hants	
572	DK	1924	4w BE		Std	Preston Corporation Electricity Dept., Lancs	
573-5		1924				Oficina Alianza (Chile)	
576-8		1924				General Post Office	Road trucks and not rail vehicles?
579	DK	1924	4w BE		Std	Cammell Laird & Co. Ltd, Birkenhead, Cheshire	
580		1924				John Brown & Co. Ltd, Clydebank, Dunbartonshire	
581	DK	1924	4w BE		3'6"	South African Rlys & Hbrs, Colenso Power Station, Natal	To Electricity Supply Commission, Colenso.
582-5	BP 6234-7	1924	BoBo WE	1100	Std	The Montreal Harbour Commission Terminal Rly	Nos 101-4 To the National Harbours Board, Montreal; later sold to CN, Nos 9180-3, (later 180-3, then 6716-9)
586	DK	1924	BE		3'6"	Imperial Govt. Rlys of Japan	
587	DK	1924	BoBo BE/WE		Std	Castner-Kellner Alkali Co. Ltd, Runcorn, Cheshire	To Imperial Chemical Industries Ltd
588-9		1925				Tokoyawa (Japan)	
590	DK	1924	BE		3'6"	Imperial Govt Rlys of Japan	
591-680	DK	1925	4w ERC		2'0"	General Post Office for Post Office Rly, London	
681-3	NBL	1924			3'6"	Imperial Govt Rlys of Japan	Replacements for locos lost in the Yokohama Earthquake
684	DK	1924	4w BE		Std	Guardbridge Paper Co. Ltd, Guard Bridge, Fife	
685-6	DK	1925	4w BE	84	Std	Ministry of Munitions, Bramley Depot, Hants	
687	DK	1925	4w BE	84	Std	War Department Tramway, Shoeburyness, Essex	Rebt to 4w DE; later No. 813, then 884
688-9	DK	1925	4w BE		2'6"	Mitchell Construction for Shropshire, Worcestershire & Staffordshire Electric Power Co., Stourport, Worcs	
690-1		1925			3'6"	Chichibu Rly (Japan)	

Works No.	Builder	Date	Type	HP	Gauge	Customer	Notes
692	DK	1925	4w WE		Std	Croydon Corporation Electricity Dept., Croydon 'A' Generating Station, Surrey	
693-4	DK	1925	4w BE		2'0"	Mitchell Construction for Salford Corporation Electricity Dept, Agecroft, Lancs	
695		1926			3'6"	Ome Rly (Japan)	No. 1
696-700	BP 6328-32	1926	BoBo WE	1100	Std	The Montreal Harbour Commission Terminal Rly	Nos 105-9 To The National Harbours Board, Montreal; later sold to CN, Nos 9184-8, (later 184-8, then 6720-4)
701	DK	1926	6w BE		Std	Aberdeen Corporation Electricity Dept.	Later to North of Scotland Hydro-electric Board; then to Carolina Power Stn, Dundee
702-4	DK	1926	4w BE		2'0"	General Post Office for Post Office Rly, London	
705	DK	1927	4w BE			Mitchell Construction Ltd, Peterborough, Cambs	
706					3'6"	Ome Rly, Japan	No. 2
707-9						Punjab Hydro Electric, India	
710-1	WBC 415-6	1927	BoBo BE	5'6"		Bombay Baroda & Cen India Rly	Overhead line maintenance vehicles
712-6	DK	1927	4w RE		Std	Roads Reconstruction Ltd, Vobster Limestone Quarries, Somerset	Automatic wagons
717	DK	1927	4w WE		Std	Blackpool Corporation Transport Dept.	
718-9		1927				Rhodesia & General Asbestos Corporation	
720-1	DK	1927	4w WE		2'0"	Mount Lyell Mining & Rly Co, Queenstown, Tasmania	
722	DK	1927	4w WE		2'6"	Oakbank Oil Co. Ltd, Winchburgh Shale Mines & Oil Works, West Lothian	
723-8	DK	1928	BoBo WE		3'6"	New Zealand Rlys	Nos EC 7-12
729-31		1928				Hokuso, Japan	
732-3		1928				Ise Denki, Japan	
734	DK	1928	BoBo DE		Std	The Montreal Harbour Commission Terminal Rly	Overhead line maintenance vehicle
735-6		1928				Ome Rly (Japan)	Nos 3 & 4
737	DK	1928	4w WE		Std	Clitheroe Corporation Gas Works, Lancs	
738-40	Leeds Forge	1928	BoBo WE		Std	British Portland Cement Manufacturers, Greenhithe, Kent	Powered hopper cars
741		1928				?	
742		1929				Punjab Hydro Electric, India	
743		1929				Rhodesia & General Asbestos Corporation	
744	DK	1929	4w BE		Std	Sheffield Corporation Electricity Dept., Meadow Hall Power Station, Yorks	
745		1929				Synthetic Ammonia & Nitrates	
746-7		1929				Achi Chuo (Japan)	
748	DK	1929	4w WE		2'0"	Mount Lyell Mining & Rly Co., Queenstown, Tasmania	
749	DK	1929	4w WE		2'0"	Sussex & Dorking United Brick Cos Ltd, Warnham, Sussex	
750-1	DK	1929	4w WE		2'11"	London Brick Co. Ltd, Stewartby, Beds	
752-63	DK	1930	A11A RE		2'0"	General Post Office for Post Office Rly, London	
764-7		1929			3'6"	New Zealand Public Works Dept., Tawa Flats	
768	DK	1930	BoBo WE		Metre	FC Guaqui-La Paz (Bolivia)	
769-71		1930				Consolidated Goldfields, Wiluna, W. Australia	
772-5		1930				Mount Isa Mines, Queensland	
776	DK	1930	4w WE		2'11"	London Brick Co. Ltd, Newton Longville, Bletchley, Bucks	
777-80	HL 3767-70	1930	BoBo WE		Metre	South Indian Rly	Nos EC 1-4 (to IR YCG 21900-3)
781-4					3'6"	New Zealand Public Works Dept, Tawa Flats	
785	DK	1930	BoBo BE		Std	War Department Tramway, Shoeburyness, Essex	Later to Royal Arsenal, Woolwich, London
786		1930				Bromford Tube Co.	
787		1930				Punjab Hydro Electric, India	
788	DK	1930	4w BE		Std	English Electric Co. Ltd, Stafford	
789		1930	BE		Metre	South Indian Rly	Overhead line maintenance vehicle
790		1930	4w		Metre	South Indian Rly	Battery tender for EE 789
791-2	DK	1930	Bo WE		2'11"	London Brick Co. Ltd, Stewartby, Beds	
793-830	DK	1930	A11A RE		2'0"	General Post Office for Post Office Rly, London	
831		1930				The Borneo Co., Pahang	
832-7	DC	1931	B2 PRC	120	Std	Bermuda Rly	Bodies built by Cravens
838-43	DC	1931	8w		Std	Bermuda Rly	Passenger trailers; bodies built by Cravens
844-5	DC	1931	B2 PRC	120	Std	Bermuda Rly	Motor freight vans; bodies built by Cravens
846-7	DC	1931	8w		Std	Bermuda Rly	Trailer freight vans; bodies built by Cravens

162

Works No.	Builder	Date	Type	HP	Gauge	Customer	Notes
848	DC	1931	4w P	120	Std	Bermuda Rly	Spare power bogie
849		1931				Workington Bridge Co.	
850-2	DC	1931	4w PM		Std	London, Midland & Scottish Rly	Inspection trolleys
853-5	DC	1931	4w		Std	London, Midland & Scottish Rly	Trailers for inspection trolleys
856	DC	1931	4w PM		5'3"	Northern Counties Committee	Inspection trolley
857	DC 2023	1932	0-4-0 DM		2'0"	Eagle Oil & Shipping Co. (Mexico)	
858		1932	E			United Steel Co.	Scale car
859		1932	DE	200		?	Probably DE railcar demonstrator
860-5	DC	1932	8w		Std	Bermuda Rly	Passenger trailers; bodies built by Cravens
866	DC	1932	4w PM		Std	London & North Eastern Rly	Inspection trolley
867-8	DC	1932	BB PM	300	Std	Bermuda Rly	Motor freight vans
869-70	DC	1932	8w		Std	Bermuda Rly	Wagons
871		1932				Simon Carves Ltd	
872		1932				Ballapur (India)	
873		1932				Edinburgh Trucks	
874	DC 2047	1933	0-4-0 DM	176	Std	London, Midland & Scottish Rly	No. 7400 (later 7050; to WD 25, later 224, then 846)
875						?	
876-87	DC 2035-46	1933	4w PM		Std	London & North Eastern Rly	Inspection trolleys
888		1933	BE			Consolidated Goldfields, Wiluna, W. Australia	
889	DC 2034	1933	PRC		5'3"	São Paulo Rly (Brazil)	
890		1933				Ballapur (India)	
891-3	DC 2052-4	1934	0-6-0 DM		2'0"	Eagle Oil & Shipping Co. (Mexico)	
894	DK	1934	4w BE		Std	Dundee Corporation Electricity Dept., Carolina Power Station, Angus	Later to North of Scotland Hydroelectric Board
895	DC 2055	1934	0-4-0 DM		2'0"	Eagle Oil & Shipping Co. (Mexico)	
896-7	DC 2056-7	1934	0-6-0 DM		2'0"	Eagle Oil & Shipping Co. (Mexico)	
898		1934				The Borneo Co., Pahang	
899	DK	1935	4w WE		Std	Bedford Brick Co., Coronation Brickworks, Beds	To London Brick Co. Ltd
900	DC 2051	1933			3'6"	South African Rlys & Hbrs	Power bogie
901	DC 2048	1933	PMRC		Metre	Burma Rlys	
902	DC 2049	1933	0-4-0 DM		2'0"	Eagle Oil & Shipping Co. (Mexico)	
903	DC 2050	1933	PRC			British Continental Oil (Venezuela)	
904		1935				Bedford Brick Co.	Powered transfer car
905	DK	1935	4w WE		Std	Derbyshire & Nottinghamshire Electric Power Co. Ltd, Spondon, Derbys	
906	DC 2058	1935	0-4-0 DM		2'0"	Eagle Oil & Shipping Co. (Mexico)	
907-8	DC 2059/62	1936	0-4-0 DM		2'0"	Eagle Oil & Shipping Co. (Mexico)	
909-10	DC 2060-1	1936	0-6-0 DM		2'0"	Eagle Oil & Shipping Co. (Mexico)	
911-6	DC 2063-8	1936	0-4-0 DM		3'6"	New Zealand Rlys	Nos Tr 13/4/8/5/7/6 (Tr 13/5-8 later TR 10, 27, 33, 56, 62)
917		1936				The Borneo Co., Pahang	
918	DC 2069	1936	0-4-0 DM		2'0"	Eagle Oil & Shipping Co. (Mexico)	
919	DC 2075	1936	0-6-0 DM		3'6"	Sudan Govt Rlys	
920-1	DC 2070-1	1936	0-6-0 DM		2'0"	Eagle Oil & Shipping Co. (Mexico)	
922	DC 2072	1936	0-4-0 DM		2'0"	Eagle Oil & Shipping Co. (Mexico)	
923-32	DK	1936	A11A RE		2'0"	General Post Office for Post Office Rly, London	
933-6	DK	1936	4w WE		2'0"	Thanet Amusements Ltd for Ramsgate Tunnel Rly	
937		1936	BE			Consolidated Goldfields, Wiluna, W. Australia	
938-9	DC 2076-7	1936	0-4-0 DM		2'0"	Eagle Oil & Shipping Co. (Mexico)	
940-1	DC 2073-4	1936			Metre	Jodhpur Rly (India)	Inspection trolleys
942	DC 2078	1936	0-4-0 DM		2'0"	Eagle Oil & Shipping Co. (Mexico)	
943	DC 2079	1936	0-6-0 DM		2'0"	Sudan Govt Public Works Dept	
944	DC 2080	1936	0-4-0 DM		2'0"	Eagle Oil & Shipping Co. (Mexico)	
945-6		1936			2'0"	Australian Iron & Steel, Port Kembla, New South Wales	
947-58	DK	1937			5'6"	Ceylon Govt Rly	Nos 501-3 (3 x 4-car sets)
959-64	DK	1937	BoBo RE		3'6"	New Zealand Govt Rlys	Nos Dm 1-6 (later DM 55, 61, 78, 84, 90, 101)
965-70	DK	1937	8w		3'6"	New Zealand Govt Rlys	Nos D 101-6 (driving trailers; later D 2007/15/23/31/58/66)
971-3	S 9267-9	1937			Metre	Federated Malay States Rly	Twin-unit steam railcars; to Malayan Rly No. 261.01-3
974-6	S 9295-7	1937			Metre	Federated Malay States Rly	Twin-unit steam railcars; to Malayan Rly Nos 261.04-6
977A	DC 1900	1937			5'6"	Buenos Aires Great Southern Rly	Spare power bogie for EE 977-1075
977-1075	DC 1901-99	1937			5'6"	Buenos Aires Great Southern Rly and Buenos Ayres Western Rly	Note 1
1076	DC 2082	1936	0-4-0 DM		2'0"	Eagle Oil & Shipping Co. (Mexico)	

Works No.	Builder	Date	Type	HP	Gauge	Customer	Notes
1077	DC 2083	1936	0-4-0 DM		2'0"	Sudan Govt Public Works Dept.	
1078-85	DC 2109-16	1937			Std	Entre Rios Rly and Argentine North Eastern Rly	Note 2
1086		1937				?	Brick transfer car
1087-92	DC 2084-9	1937	0-4-0 DM	102	5'6"	Buenos Aires Great Southern Rly	Nos DM 21-6
1093-5	DC 2091-3	1937	0-4-0 DM	102	5'6"	Buenos Aires Western Rly	Nos DM 41-3
1096-7	DC 2095-6	1937	0-4-0 DM	102	5'6"	Buenos Aires Great Southern Rly	Nos DM 27-8
1098	DC 2097	1937	0-4-0 DM		3'6"	Ohai Rly Board, Invercargill, S. Island, New Zealand	Later to New Zealand Rlys No. Tr 81, then TR 309
1099-102	DC 2117-20	1937			3'6"	Tasmanian Govt Rlys	Nos DP 11-4 power units only
1103-9	DC 2121-7	1937	0-6-0 DM		3'6"	New Zealand Govt Rlys	Nos Tr 28/9/4/6/7/3/5 (Tr 23/5-7/9 later TR 102/25/31/48/54)
1110-3	DC 2131-4	1937	DRC		5'6"	Nizam's State Rly (India)	Nos 1-4
1114	DC 2135	1937			5'6"	Nizam's State Rly (India)	Spare power bogie for EE 1110-3
1115-6	DC 2098/101	1937	0-4-0 DM		3'6"	New Zealand Govt Rlys	Nos Tr 21-2 (later TR 85, 91)
1117	DC 2128	1938	0-4-0 DM		5'6"	Calcutta Electric Supply Co. (India)	
1118-9	DC 2129-30	1938			3'6"	Tasmanian Govt Rlys	Nos DP 15-6 (power bogies only)
1120	DC 2138	1938	0-4-0 DM		3'6"	New Zealand Govt Rlys	No. Tr 20 (later TR 79)
1121	DC 2142	1938	0-6-0 DM		2'0"	Hubert Davies for Zululand Sugar Planters, Natal, S Africa	
1122-8	DC 2143-9	1938	0-4-0 DM		3'6"	New Zealand Govt Rlys	Nos Tr 30/5/1-3/6/4 (30-6 later TR 160/77/83, 200/17/23/46)
1129	DC 2153	1939	0-4-0 DM		3'6"	New Zealand Refrigerating Co.	
1130	DK	1939	4w WE		Std	Derbyshire & Nottinghamshire Electric Power Co. Ltd, Spondon, Derbys	
1131	DK	1940	4w WE		Std	Fairfield Shipbuilding & Engineering Co. Ltd, Govan, Glasgow	
1132-9		1940				War Office	Mobile power units
1140	DK	1940	4w BE		Std	Ayrshire Electricity Board, Kilmarnock, Ayrshire	To South of Scotland Electricity Board; later to Yoker, Lanarks
1141-52	DK	1940	Bo2 RE		Std	Southern Rly (Waterloo & City)	Nos 51-62. Note 3
1153-68	DK	1940	8w		Std	Southern Rly (Waterloo & City)	Nos 71-86 (trailer cars). Note 3
1169-76	DK	1940			5'6"	Ceylon Govt Rly	Not built?
1177-82	DC	1940			3'6"	Tasmanian Govt Rlys	Nos DP 21-4 (power bogies only. Two lost in transit?)
1183-6		1940	8w			British Guiana Govt Rly	1st class cars
1187-96	DC 2156-65	1940	0-4-0 DM	153	Std	Ministry of Supply	Nos WD 29-38 (later 70029-38)
1197	DK	1941	4w BE	31	Std	Swindon Corporation Electricity Dept, Wilts	
1198-209		1941				Portugal	Not built?
1210-1		1941				War Office	Mobile power units
1212-3		1942				War Office	Mobile power units
1214	DK	1942	4w WE	400	Std	Sunderland Corporation Electricity Dept, Co. Durham	
1215-23	DK	1943	WE		600mm	Ministry of Supply for USSR	
1224-6	DK	1943	WE		900mm	Ministry of Supply for USSR	
1227	DK	1943	BE		Std	Imperial Chemical Industries Ltd, Billingham, Co. Durham	
1228-86	DK	1943	WE		600mm	Ministry of Supply for USSR	
1287-306	DK	1943	WE		900mm	Ministry of Supply for USSR	
1307-36	DK	1943	BE		600mm	Ministry of Supply for USSR	
1337-56	DK	1943	BE		900mm	Ministry of Supply for USSR	
1357-61	DK	1943	WE		600mm	Ministry of Supply for USSR	
1362-7	DK	1943	WE		600mm	Ministry of Supply for USSR	
1368-74	DK	1943	WE		750mm	Ministry of Supply for USSR	
1375-7	DK	1943	BE		600mm	Ministry of Supply for USSR	
1378	DK	1944	4w BE/WE		Std	South Wales Electric Power Co., Upper Boat Power Station, Treforest, Glam.	
1379	DK	1945	4w WE		Std	Derbyshire & Nottinghamshire Electric Power Co. Ltd, Spondon, Derbys	
1380-439	DK	1943	4w			Ministry of Supply for USSR	Battery tenders
1440-79	DK	1943	4w			Ministry of Supply for USSR	Battery tenders
1480-2	DK	1945	BoBo ERC		3'6"	New Zealand Govt Rlys	Nos Dm 7-9 (later DM 118/24/30)
1483-4	DK	1945	8w		3'6"	New Zealand Govt Rlys	Nos D 107-8 (driving trailers; later D 2074/82)
1485-504	DK	1948	0-6-0 DE	350	Metre	Malayan Rly	Nos 151.01-20
1505-27		1946	DRC		5'6"	Ceylon Govt Rly	T1 504-26. Note 4
1528-42	DK	1948	0-6-0 DE	350	Std	Egyptian Rly	Nos 4001-15
1543-8	DK	1948	1ADoA1 DE	1600	Std	Egyptian Rly	Nos 3001-6

164

Works No.	Builder	Date	Type	HP	Gauge	Customer	Notes
1549	DK	1948	0-6-0 DE	350	Std	English Electric Co. Ltd	Demonstrator
1550-1	DK	1948	0-6-0 DE	350	Std	Statens Jarnvagar (Sweden)	Nos V1 3-4. Note 5
1552-3	DK	1948	0-6-0 DE	350	Std	Imperial Chemical Industries Ltd, Wilton, Middlesbrough, Yorks	EE 1552 later to ICI, Winnington, Cheshire. Note 5
1554	DK	1948	0-6-0 DE	350	Std	Imperial Chemical Industries Ltd, Billingham, Co Durham	Later to ICI, Wilton, Middlesbrough, Yorks. Note 5
1555-67	DK	1948	BoBo ERC		3'6"	New Zealand Govt Rlys	Nos DM 10-22 (10-2/4-22 later DM 147/53 176/82/99, 216/22/39/45/51/68/74)
1568-80	DK	1949	BoBo ERC		3'6"	New Zealand Govt Rlys	Nos DM 23-35 (later DM 280/97, 308/14 320/37/43/66/72/89/ 95, 406/12)
1581-94	DK	1950	BoBo ERC		3'6"	New Zealand Govt Rlys	Nos DM 36-49 (later DM 429/35/41/58/64, 470/87/93, 504/10/ 27/33/56/62)
1595-617	DK	1948	8w		3'6"	New Zealand Govt Rlys	Nos D 109-31 (driving trailers; later D 2090/106/14/22/ 30/49/57/65/73/81/ 2205/13/21/48/56/64/ 72/80/99/304, 2312/ 20/39)
1618-41	DK	1949	8w		3'6"	New Zealand Govt Rlys	Nos D 132-55 (driving trailers; later D 2347/55/63/71/98/ 403/11/38/46/54, 2462/70/89/97/502/ 10/29/37/45/53, 2561/88/96/601)
1642-65	DK	1950	8w		3'6"	New Zealand Govt Rlys	Nos D 156-79 (driving trailers; later D 2628/36/44/52/60/ 79/87/95/700/19/ 2727/35/43/51/78/86/ 94/818/26/34, 2842/ 50/69/77)
1666-97	DK	1948	BoBo ERC		5'6"	Great Indian Peninsula Rly	
1698-729	DK	1948	8w		5'6"	Great Indian Peninsula Rly	Trailer cars
1730-6	RSH 7486-92	1951	BoBoBo WE		3'6"	New Zealand Govt Rlys	Nos EW 1800-6 (later EW 107/13/36/ 42/59/65/71)
1737-8			WE			Bibiani (1927) Ltd	
1739-53	DK	1951	BoBo DE		3'6"	New Zealand Govt Rlys	Nos DE 501-15 (later DE 1308/14/20/ 37, 1343/66/72/89/ 95/406/12/29/35/ 41/58)
1754-63	DK	1951	0-6-0 DE	350	5'3"	Victorian Rlys (Australia)	Nos F 310-9 (later F 201-10)
1764-8	DK	1951	0-6-0 DE	350	3'6"	Sudan Govt Rlys	Nos 403-7
1769	DK	1949	0-6-0 DE	350	Std	Nederlandse Spoorwegen (Holland)	No. 511
1770-5	DK	1950	0-6-0 DE	350	Std	Nederlandse Spoorwegen (Holland)	Nos 512-7
1776-8	DK	1951	0-6-0 DE	350	Std	Nederlandse Spoorwegen (Holland)	Nos 518-20
1779-93	VF E32-46	1949/50	CoCo WE	3000	5'3"	EF Santos a Jundiai (Brazil)	Nos 1000-14 To RFFSA 9001-15
1794-5	Bg 3350-1	1951	BoBo WE	400	Std	National Coal Board, Harton Rly, South Shields, Co. Durham	
1796-805	VF D88-97	1950	BoBo DE	600	3'6"	Tasmanian Govt Rlys	Nos X 1-10
1806-8	DK	1951	0-6-0 DE	350	5'3"	State Electricity Commission, Victoria, Australia	Later to VR Nos F 215, 216, 211
1809	Bg 3353	1952	4w BE	64	2'0"	NCB, Wardley, Co. Durham	Underground loco
1810	Bg 3354	1952	4w BE	64	2'6"	NCB, Littleton, Staffs	Underground loco
1811-6	VF D105-10	1950	BoBo DE	600	3'6"	Tasmanian Govt Rlys	Nos X 11-6
1817-20	VF D111-4	1951	BoBo DE	600	3'6"	Tasmanian Govt Rlys	Nos X 17-20
1821-3	DK	1951	BoBo DE	600	3'6"	Tasmanian Govt Rlys	Nos X 21-3
1824-32	DK	1952	BoBo DE	600	3'6"	Tasmanian Govt Rlys	Nos X 24-32
1833-47	DK	1952	0-6-0 DE		Std	Nederlandse Spoorwegen (Holland)	Nos 551-65 Later 451-65, then 701-15. Delivered without engines, these being fitted in Holland
1848-9	Isl	1951	A1AA1A DE	1588	5'3"	South Australian Rlys	Nos 900-1
1850-3	Isl	1952	A1AA1A DE	1588	5'3"	South Australian Rlys	Nos 902-5
1854-7	Isl	1953	A1AA1A DE	1588	5'3"	South Australian Rlys	Nos 906-9
1858-63	VF D132-7	1952	A1AA1A DE		Metre	Buenos Aires Provincial Rly	Order Cancelled?
1864-74	VF E47-57	1952	CoCo WE	3000	5'6"	RENFE (Spain)	Nos 7701-11 (later 277.001-11)

Works No.	Builder	Date	Type	HP	Gauge	Customer	Notes
1875-83	VF E58-66	1953	CoCo WE	3000	5'6"	RENFE (Spain)	Nos 7712-20 (later 277.012-20)
1884-900	DK	1953	CoCo WE	2400	5'3"	Victorian Rlys (Australia)	Nos L 1150-66
1901-4	DK	1951	0-6-0 DE	350	Std	Imperial Chemical Industries Ltd, Winnington, Cheshire	
1905-14	VF D146-55	1953	CoCo DE	1290	3'6"	Queensland Govt Rlys	Nos 1200-9
1915-7	DK	1953	0-6-0 DE	350	5'3"	State Electricity Commission, Victoria, Australia	Later to VR Nos F 212-4
1918	Bg	1951	4w BE		Std	English Electric Co. Ltd, Willans Works, Rugby, Staffs	
1919-26	DK	1953	CoCo WE	2400	5'3"	Victorian Rlys (Australia)	Nos L 1167-74
1927-36	DK	1954	2CoCo2 DE	1500	3'6"	New Zealand Rlys	Nos Df 1501-9, 1500 (later 1301-9, 1300)
1937-57	DK		2CoCo2 DE	1500	3'6"	New Zealand Rlys	Order Cancelled. Note 7
1958-9	Bg	1951				Mount Isa Mines, Queensland, Australia	
1960-1	Bg 3379-80	1954	4w BE	64	2'0"	NCB, Llay Main, Denbighs	Underground locos
1962-3	Bg 3382/1	1954	4w BE	64	2'0"	NCB, Llay Main, Denbighs	Underground locos
1964-74	VF E117-27	1953	CoCo WE	3000	5'6"	RENFE (Spain)	Nos 7721-31 (later 277.021-31)
1975-83	VF E128-36	1954	CoCo WE	3000	5'6"	RENFE (Spain)	Nos 7732-40 (later 277.032-40)
1984	VF E74	1954	CoCo WE	3000	5'6"	RENFE (Spain)	Nos 7741 (later 277.041)
1985-98	VF E75-88	1955	CoCo WE	3000	5'6"	RENFE (Spain)	Nos 7742-55 (later 277.042-55)
1999-2003	VF E89-93	1956	CoCo WE	3000	5'6"	RENFE (Spain)	Nos 7756-60 (later 277.056-60)
2004-6	Bg 3397-9	1954	4w BE		3'6"	NCB, Bankhall Colliery, Burnley, Lancs	Underground locos
2007	DK	1955	CoCo DE	3300	Std	English Electric Co. Ltd	*Deltic*. Demonstrated on BR: later returned to EE
2008-17	DK	1953	0-6-0 DE	350	Std	Nederlandse Spoorwegen (Holland)	Nos 521-30
2018-22	DK	1954	0-6-0 DE	350	Std	Nederlandse Spoorwegen (Holland)	Nos 531-5
2023	VF E94	1955	CoCo WE	3000	5'3"	E.R. Santos a Jundiai (Brazil)?	No. 1015. Note 8
2024-5	VF E95-6	1955	CoCo WE	3000	5'6"	RENFE (Spain)?	Note 8
2026	Bg 3413	1954	4w BE	64	2'0"	NCB, Wardley, Co. Durham	Underground loco
2027-8	Bg 3414-5	1954	4w BE	64	2'0"	NCB, Washington 'F' Pit, Co. Durham	Underground locos
2029-31	Bg 3418-20	1954	4w BE		2'6"	NCB, Betteshanger, Kent	Underground locos
2032-44	VF D195-207	1954	A1AA1A DE	1000	Metre	RFFSA RF Nordeste (Brazil)	Nos 701-13
2045-51	VF E67-73	1955	CoCo WE	3215	5'6"	Indian Railways	Nos 4100-6 (later WCM1 20066-72)
2052-61	DK	1954	BoBo DE	750	3'6"	Gold Coast Rly	Nos 751-60
2062-5	VF D236-9	1954	BoBo DE	750	3'6"	Gold Coast Rly	Nos 761-4
2066	DK	1954	BoBo DE	750	3'6"	African Explosives & Chemical Industries Ltd, Modderfontein Transvaal, S. Africa	
2067-75	DK	1954	0-6-0 DE	350	Std	Nederlandse Spoorwegen (Holland)	Nos 536-44
2076-8	Bg 3427-9	1954	4w BE	64	2'6"	NCB, Whitburn, Co. Durham	Underground locos
2079	Bg 3430	1954	4w BE	64	2'0"	NCB, Wardley, Co. Durham	Underground loco
2080	Bg 3439	1954	4w BE	64	2'6"	NCB, Whitburn, Co. Durham	Underground loco
2081-2	Bg 3448-9	1954	4w BE		2'0"	NCB, Snowdown, Kent	Underground locos
2083	Bg 3435	1954	4wBE		2'0"	NCB, Snowdown, Kent	Underground loco
2084-6	Bg 3432-4	1954	4w BE		2'0"	NCB, Tilmanstone, Kent	Underground loco
2087-90	DK	1954	BoBo DE	750	3'6"	Nigerian Govt Rlys	Nos 1001-4
2091-6	VF D230-5	1954	BoBo DE	750	3'6"	Nigerian Govt Rlys	Nos 1005-10
2097	DK	1954	0-6-0 DE	350	Std	Nederlandse Spoorwegen (Holland)	No. 545
2098-107	DK	1955	0-6-0 DE	350	Std	Nederlandse Spoorwegen (Holland)	Nos 601-10
2108-14	VF D298-304	1955	0-6-0 DE	350	Std	Nederlandse Spoorwegen (Holland)	Nos 611-7
2115-60	VF D305-50	1956	0-6-0 DE	350	Std	Nederlandse Spoorwegen (Holland)	Nos 618-63
2161-2	VF D351-2	1957	0-6-0 DE	350	Std	Nederlandse Spoorwegen (Holland)	Nos 664-5
2163-8	DK	1954	BoBo WE	2050	3'6"	South African Rlys & Hbrs	Nos 5E E259-64
2169-82	DK	1955	BoBo WE	2050	3'6"	South African Rlys & Hbrs	Nos 5E E265-78
2183-97	DK	1956	BoBo WE	2050	3'6"	South African Rlys & Hbrs	Nos 5E E279-93
2198-210	DK	1957	BoBo WE	2050	3'6"	South African Rlys & Hbrs	Nos 5E E294-306
2211-22	VF E137-48	1955	BoBo WE	2050	3'6"	South African Rlys & Hbrs	Nos 5E E307-18
2223-4	Bg 3440-1	1954	4w WE		2'6"	NCB, Cardowan, Lanarks	Underground locos
2225-6	Bg 3442-3	1954	4w WE		2'6"	NCB, Bedlay, Lanarks	Underground locos
2227-9	Bg 3444-6	1954	4w BE	64	2'6"	NCB, Boldon, Co. Durham	Underground locos
2230	Bg 3431	1954	4w BE	64	2'0"	NCB, Wardley, Co. Durham	Underground loco
2231-45	DK	1955	1CoCo1 DE	2000	3'6"	Rhodesia Rlys	Nos 1200-14
2246-53	DK	1956	1CoCo1 DE	2000	3'6"	Rhodesia Rlys	Nos 1215-22
2254-73	RSH 7821-40	1955	A1AA1A DE	750	3'6"	New Zealand Rlys	Nos Dg 750-69 (later 2007/474/036/42/59, 2065/71/88/94/105/ 11/28/34/40/57/63, 2186/92/480/226)
2274-84	VF D353-63	1956	A1AA1A DE	750	3'6"	New Zealand Rlys	Nos Dh 770-80 (to Dg class; later 2232/ 49/55/61/78/84/90, 2301/18/24/30
2285-95	VF D364-74	1956	A1AA1A DE	750	3'6"	New Zealand Rlys	Nos Dg 781-91 (later 2347/53/76/82/99, 2416/22/39/45/51/68)

166

Works No.	Builder	Date	Type	HP	Gauge	Customer	Notes
2296	Bg 3454	1956	4w BE		2'6"	NCB, Littleton, Staffs	Underground loco
2297-8	Bg 3455-6	1956	4w BE		2'6"	NCB, Wyrley No. 3, Staffs	Underground locos
2299	Bg	1957	4w WE		3'6"	Stewarts & Lloyds Minerals Ltd, Thistleton Ironstone Mines, Lincs	
2300-1	Bg 3436-7	1956	4w WE		2'0"	NCB, Snowdown, Kent	Underground locos
2302	Bg 3466	1955	4w BE		2'0"	NCB, Hafodrynys, Glam.	Underground loco
2303-7 \	DK	1956	A1AA1A DE	940	Metre	Buenos Aires Provincial Rly	Nos DE31-5 (to EFEA Gen Belgrano 5771-5)
2308	Bg 3469	1957	BoBo WE	400	Std	NCB, Harton Rly, South Shields, Co. Durham	
2309-20	VF E97-108	1957	CoCo		5'6"	Indian Railways	Nos 4107-18 (later WCM2 20175-86)
2321-7	DK	1956	BoBo DE		Std	Jamaica Govt Rly	Nos 81-7
2328	Bg 3470	1956	4w BE	64	2'6"	NCB, Wearmouth, Co. Durham	Underground loco
2329	Bg 3471	1956	4w BE	64	2'6"	NCB, Wearmouth, Co. Durham	Underground loco
2330	Bg 3473	1956	4w BE	64	2'6"	NCB, Whitburn, Co. Durham	Underground loco
2331	Bg 3472	1956	4w BE	64	2'6"	NCB, Boldon, Co. Durham	Underground loco
2332-6	Bg 3475-9	1956	4w BE		2'6"	NCB, Hem Heath, Staffs	Underground locos
2337-8	Bg 3480-1	1956	4w BE		2'6"	NCB, Florence, Staffs	Underground locos
2339-41	DK	1956	BoBo DE		Std	Jamaica Govt Rly	Nos 88-90
2342-4	RSH 7930-2	1957	4w BE	64	3'0"	NCB, Easington, Co. Durham	Underground locos
2345	VF D226	1956	0-6-0 DE	500	Std	English Electric Co. Ltd	No. D226 Demonstrator; later D0226
2346	VF D227	1956	0-6-0 DH	500	Std	English Electric Co. Ltd	No. D227 Demonstrator; later D0227
2347-62	VF D375-90	1957	BoBo DE	1000	Std	British Railways	Nos D8000-15 (later 20050/01-15)
2363-6	VF D391-4	1958	BoBo DE	1000	Std	British Railways	Nos D8016-9 (later 20016-9)
2367-76	VF D395-404	1958	1CoCo1 DE	2000	Std	British Railways	Nos D200-9 (later 40122/001-9)
2377-86	VF D417-26	1959	BoBo DE	1100	Std	British Railways	Nos D5900-9
2387-93	Bg 3485-91	1958	4w BE		3'0"	NCB, Silverwood, Yorks	Underground locos
2394-5	Bg 3492-3	1957	4w BE		2'6"	NCB, Kinneil, West Lothian	Underground locos
2396-405	DK	1957	CoCo DE	1500	Metre	Malayan Rly	Nos 20101-10
2406-15	RSH 7953-62	1957	CoCo DE	1500	Metre	Malayan Rly	Nos 20111-20
2416-7	RSH 7935-6	1957	4w BE	64	2'3½"	NCB, Granville, Shropshire	Underground locos
2418-20	Bg 3497-9	1958	4w BE	64	2'6"	NCB, Westoe, Co. Durham	Underground locos
2421-65	VF E149-93	1957	BoBo WE	2050	3'6"	South African Rlys & Hbrs	Nos 5E E319-63
2466	Bg 3501	1957	4w BE	64	2'0"	NCB, Wardley, Co. Durham	Underground loco
2467	Bg 3495	1957	4w BE	64	2'0"	NCB, Wardley, Co. Durham	Underground loco
2468	Bg					Furuholmen A/S, Norway	
2469-74	RSH 7937-42	1958	4w BE	64	2'0"	NCB, Murton, Co. Durham	Underground locos
2475-6	RSH 7979-80	1958	4w BE	64	2'0"	NCB, Eppleton, Co. Durham	Underground locos
2477	RSH 7981	1959	4w BE	64	2'0"	NCB, Eppleton, Co. Durham	Underground loco
2478	RSH 7982	1959	4w BE	64	2'0"	NCB, Murton, Co. Durham	Underground loco
2479	RSH 7994	1958	4w BE	64	2'0"	NCB, Murton, Co. Durham	Underground loco
2480	RSH 7993	1958	4w BE	64	2'0"	NCB, Murton, Co. Durham	Underground loco
2481-4	RSH 7992-89	1958	4w BE	64	2'0"	NCB, Eppleton, Co. Durham	Underground locos; RSH Nos in reverse order
2485	RSH 7988	1958	4w BE	64	2'0"	NCB, Murton, Co. Durham	Underground loco
2486	RSH 7987	1958	4w BE	64	2'0"	NCB, Eppleton, Co. Durham	Underground loco
2487-8	RSH 7986/5	1958	4w BE	64	2'0"	NCB, Murton, Co. Durham	Underground locos
2489-90	RSH 7984/3	1958	4w BE	64	2'0"	NCB, Eppleton, Co. Durham	Underground locos
2491	RSH 7978	1958	4w BE	64	3'0"	NCB, Hafodrynys, Glam	Underground loco
2492-503	VF D405-16	1958	1CoCo1 DE	2000	3'6"	Rhodesia Rlys	Nos 1223-34
2504-18	VF D194-208	1958	CoCo WE	3000	5'6"	RENFE (Spain)	Nos 7761-75 (later 277.061-75)
2519	Bg 3500	1958	4w BE	64	2'0"	NCB, Heworth, Co. Durham	Underground loco
2520	RSH 8022	1958	4w BE	64	2'6"	NCB, Kinneil, West Lothian	Underground loco
2521	RSH 7963	1957	4w BE	64	2'0"	NCB, Snowdon, Kent	Underground loco
2522	RSH 7964	1958	4w BE	64	2'0"	NCB, Snowdon, Kent	Underground loco
2523	Bg 3496	1957	4w BE	64	2'6"	NCB, Boldon, Co. Durham	Underground loco
2524-6	RSH 8047-9	1958	4w BE	64	3'0"	NCB, Ogilvie, Glam	Underground locos
2527	RSH 8046	1958	4w BE	64	2'0"	NCB, Chislet, Kent	Underground loco
2528-43	VF					Central Rly of Peru	Order cancelled?
2544-98	VF E209-63	1959	BoBo WE	2050	3'6"	South African Rlys & Hbrs	Nos 5E E536-90
2599-600	Bg 3519-20	1959	BoBo WE	400	Std	NCB, Harton Rly, South Shields, Co. Durham	
2601	RSH 7947	1959	4w BE	64	2'6"	NCB, Manor Powis, Stirlingshire	Underground loco
2602-22	RSH 8001-21	1959	A1AA1A DE	1000	Metre	EFEA, General Belgrano, Argentina	Nos 5776-96
2623-5	RSH 8083-5	1958	4w BE	64	2'0"	NCB, Baddesley, Staffs	Underground locos
2626	Bg 3521	1958	4w BE	64	2'6"	NCB, Westoe, Co. Durham	Underground loco
2627-8	Bg 3522-3	1958	4w BE	64	2'6"	NCB, Wearmouth, Co. Durham	Underground locos
2629-34	RSH 7995-8000	1958	CoCo DE	1500	Metre	Malayan Rly	Nos 20121-6
2635-9	RSH 8028-32	1960	4w BE	64	2'0"	NCB, Wallsend, Northumberland	Underground locos
2640-52	RSH 7965-77	1959	BoBo DE	420	5'6"	Hindustan Steel Ltd, Durgapur, India	Note 6
2651-2A	Bg 3527-8	1960	4w BE		3'0"	NCB, Killoch, Ayrshire	Underground locos Note 6
2653-4	Bg 3529-30	1960	4w BE		3'0"	NCB, Killoch, Ayrshire	Underground locos
2655-6	Bg 3531-2	1961	4w BE		3'0"	NCB, Killoch, Ayrshire	Underground locos
2657-9	Bg 3533-5	1963	4w BE		3'0"	NCB, Killoch, Ayrshire	Underground locos
2660	RSH 7945	1959	4w BE	64	2'6"	NCB, Littleton, Staffs	Underground loco
2661-2	RSH 8094-5	1959	4w BE	64	2'6"	NCB, Silksworth, Co. Durham	Underground locos

Works No.	Builder	Date	Type	HP	Gauge	Customer	Notes
2663-4	RSH 8086-7	1959	BoBo DE	750	3'6"	Roan Antelope Copper Mine, Ndola, Northern Rhodesia	
2665	RSH 8045	1958	4w BE	64	2'6"	NCB, Cardowan, Lanarks	Underground loco
2666-95	VF D427-56	1959	1CoCo1 DE	2000	Std	British Railways	Nos D210-39 (later 40010-39)
2696	RSH 8096	1959	4w BE	64	2'0"	NCB, Chislet, Kent	Underground loco
2697	Bg 3537	1959	4w BE		2'0"	NCB, Llay Main, Denbighs	Underground loco
2698-709	RSH 8033-44	1959	BoBo DE	750	3'6"	Ghana Rlys	Nos 765-76
2710-1	RSH 8023-4	1959	4w BE	64	2'7½"	NCB, Polmaise, Stirlingshire	Underground locos
2712	RSH 8025	1959	4w BE	64	2'6"	NCB, Barony, Ayrshire	Underground loco
2713	RSH 8026	1960	4w BE	64	2'6"	NCB, Kinneil, West Lothian	Underground loco
2714	RSH 8027	1961	4w BE	64	2'6"	NCB, Cardowan, Lanarks	Underground loco
2715-24	VF D457-66	1959	1CoCo1 DE	2000	Std	British Railways	Nos D240-9 (later 40040-9)
2725-34	RSH 8135-44	1960	1CoCo1 DE	2000	Std	British Railways	Nos D305-14 (later 40105-14)
2735	RSH 8105	1960	4w BE	64	2'0"	NCB, Baddesley, Staffs	Underground loco
2736	RSH 8106	1959	4w BE	64	2'0"	NCB, Murton, Co. Durham	Underground loco
2737	RSH 8107	1960	4w BE	64	2'0"	NCB, Murton, Co. Durham	Underground loco
2738-9	RSH 8108-9	1960	4w BE	64	2'0"	NCB, Abernant, Glam.	Underground locos
2740	Bg 3542	1959	4w BE	64	2'6"	NCB, Westoe, Co. Durham	Underground loco
2741	RSH 8129	1959	4w BE	64	2'0"	NCB, Littleton, Staffs	Underground loco
2742-52	RSH 8052-62	1959	BoBo DE	1000	Std	British Railways	Nos D8020-30 (later 20020-30)
2753-6	RSH 8063-6	1960	BoBo DE	1000	Std	British Railways	Nos D8031-4 (later 20031-4)
2757-71	VF D482-96	1959	BoBo DE	1000	Std	British Railways	Nos D8035-49 (later 20035-49)
2772-6	VF D467-71	1959	1CoCo1 DE	2000	Std	British Railways	Nos D250-4 (later 40050-40)
2777-81	VF D472-6	1960	1CoCo1 DE	2000	Std	British Railways	Nos D255-9 (later 40055-9)
2782-826	VF D497-541	1960	1CoCo1 DE	2000	Std	British Railways	Nos D260-304 (later 40060-104)
2827-41	VF D542-56	1960	CoCo DE	2000	3'6"	Sudan Govt Rlys	Nos 1000-14
2842-3	Bg 3547-8	1960	4w BE		2'6"	NCB, Highley, Shropshire	Underground locos
2844-7	RSH 8131-4	1960	4w BE	64	2'6"	NCB, Cannock Wood, Staffs	Underground locos
2848-9	RSH 8201-2	1960	4w BE	64	2'0"	NCB, Murton, Co. Durham	Underground locos
2850-9	RSH 8145-54	1961	1CoCo1 DE	2000	Std	British Railways	Nos D315-24 (later 40115-21/3/4)
2860	RSH 8203	1960	4w BE	64	2'6"	NCB, Cannock Wood, Staffs	Underground loco
2861	RSH 8204	1960	4w BE	64	2'6"	NCB, Lea Hall, Staffs	Underground loco
2862	RSH 8205	1960	4w BE	64	2'6"	NCB, Littleton, Staffs	Underground loco
2863-6	VF D579-82	1960	CoCo DE	1750	Std	British Railways	Nos D6700-3 (later 37119/001-3)
2867-94	VF D583-610	1961	CoCo DE	1750	Std	British Railways	Nos D6704-31 (later 37004-31)
2895-904	VF D611-20	1962	CoCo DE	1750	Std	British Railways	Nos D6732-41 (later 37032-41)
2905-24	VF D557-76	1961	CoCo DE	3300	Std	British Railways	Nos D9000-19 (later 55022/01-19)
2925-6	VF D577-8	1962	CoCo DE	3300	Std	British Railways	Nos D9020-1 (later 55020-1)
2927	RSH 8206	1960	4w BE	64	2'6"	NCB, Littleton, Staffs	Underground loco
2928-37	VF E264-73	1960	BoBo WE	2950	Std	British Railways	Nos E3024-33 (later 83001-10)
2938	VF E274	1961	BoBo WE	2950	Std	British Railways	No. E3034 (later 83011)
2939-40	VF E275-6	1961	BoBo WE	2950	Std	British Railways	Nos E3303-4 (later E3098-9, then 83013-4)
2941	VF E277	1961	BoBo WE	2950	Std	British Railways	No. E3035 (later 83012)
2942	VF E278	1962	BoBo WE	2950	Std	British Railways	No. E3305 (reno. E3100 before delivery; later 83015)
2943-52	RSH 8110-9	1960	1CoCo1 DE	1875	Metre	East African Rlys & Hbrs	Nos 9001-10 (later 8701-10)
2953-4	RSH 8286-7	1960	4w BE	64	2'6"	NCB, Barony, Ayrshire	Underground locos
2955	Bg 3566	1960	4w BE	64	2'6"	NCB, Boldon, Co. Durham	Underground loco
2956-3015	RSH 8208-67	1961	BoBo DE	1000	Std	British Railways	Nos D8050-96/8/7/9-109 (later 20128/051-96/8/7/9-109)
3016-33	RSH 8268-85	1962	BoBo DE	1000	Std	British Railways	Nos D8110-27 (later 20710-27)
3034-60	VF D696-722	1962	CoCo DE	1750	Std	British Railways	Nos D6742-68 (later 37042-68)
3061-70	RSH 8315-24	1962	CoCo DE	1750	Std	British Railways	Nos D6769-78 (later 37069-78)
3071-3	VF D621-3	1960	1CoCo1 DE	2000	Std	British Railways	Nos. D325-7 (later 40125-7)
3074-117	VF D624-67	1961	1CoCo1 DE	2000	Std	British Railways	Nos D328-71 (later 40128-71)

Works No.	Builder	Date	Type	HP	Gauge	Customer	Notes
3118-45	VF D668-95	1962	1CoCo1 DE	2000	Std	British Railways	Nos D372-99 (later 40172-99)
3146-7	RSH 8288-9	1961	4w BE	64	2'6"	NCB, Lea Hall, Staffs	Underground locos
3148	RSH 8200	1960	BoBo DE	750	3'6"	African Explosives & Chemical Industries Ltd, Modderfontein, Transvaal, S. Africa	
3149	RSH 8290	1960	4w BE	64	2'6"	NCB, Silksworth, Co. Durham	Underground loco
3150	Bg 3567	1960	4w BE	64	2'6"	NCB, Westoe, Co. Durham	Underground loco
3151-2	RSH 8291-2	1961	4w BE	64	2'6"	NCB, Littleton Staffs	Underground locos
3153	RSH 8293	1961	4w BE	64	2'0"	NCB, Tilmanstone, Kent	Underground loco
3154	RSH 8294	1960	4w BE	64	2'6"	NCB, Cardowan, Lanarks	Underground loco
3155	RSH 8295	1961	4w BE	64	2'6"	NCB, Silksworth, Co. Durham	Underground loco
3156-7	RSH 8296-7	1961	4w BE	64	2'6"	NCB, West Cannock Staffs	Underground locos
3158-9	RSH 8299-8300	1961	4w BE	64	3'0"	NCB, Penallta, Glam.	Underground locos
3160	RSH 8301	1962	4w BE	64	3'0"	NCB, Penallta, Glam.	Underground loco
3161	RSH 8302	1961	4w BE	64	2'6"	NCB, West Cannock, Staffs	Underground locos
3162	Bg 3574	1961	4w BE		2'6"	NCB, Highley, Shropshire	Underground loco
3163	RSH 8303	1961	4w BE	64	2'3½"	NCB, Granville, Shropshire	Underground loco
3164	RSH 8304	1961	4w BE	64	2'0"	NCB, Tilmanstone, Kent	Underground loco
3165-6	RSH 8310-1	1961	4w BE	64	2'6"	NCB, Cardowan, Lanarks	Underground loco
3167	RSH 8312	1961	4w BE	64	2'0"	NCB, Murton, Co. Durham	Underground loco
3168	RSH 8340	1962	4w BE	64	2'6"	NCB, Barony, Ayrshire	Underground loco
3169-72	RSH 8306-9	1962	4w WE		2'0"	NCB, Chislet, Kent	Underground locos
3173	Bg 3583	1962	4w BE	64	2'6"	NCB, Westoe, Co. Durham	Underground loco
3174	Bg 3584	1962	4w BE	64	2'0"	NCB, Usworth, Co. Durham	Underground loco
3175-84	VF D723-32	1961	CoCo DE	2000	3'6"	Sudan Govt Rlys	Nos 1015-24
3185-204	VF E279-98	1961	BoBo	2720	Std	PKP (Poland)	Nos EU06.01-20
3205	VF D733	1961	CoCo DE	2700	Std	English Electric Co. Ltd	No. DP2 Demonstrator
3206-14	RSH 8325-33	1962	CoCo DE	1750	Std	British Railways	Nos D6779-87 (later 37079-87)
3215-20	RSH 8334-9	1963	CoCo DE	1750	Std	British Railways	Nos D6788-93 (later 37088-93)
3221-2	RSH 8341-2	1963	CoCo DE	1750	Std	British Railways	Nos D6794-5 (later 37094-5)
3223-4	RSH 8344-5	1962	4w BE	64	2'6"	NCB, Lea Hall, Staffs	Underground loco
3225-30	VF D750-5	1962	CoCo DE	1750	Std	British Railways	Nos D6796-801 (later 37096-101)
3231-47	VF D756-72	1963	CoCo DE	1750	Std	British Railways	Nos D6802-18 (later 37102-18)
3248-63	VF D734-49	1962	1CoCo1 DE	2000	3'6"	Rhodesia Rlys	Nos 1300-15
3264-73	RSH 8379-88	1963	CoCo DE	1750	Std	British Railways	Nos D6819-28 (later 37283/120-8)
3274-83	VF D803-12	1963	CoCo DE	1750	Std	British Railways	Nos D6829-38 (later 37129-38)
3284-313	VF D773-802	1964	CoCo DE	2000	3'6"	Sudan Govt Rlys	Nos 1025-54
3314-33	VF D813-32	1963	CoCo DE	1750	Std	British Railways	Nos D6839-58 (later 37139-58)
3334-5	RSH 8313-4	1962	A11A RE		2'0"	General Post Office, for Post Office Railway, London	
3336	Bg 3595	1963	4w BE	64	2'6"	NCB, Westoe, Co. Durham	Underground loco
3337-46	RSH 8390-9	1963	CoCo DE	1750	Std	British Railways	Nos D6859-68 (later 37159-68)
3347-56	VF D833-42	1963	CoCo DE	1750	Std	British Railways	Nos D6869-78 (later 37169-78)
3357-64	RSH 8400-7	1963	CoCo DE	1750	Std	British Railways	Nos D6879-86 (later 37179-86)
3365-76	RSH 8408-19	1964	CoCo DE	1750	Std	British Railways	Nos D6887-98 (later 37187-98)
3377-89	VF D843-55	1963	CoCo DE	1750	Std	British Railways	Nos D6899-911 (later 37199-211)
3390-6	VF D856-62	1964	CoCo DE	1750	Std	British Railways	Nos D6912-8 (later 37212-8)
3397-8	RSH 8362-3	1963	BoBo DE	750	Std	Jamaica Govt Rly	Nos 91-2
3399	Bg 3599	1963	4w BE	64	2'6"	NCB, Westoe, Co. Durham	Underground loco
3400	RSH 8420	1963	4w BE	64	2'6"	NCB, Lea Hall, Staffs	Underground loco
3401	RSH 8422	1963	4w BE	64	2'0"	NCB, Eppleton, Co. Durham	Underground loco
3402	RSH 8421	1963	4w BE	64	2'6"	NCB, West Cannock, Staffs	Underground loco
3403	RSH 8425	1963	4w BE	64	2'6"	NCB, Manor Powis, Stirlingshire	Underground loco
3404	Bg 3603	1963	4w BE	64	2'6"	NCB, Wearmouth, Co. Durham	Underground loco
3405-24	VF D863-82	1964	CoCo DE	1750	Std	British Railways	Nos D6919-38 (later 37219-38)
3425	RSH 8450	1963	4w BE	64	3'0¼"	NCB, Ogilvie, Glam	Underground loco. Note 9
3426	RSH 8455	1963	4w BE	64	2'3½"	NCB, Granville, Shropshire	Underground loco. Note 9
3425-38	VF D883-96	1964	1CoCo1 DE	1800	Metre	East African Rlys & Hbrs	Nos 9011-24 (later 8711-24). Note 9
3439-49	VF D897-907	1964	BoBo DE	750	3'6"	Ghana Rly & Ports Admin	Nos 777-87
3450-1						Blank	Note 9
3452	VF	1964	4w BE	64	2'6"	NCB, Manor Powis, Stirlings	Underground loco
3453-89	VF E299-335	1965	BoBo WE	3600	Std	British Railways	Nos E3161-97 (later re No. in 86xxx series)

Works No.	Builder	Date	Type	HP	Gauge	Customer	Notes
3490-2	VF E336-8	1966	BoBo WE	3600	Std	British Railways	Nos E3198-200 (later re No. in 86xxx series)
3493-4	VF	1964	4w BE	64	2'6"	NCB, West Cannock, Staffs	Underground locos
3495	VF	1964	4w BE	64	2'6"	NCB, West Cannock, Staffs	Underground loco
3496-508	VF D927-39	1964	CoCo DE	1750	Std	British Railways	Nos D6939-51 (later 37239-51)
3509-15	VF D940-6	1965	CoCo DE	1750	Std	British Railways	Nos D6952-8 (later 37252-8)
3516	VF	1964	4w BE	64	3'0"	NCB, Penallta, Glam.	Underground loco
3517	VF D947	1965	BoBo DE	750	Std	Jamaica Govt Rly	Rebuild of damaged loco
3518	VF	1964	4w BE	64	2'0"	NCB, Baddesley, Warwicks	Underground loco
3519-59	VF D948-88	1965	CoCo DE	1750	Std	British Railways	Nos D6959-99 (later 37259-82/4-99)
3560-8	VF D989-97	1965	CoCo DE	1750	Std	British Railways	Nos D6600-8 (later 37300-8)
3569-75	VF E339-45	1965	BoBo ED	1600	Std	British Railways	Nos E6007-13 (later 73101-7)
3576-98	VF E346-68	1966	BoBo ED	1600	Std	British Railways	Nos E6014-36 (later 73108-20/21-9)
3599-648	VF D998-D1047	1966	BoBo DE	1000	Std	British Railways	Nos D8128-77 (later 20228/129-77)
3649-50	VF	1964	4w BE	64	2'6"	NCB, Kinneil, West Lothian	Underground locos
3651	VF	1965	4w WE		2'0"	NCB, Chislet, Kent	Underground loco
3652	VF	1965	4w BE	64	2'6"	NCB, Littleton, Staffs	Underground loco
3653-4	VF	1965	4w BE	64	2'6"	NCB, Barony, Ayrshire	Underground locos
3655	VF	1965	4w BE	64	3'0"	NCB, Bates, Northumb	Underground loco
3656-7	VF					Newstan Colliery, Australia	
3658	VF	1965	4w BE	64	2'6"	NCB, Cardowan, Lanarks	Underground loco
3659-65	VF D1054-60	1966	BoBo DE	1000	Std	British Railways	Nos D8178-84 (later 20178-84)
3666-80	VF D1061-75	1967	BoBo DE	1000	Std	British Railways	Nos D8185-99 (later 20185-99)
3681-708	VF D1076-D1103	1967	BoBo DE	1000	Std	British Railways	Nos D8300-27 (later 20200-27)
3709-20	VF E369-80	1966	BoBo ED	1600	Std	British Railways	Nos E6037-48 (later 73130-41)
3721	VF E381	1967	BoBo ED	1600	Std	British Railways	No. E6049 (later 73142)
3722-41	VF E382-401	1966	BoBo WE	3600	Std	British Railways	Nos E3141-60 (later re No. in 86xxx series)
3742-3	VF	1965	4w BE	64	3'0"	NCB, Bedwas, Glam.	Underground locos
3744	VF	1965	4w BE	64	2'6"	NCB, Bedlay, Lanarks	Underground loco
3745	Bg 3614	1965	4w BE		3'0"	NCB, Killoch, Ayrshire	Underground loco
3746-57	VF D1104-15	1966	1CoCo1 DE	1800	Metre	East African Rlys & Hbrs	Nos 9025-36 (later 8725-36)
3758-67	VF D1127-36	1966	BoBo DE	1350	5'6"	Camhinos de Ferro Portugueses	Nos 1401-10
3768	VF	1966	4w BE	64	2'6"	NCB, Hilton Main, Staffs	Underground loco
3769	VF	1966	4w BE	64	2'6"	NCB, Littleton, Staffs	Underground loco
3770-2	VF D1141-3	1967	CoCo DE	2700	Std	EE Leasings Ltd	Nos D400/2/1 Leased, later sold, to BR (later 50050/02/1)
3773-819	VF D1144-90	1968	CoCo DE	2700	Std	EE Leasings Ltd	Nos D403-49 Leased, later sold, to BR (later 50003-49)
3820	Bg 3642	1966	4w BE	64	2'6"	NCB, Westoe, Co. Durham	Underground loco
3821	VF					Newstan Colliery, Australia	
3822-31	VF D1208-17	1968	1BoBo1 DE	1300	Metre	East African Rlys & Hbrs	Nos 9101-10 (later 7101-10)
3832-9	VF D1218-25	1969	1CoCo1 DE	1800	Metre	East African Rlys & Hbrs	Nos 9037-44 (later 8737-44)
3840	VF	1967	4w BE	64	2'6"	NCB, Lea Hall, Staffs	Underground loco
3841	VF	1967	4w BE	64	2'6"	NCB, Hilton Main, Staffs	Underground loco
3842	Bg 3645	1967	4w BE	64	2'6"	NCB, Westoe, Co. Durham	Underground loco
3843-4	VF					New State Mines Control Authority, Australia	
3845	VF	1968	4w BE	64	3'0"	NCB, Easington, Co. Durham	Underground loco
3846-7	VF D1234-5	1968	BoBo DE	750	Std	Jamaica Rly Corporation	Nos 93-4
3848	Bg 3643	1967	4w BE		3'0"	NCB, Killoch, Ayrshire	Underground loco
3849	VF	1967	4w BE	64	2'6"	NCB, Silksworth, Co. Durham	Underground loco
3850-9	VF D1269-78	1969	CoCo DE	1800	3'6"	Ghana Rlys & Ports Admin	Nos 1851-60
3860						Argentina	Locomotive not completed
3861-3							Not built?
3864-9	VF D1281-6	1969	CoCo DE	1800	3'6"	Ghana Rlys & Ports Admin	Nos 1861-6
3870	VF	1969	0-6-0 DH	274	Std	Monsanto Chemicals Ltd, Seal Sands, Co. Durham	
3871	Bg 3649	1968	4w BE	64	2'6"	NCB, Westoe, Co. Durham	Underground loco
3872-81	VF 3872-81	1969	1BoBo1 DE	1300	Metre	East African Rlys & Hbrs	Nos 7201-10
3882-91	VF 3882-91	1968	CoCo DE	2700	5'6"	Caninhos de Ferro Portugueses	Nos 1801-10
3892-943						Blank	Note 10
3944-7	VF D1256-9	1968	0-6-0 DH	450	Std	Richard Thomas & Baldwins Ltd, Llanwern, Mon.	

Works No.	Builder	Date	Type	HP	Gauge	Customer	Notes
3948	VF D1260	1968	0-6-0 DH	380	Std	NCB, Nailstone, Leics	
3949-50	VF D1261-2	1968	0-6-0 DH	500	Std	Lancashire Steel Coporation Ltd, Irlam, Lancs	
3951	VF D1263	1968	0-6-0 DH	500	Std	Richard Thomas & Baldwins Ltd Llanwern, Mon.	
3952	VF D1264	1968	0-6-0 DH	500	Std	Lancashire Steel Corporation Ltd, Irlam, Lancs	
3953	VF D1265	1968	0-6-0 DH	500	Std	Sierra Leone Development Co.	No. 152
3954-6	VF D1266-8	1969	0-6-0 DH	620	5'3"	Northern Ireland Rlys	Nos 1-3
3957-66	VF	1969	CoCo DE	2000	3'6"	Sudan Govt Rlys	Nos 1055-64
3967	VF D1279	1969	0-4-0 DH	305	Std	Stewarts & Lloyds Ltd, Newport, Mon.	
3968						?	
3969	Bg	1969	4w BE			New South Wales State Mines, Australia	
3970-1	VF	1969	0-6-0 DH	447	Std	Stewarts & Lloyds Ltd, Corby, Northants	
3972-7	CAF 197-202	1969	0-4-0 DH	345	5'6"	Union Nacional de Siderurgicas Asturianas (UNISA), Verina, Gijon, Spain	
3978-83	CAF 203-8	1969	0-6-0 DH	620	5'6"	Union Nacional de Siderurgicas Asturianas (UNISA), Verina, Gijon, Spain	
3984	VF	1970	4w BE		3'6"	Elcom, Newvale No. 2, New South Wales, Australia	
3985-6	VF	1970	0-6-0 DH	500	Std	John Summers & Sons Ltd, Shotton, Flint.	
3987	VF D1280	1970	0-4-0 DH	272	Std	English Clays Lovering Pochin & Co. Ltd, Marsh Mills, Devon	
3988	VF	1970	0-4-0 DH	305	Std	Koninklijke Soda, Holland	
3989	VF	1970	0-6-0 DH	286	Std	British Petroleum Ltd, Baglan Bay, Glam.	
3990	VF	1970	0-6-0 DH	344	Std	Shanks & McEwan Ltd, Corby, Northants	
3991	VF	1970	0-4-0 DH	300	Std	Stewarts and Lloyds Ltd, Newport, Mon.	
3992-3	VF	1971	4w BE	64	3'0"	NCB, Seafield, Fife	Underground locos
3994	VF	1970	0-6-0 DH	391	Std	Derek Crouch (Contractors) Ltd, Llanharan	
3995	VF	1971	4w BE	64	2'6"	NCB, Lea Hall, Staffs	Underground loco
3996-7						?	
3998-9	VF	1970	0-6-0 DH	500	Std	John Summers & Sons Ltd, Shotton, Flint.	
4000	VF	1971	4w BE	64	2'6"	NCB, Bilston Glen, Midlothian	Underground loco
4001-2	VF	1971	4w BE	64	3'0"	NCB, Seafield, Fife	Underground locos
4003	VF	1971	0-6-0 DH	286	Std	British Petroleum Ltd, Sully, Glam.	

NRZ No. 1408, Class DE4 Co-Co locomotive built by Brush in 1964, with a Mirrlees diesel engine. In 1982, the class was re-engined with the Ruston 8RK3CT engine, built at Vulcan Foundry. The companion classes DE2 and DE3 each have English Electric diesel engines, and all have given good service in Zimbabwe. (This might look like a Brush locomotive, but it houses English Electric power!)

Appendix V

GEC Traction Ltd: Locomotive Works List

Works No.	In Conj. With	Date	Type	HP	Gauge	Customer	Notes
5276-301	MCW	1970	BoBo DE	550	Metre	Bangladesh Rlys	Nos 3101-26
5302-41	MCW	1971	CoCo DE	1760	Metre	Malayan Rly	Nos 22101-40
5342-51						No details known	
5352-3	VF	1971	0-6-0 DH	500	Std	John Summers & Sons Ltd, Shotton, Flint.	
5354-8	VF	1971	0-6-0 DH	447	Std	Stewarts & Lloyds Ltd, Corby, Northants	
5359	VF	1971	4w BE		2'6"	NCB, Kinneil, West Lothian	Underground loco
5360-1	VF	1971	0-4-0 WE		Std	British Steel Corporation, Ravenscraig, Lanarks.	Coke ovens locos
5362	VF	1971	4w BE		2'6"	NCB, Barony, Ayrshire	Underground loco
5363	VF	1971	4w BE		2'6"	NCB, Seafield, Fife.	Underground loco
5364						No details known	
5365-7	VF	1972	0-6-0 DH	447	Std	British Steel Corporation, Corby, Northants.	
5368-9	VF	1973	0-6-0 DH	500	Std	NCB, Maesteg, Glam.	
5370	BD 3684	1973	0-4-0 WE		Std	British Steel Corporation, Ravenscraig, Lanarks.	Coke ovens loco
5371						No details known	
5372-7	MCW	1972	CoCo DE	1760	3'6"	CF du Grands Lacs, Zaire	Nos 400-5
5378-81	VF	1972	0-6-0 DH	500	Std	British Steel Corporation, Llanwern, Mon.	
5382-3	VF	1973	0-6-0 DH	500	Std	British Steel Corporation, Llanwern, Mon.	
5384-6	VF	1973	4w BE		3'0"	NCB, Seafield, Fife.	Underground locos
5387-8	VF	1974	0-6-0 DH	447	Std	British Steel Corporation, Corby, Northants.	
5389-90	VF	1973	0-4-0 WE		Std	British Steel Corporation, Llanwern, Mon.	Coke ovens locos
5391-2	VF	1974	0-6-0 DH	500	Std	British Steel Corporation, Shotton, Flint.	
5393	VF	1974	4w BE		2'6"	NCB, Cardowan, Lanarks	Underground loco
5394-5	VF	1974	0-6-0 DH	447	Std	British Steel Corporation, Corby, Northants.	
5396-402	VF	1975	0-6-0 DH	500	Std	British Steel Corporation, Shotton, Clwyd	
5403-6	VF	1975	4w BE		3'0"	NCB, Seafield, Fife.	Underground locos
5407-8	VF	1976	0-6-0 DH	447	Std	British Steel Corporation, Corby, Northants.	
5409-13	VF	1976	0-6-0 DE		Std	British Steel Corporation, Llanwern, Gwent	
5414-8	VF	1976	0-6-0 DE		Std	British Steel Corporation, Middlesbrough, Cleveland	
5419-20	VF	1977	4w BE		2'6"	NCB, West Cannock, Staffs	Underground locos
5421-2	VF	1977	0-6-0 DE		Std	NCB, Littleton, Staffs	
5423-4	VF	1976	4w BE		2'0"	NCB, Tilmanstone, Kent	Underground locos
5425-32	VF	1977	0-6-0 DE		Std	British Steel Corporation, Middlesbrough, Cleveland	
5433	VF	1977	4w BE		2'6"	NCB, West Cannock, Staffs	Underground loco
5434-40	BD 3734-40	1977	0-4-0 DE		Std	British Steel Corporation, Scunthorpe, Humberside	
5441-4	UCW	1976	BoBo WE	2840	3'6"	Taiwan Rly Administration	Nos E101-4
5445-60	UCW	1977	BoBo WE	2840	3'6"	Taiwan Rly Administration	Nos E105-20
5461-7	VF	1977	0-6-0 DE		Std	British Steel Corporation, Middlesbrough, Cleveland	
5468	VF	1978	0-6-0 DE		Std	NCB, Littleton, Staffs	
5469-75	VF	1978	0-6-0 DE		Std	British Steel Corporation, Middlesbrough, Cleveland	
5476-7	BD 3748-9	1979	0-4-0 WE		Std	British Steel Corporation, Port Talbot, West Glamorgan	Coke ovens locos
5478	VF	1979	0-6-0 DE		Std	NCB, Lea Hall, Staffs	
5479-80	VF	1979	0-6-0 DE		Std	NCB, Bickershaw, Greater Manchester	
5481-545						No details known	
5546-70	UCW	1978/9	CoCo WE		3'6"	South African Rlys & Hbrs	Nos 9E E9001-25
5571-2	VF	1978	4w BE		2'6"	NCB, Lea Hall, Staffs	Underground locos
5573	BD 3747	?	4w WE		3'6"	Zambia	
5574	VF	1979	0-4-0 WE		Std	British Steel Corporation, Ravenscraig, Strathclyde	Coke ovens loco
5575-7	VF	1979	0-4-0 DH	165	Std	British Steel Corporation, Shotton, Clwyd	
5578	VF	1979	0-6-0 DE		Std	Imperial Chemical Industries, Northwich, Cheshire	
5579	VF	1981	4w BE		3'0"	NCB, Penallta, Mid Glamorgan	Underground loco
5580-5	VF	1980	4w BE		3'0"	NCB, Easington, Co. Durham	Underground locos.
5586-9						No details known	Note 11
5590-3	VF	?	4w WE		3'6"	Amax Corporation (USA)	
5594						No details known	
5595-600	UCW	1982	CoCo WE		3'6"	South African Rlys & Hbrs	Nos 9E E9026-31
5601-58						No details known	
5659-708	UCW	1987-9	CoCo WE		3'6"	South African Rlys	Nos 10E E10051-100
5709-38						No details known	
5739-88	UCW	1990/1	CoCo WE		3'6"	South African Rlys	Nos 10E E10126-75

Abbreviations

Builders
BD – Baguley Drewry Ltd
Bg – E. E. Baguley Ltd
BP – Beyer Peacock & Co. Ltd
CAF – Construcciones y Auxiliar de Ferrocurriles SA (Spain)
DC – Drewry Car Co. Ltd
DK – Dick, Kerr & Co. Ltd
HL – R. & W. Hawthorn, Leslie & Co. Ltd
Isl – Islington Works, South Australian Railways
MCW – Metropolitan Carriage & Wagon Co. Ltd
NBL – North British Locomotive Co. Ltd
RSH – Robert Stephenson & Hawthorns Ltd
S – Sentinel (Shrewsbury) Ltd
UCW – Union Carriage & Wagon Co. Ltd
VF – Vulcan Foundry
WBC –

Type – wheel arrangement followed by:
BE – battery electric
DE – diesel with electric transmission
DH – diesel with hydraulic transmission
DM – diesel with mechanical transmission
ED – electro-diesel
ERC – electric rail car
PM – petrol with mechanical transmission
PRC – petrol rail car
RE – electric with rail pick up
WE – –electric with overhead wire supply

Notes

(1) EE 977A, 977-1075 were split between the BAGS & BAW Rlys. There were different internal layouts of the railcars, viz: 38 Type A Cars: 2nd class, light luggage and postal compartments; 30 Type B Cars: 1st class, light luggage compartment; 2 Type B1 Cars: 1st class, buffet; 14 Type C Cars: 1st and 2nd class; 15 Type D Cars: Goods/parcels and postal compartments. It is not known how many of each type went to each railway.
(2) EE 1078-85 were split between the Entre Rios and ANE Rlys (which were under common management).
(3) EE 1141-52 and 1153-68 each had two order Nos shown. Therefore it is presumed that there was some detail within each batch, but the nature of this is not known.
(4) EE 1505-27 had two order Nos, (4K0176 & 6S0542), but further details as to why are not known.
(5) EE 1550-4 were built for stock but were later sold as shown.
(6) EE 2651-2 allotted twice in error; EE records show the two underground locos (Bg 3527-8) as works Nos 2651-2A.
(7) Order No. 6B0742 was originally for 31 1,500hp 1CoCo1 DE locos for the NZR, but only the first ten were built. The remaining 21 were cancelled and replaced by an order for 42 750hp A1AA1A DEs, built as EE works Nos 2254-95. Hence, works Nos 1937-57 remained blank.

(8) EE 2023-5 are stated to have been built for the RENFE, but cannot be traced in RENFE lists. They could possibly be replacements for earlier locomotives of the batches 1864-83, 1964-2003 lost in transit. There is also an additional locomotive built for the EF Santos a Jundiai in 1955 which does not appear in EE records; this could well be one of EE 2023-5.
(9) EE 3425-6 allotted twice in error. EE 3450-1 were left blank to compensate for this.
(10) EE 3892-943 were left blank to cover industrial locomotives built prior to 1968. Possibly these were intended to cover VF D913-26, D1048-53, D1116-26, D1137-40, D1191-205, D1226-33 which were built to an RSH design, but not allotted either RSH or EE works Nos. However, there are 58 of these but only 52 EE Nos left blank.
(11) GECT 5580-5 were rebuilds of EE 2393/87/90/91/89/92 respectively. EE 2388 was used for spare parts.

The names of Malayan Railway Nos 20101–26 (EE 2396–415, 2629–34) were as follows:

20101	Bunga Raya	20114	Bunga Kala
20102	Bunga Chempaka	20115	Bunga Mata Hari
20103	Bunga Kenenga	20116	Bunga Medan
20104	Bunga Melor	20117	Bunga Kekwa
20105	Bunga Teratai	20118	Bunga Pandan
20106	Bunga Tanjong	20119	Bunga Butang
20107	Bunga Kiambang	20120	Bunga Tongking
20108	Bunga Melati	20121	Bunga Kemboja
20109	Bunga Mawar	20122	Bunga Kemuning
20110	Bunga Anggerek	20123	Bunga Kantan
20111	Bunga Telang	20124	Bunga Seroja
20112	Bunga Siantan	20125	Bunga Chinta Berahi
20113	Bunga Baka Wali	20126	Bunga Putri Malu
(Bunga=Flower)			

22101	Shah Alam	22121	Anak Bukit
22102	Seri Menanti	22122	Changkat Tenggara
22103	Alor Setar	22123	Seri Gading
22104	Kuala Kangsar	22124	Tanjong Malim
22105	Kelian Intan	22125	Telok Chempedak
22106	Changkat Budiman	22126	Merlimau
22107	Petaling Jaya	22127	Tanjong Bunga
22108	Kota Tinggi	22128	Tanjong Tenteram
22109	Kuala Perlis	22129	Telaga Batin
22110	Rantau Abang	22130	Mahsuri
22111	Langkawi	22131	Limau Kasturi
22112	Pasir Mas	22132	Seri Medan
22113	Bandar Maharani	22133	Malim Nawar
22114	Mambang Di-Awan	22134	Durian Tunggal
22115	Kuala Lipis	22135	Geliga
22116	Alor Gajah	22136	Jitra
22117	Bayan Lepas	22137	Pantai Irama
22118	Nilam Puri	22138	Bagan Serai
22119	Mata Ayer	22139	Sungai Petani
22120	Chendering	22140	Manek Urai

These names are towns in West Malaysia

Metropolitan-Vickers 'Metadyne' equipped stock for London Transport, finished in their distinctive silver livery.

(London Transport Museum)

Index

174